# User's Guide

## Microsoft® MS-DOS® 6

For the MS-DOS Operating System

Microsoft Corporation

Document No. MS55892-1193

Printed in the United States of America.

# Contents

# Welcome

Welcome to Microsoft ® MS-DOS ®, the most widely used operating system for personal computers. MS-DOS 6 includes many new features that turn your computer into a powerful tool for business or personal use. These features are described in detail later in this introduction.

If MS-DOS 6 is not yet set up on your computer, see the chapter "Getting Started" for information about how to use the Setup program.

This introduction to the *Microsoft MS-DOS 6 User's Guide* includes a list of the printed and online documentation included with MS-DOS 6, an introduction to new and improved MS-DOS 6 features, a list of the typographic conventions used in this guide, and information about how to get product support.

## About Your MS-DOS Documentation

MS-DOS 6 documentation consists of the *Microsoft MS-DOS 6 User's Guide,* MS-DOS Help, and several other online documents.

This guide includes information for users who have little experience with computers, in addition to advanced topics for those who are familiar with MS-DOS. You can use the detailed table of contents and index to find information about the features you work with most often.

MS-DOS Help is a comprehensive online reference to MS-DOS commands. The reference includes information about how to type commands and their parameters and switches, notes about commands, and examples of how to use commands.

After you've set up MS-DOS 6 on your computer, you can display the MS-DOS Help table of contents by typing **help** at the command prompt and then pressing ENTER. You can also get information about a command without displaying the table of contents. For example, to display information about the **copy** command, type **help copy** at the command prompt.

For more information about using MS-DOS Help, see the chapter "MS-DOS Basics."

When you install MS-DOS 6, Setup copies to your hard disk two online documents that contain information that was unavailable when this guide was printed. You can read (and print) the documents by using any text editor.

After you set up MS-DOS 6, you will find the following files in the directory that contains your MS-DOS files:

- The README.TXT file, which provides information about how MS-DOS 6 interacts with certain types of hardware and software.

- The NETWORKS.TXT file, which provides information about making your network compatible with MS-DOS 6.

# New Features of MS-DOS 6

If you have used earlier versions of MS-DOS, you will find many improvements in MS-DOS 6. These improvements include new commands and programs that make using your computer easier and more efficient.

MS-DOS 6 includes the following new or improved features:

- Microsoft DoubleSpace, integrated disk compression that increases your available disk space by compressing files. You can use DoubleSpace to increase available space on both hard disks and floppy disks. DoubleSpace is easy to install. For more information about DoubleSpace, see the chapter "Freeing Disk Space."

- A new **/c** switch for the **dir** command that displays information about file-compression ratios on compressed DoubleSpace drives. For more information, type **help dir** at the MS-DOS command prompt, and then press ENTER.

- Microsoft MemMaker, a memory-optimization program that makes it easy to free conventional memory by moving device drivers and memory-resident programs from conventional memory into the upper memory area. If your computer has an 80386 or higher processor, you can use MemMaker to maximize available conventional memory so that programs run faster and more efficiently. For more information about using MemMaker, see the chapter "Making More Memory Available."

- An enhanced EMM386 device driver that provides access to more upper memory blocks and uses extended memory to simulate expanded memory as needed, without requiring you to change configuration commands or restart your computer. For more information, see the chapter "Making More Memory Available."

- An enhanced **mem** command that provides more information about the memory your computer is using and the programs that are loaded in memory. For more information, type **help mem** at the MS-DOS command prompt, and then press ENTER.

- Enhanced **loadhigh** and **devicehigh** commands that enable you to specify the memory region in which you want to load a program. For more information, type **help loadhigh** or **help devicehigh** at the MS-DOS command prompt, and then press ENTER.

- Microsoft Backup, a program that makes it easy to back up your data. MS-DOS 6 includes both Backup for MS-DOS, a program you can start from the command prompt, and Backup for Windows, a program you can use with the Microsoft Windows™ operating system. For more information about Backup, see the chapter "Managing Your System."

- Microsoft Anti-Virus, a program that can identify and remove more than 800 different computer viruses from your system. MS-DOS 6 includes both Anti-Virus for MS-DOS, a program you can start from the command prompt, and Anti-Virus for Windows, a program you can use with Windows. For more information about Anti-Virus, see the chapter "Managing Your System."

- Microsoft Undelete, an enhanced program that enables you to choose one of three levels of protection in case you accidentally delete a file. MS-DOS 6 includes Undelete for MS-DOS, a program you can run from the command prompt, and Undelete for Windows, a program you can use with Windows. For more information about Undelete, see the chapter "Managing Your System."

- When you set up MS-DOS 6 and choose to install the Windows-based versions of Backup, Anti-Virus, and Undelete, Setup creates a new group in Program Manager named Microsoft Tools that contains icons for each program. Setup also adds a Tools menu to the menu bar in File Manager. If you have Windows for Workgroups, Setup also adds buttons to the toolbar in File Manager.

- The ability to define more than one configuration in your CONFIG.SYS file. This can be especially useful if you share a computer with several people. If your CONFIG.SYS file defines multiple configurations, MS-DOS displays a menu that enables you to choose the configuration you want to use each time you start your computer. For more information about multiple configurations, see the chapter "Configuring Your System."

- The ability to bypass startup commands when you turn on your computer. With this feature, you can choose which CONFIG.SYS commands MS-DOS should carry out and whether MS-DOS should run your AUTOEXEC.BAT file. By controlling the commands your computer uses to start up, you can pinpoint problems more quickly and easily. For more information about bypassing startup commands, see the chapter "Configuring Your System."

- Microsoft Defragmenter, a program that reorganizes files on your hard disk to minimize the time it takes your computer to access the files. For more information about the Defragmenter, see the chapter "Managing Your System."

- MS-DOS Help, a complete online reference to MS-DOS commands. The reference includes information about how to type commands and their parameters and switches, notes about commands, and examples of how to use commands. For more information about using MS-DOS Help, see the chapter "MS-DOS Basics."

- An enhanced SMARTDrive program that speeds up your computer by using a disk cache, which stores information to be written to your hard disk and writes it to the disk later, when system resources are in less demand. For more information, see the chapter "Managing Your System," or type **help smartdrv** at the MS-DOS command prompt, and then press ENTER.

- Microsoft Diagnostics (MSD), a program that gathers and displays technical information about your computer. For more information, type **help msd** at the MS-DOS command prompt, and then press ENTER.

- Interlnk, a program that enables you to easily transfer files between computers. With Interlnk and a cable, you can access information on another computer without having to copy files to that computer by using floppy disks. For more information about Interlnk, see the chapter "Features for Your Laptop Computer."

- Power, a program that conserves battery power when applications and hardware devices are idle. With this feature, your batteries will last up to 25 percent longer. For more information about the Power program, see the chapter "Features for Your Laptop Computer."

- A **move** command that moves one or more files from one directory or drive to another. You can also use the **move** command to rename directories. For more information, type **help move** at the MS-DOS command prompt, and then press ENTER.

- The ability to prompt a user for input easily when running a batch program. With the **choice** command, you can display a specified prompt, pause for user input, and return an errorlevel parameter to the batch program. For more information about the **choice** command, type **help choice** at the MS-DOS command prompt, and then press ENTER.

- A **deltree** command that deletes a directory and all of its files and subdirectories. For more information, type **help deltree** at the MS-DOS command prompt, and then press ENTER.

- Fewer technical status messages appear when your computer starts. By default, the HIMEM, EMM386, and SMARTDrive programs now display no confirmation messages when they are loaded.

# Conventions

This guide uses document and keyboard conventions to help you locate and identify information.

## Document Conventions

To help you locate and interpret information easily, this guide uses consistent visual cues and a standard key-combination format. These conventions are explained as follows.

| This | Represents |
| --- | --- |
| **bold** | Commands and the switches that follow them. You must type commands and their switches exactly as they appear. To carry out a command, type the command and its switches, if any, and then press the ENTER key. For example, if you are instructed to type **net view**, type all the bold characters exactly as they are printed, and then press ENTER. |
| *italic* | Placeholders that represent information you must provide. For example, if you are asked to type *filename,* you would type the actual name of a file instead of the word shown in italic. |
| | Italic type also signals a new term. An explanation precedes or follows the italicized term. |
| ALL CAPITALS | The names of computers, printers, directories, and files. |

Microsoft documentation uses the term *MS-DOS* to refer to the Microsoft MS-DOS and IBM ® PC-DOS operating systems.

## Keyboard Conventions

Key combinations and key sequences appear in the following format:

| Notation | Meaning |
| --- | --- |
| KEY1+KEY2 | A plus sign (+) between key names means you must press the keys at the same time. For example, "Press CTRL+C" means that you press CTRL and hold it down while you press C. |
| KEY1, KEY2 | A comma (,) between key names means you must press the keys in sequence—for example, "Press ALT, F10" means that you press the ALT key and release it, and then press the F10 key and release it. |

# Microsoft Support Services

If you have a question about MS-DOS, first look in the *MS-DOS 6 User's Guide* or consult online Help. You can also find late-breaking updates and technical information in the README file that came with your MS-DOS 6.2 Upgrade disks. If you cannot find the answer, contact the Microsoft Support Network.

Outside the United States, contact Microsoft Product Support Services at the Microsoft subsidiary office that serves your area. For information about Microsoft subsidiary offices, see "Product Support Worldwide" later in this section.

# The Microsoft Support Network

The Microsoft Support Network offers you a wide range of choices and access to high-quality, responsive technical support. Microsoft recognizes that support needs vary from user to user; the Microsoft Support Network allows you to choose the type of support that best meets your needs, with options ranging from electronic bulletin boards to annual support programs.

Services vary outside the United States and Canada. In other locations, contact a local Microsoft subsidiary for information. The Microsoft Support Network is subject to Microsoft's then-current prices, terms, and conditions, and is subject to change without notice.

# Product Support Within the United States and Canada

In the United States and Canada, the following support services are available through the Microsoft Support Network.

### Electronic Services

These services are available 24 hours a day, 7 days a week, including holidays.

**Microsoft FastTips**   (800) 936-4200 on a touch-tone telephone. Receive automated answers to common questions, and access a library of technical notes, all delivered by recording or fax. You can use the following keys on your touch-tone telephone after you reach FastTips:

| To | Press |
| --- | --- |
| Advance to the next message | * |
| Repeat the current message | 7 |
| Return to the beginning of FastTips | # |

**CompuServe**   Interact with other users and Microsoft support engineers, or access the Microsoft Knowledge Base to get product information. At any ! prompt, type

**go microsoft** to access Microsoft forums, or type **go mskb** to access the Microsoft Knowledge Base. For an introductory CompuServe membership kit, call (800) 848-8199, operator 520.

**Microsoft Download Service**  Access, via modem, the Driver Library and the most current technical notes (1200, 2400, or 9600 baud; no parity; 8 data bits; 1 stop bit). In the United States, call (206) 936-6735.  In Canada, call (905) 507-3022.

**Internet**  Access the Driver Library and the Microsoft Knowledge Base. The Microsoft Internet FTP archive host, ftp.microsoft.com, supports anonymous login. When logging in as anonymous, you should type your complete electronic mail name as your password.

## Standard Support

In the United States, no-charge support from Microsoft support engineers is available via a toll call between 6:00 A.M. and 6:00 P.M. Pacific time, Monday through Friday, excluding holidays. This support is available for 90 days after your first call to a support engineer.

- For technical support for MS-DOS, call (206) 646-5104.

In Canada, support engineers are available via a toll call between 8:00 A.M. and 8:00 P.M. Eastern time, Monday through Friday, excluding holidays. Call (905) 568-3503. This support is available for 90 days after your first call to a support engineer.

When you call, you should be at your computer and have the appropriate product documentation at hand.  Be prepared to give the following information:

- The version number of the Microsoft product that you are using
- The type of hardware that you are using, including network hardware if applicable
- The operating system that you are using
- The exact wording of any messages that appeared on your screen
- A description of what happened and what you were doing when the problem occurred
- A description of how you tried to solve the problem

## Priority Support

The Microsoft Support Network offers priority telephone access to Microsoft support engineers 24 hours a day, 7 days a week, except holidays.

- In the United States, call (900) 555-2000; $2 (U.S.) per minute, $25 (U.S.) maximum. Charges appear on your telephone bill. Not available in Canada.

- In the United States, call (800) 936-5700; $25 (U.S.) per incident, billed to your VISA card, MasterCard, or American Express card. In Canada, call (800) 668-7975; $30 per incident, billed to your VISA card, MasterCard, or American Express card.

### Text Telephone

Microsoft text telephone (TT/TDD) services are available for the deaf or hard-of-hearing. In the United States, using a TT/TDD modem, dial (206) 635-4948 between 6:00 A.M. and 6:00 P.M. Pacific time, Monday through Friday, excluding holidays. In Canada, using a TT/TDD modem, dial (905) 568-9641 between 8:00 A.M. and 8:00 P.M. Eastern time, Monday through Friday, excluding holidays.

### Other Support Options

The Microsoft Support Network offers annual support plans. For information, in the United States, contact the Microsoft Support Network Sales and Information group at (800) 936-3500 between 6:00 A.M. and 6:00 P.M. Pacific time, Monday through Friday, excluding holidays. In Canada, call (800) 668-7975 between 8:00 A.M. and 8:00 P.M. Eastern time, Monday through Friday, excluding holidays.

## Product Training and Consultation

Microsoft Solution Providers are independent organizations that provide consulting, integration, customization, development, technical support and training, and other services for Microsoft products. These companies are called Solution Providers because they apply technology and provide services to help solve real-world problems.

In the United States, for more information about the Microsoft Solution Providers program or the Microsoft Solution Provider nearest to you, please call (800) 426-9400 between 6:30 A.M. and 5:30 P.M. Pacific time, Monday through Friday, excluding holidays. In Canada, call (800) 668-7975 between 8:00 A.M. and 8:00 P.M. Eastern time, Monday through Friday, excluding holidays.

# Product Support Worldwide

If you are outside the United States and have a question about a Microsoft product, first:

- Consult the documentation and other printed information included with your product.
- Check online Help.

- Check the README files that come with your product disks. These files provide general information that became available after the books in the product package were published.
- Consult electronic options such as CompuServe forums or bulletin boards, if available.

If you cannot find a solution, you can receive information on how to obtain product support by contacting the Microsoft subsidiary office that serves your country.

# Calling a Microsoft Subsidiary Office

When you call, you should be at your computer and have the appropriate product documentation at hand. Be prepared to give the following information:

- The version number of the Microsoft product that you are using
- The type of hardware that you are using, including network hardware, if applicable
- The operating system that you are using
- The exact wording of any messages that appeared on your screen
- A description of what happened and what you were doing when the problem occurred
- A description of how you tried to solve the problem

Microsoft subsidiary offices and the countries they serve are listed below. If there is no Microsoft office in your country, please contact the establishment from which you purchased your Microsoft product.

| Area | Telephone Numbers |
| --- | --- |
| Argentina | Microsoft de Argentina S.A. <br> Phone: (54) (1) 814-5105 <br> (54) (1) 814-4807 <br> (54) (1) 814-4808 <br> (54) (1) 814-7199 <br> Fax: (54) (1) 814-0372 |
| Australia | Microsoft Pty. Ltd. <br> Install & Setup: (61) (02) 870-2870 <br> Fax: (61) (02) 805-1108 <br> Bulletin Board Service: (61) (02) 870-2348 <br> Technical Support: (61) (02) 870-2131 <br> Sales Information Centre: (61) (02) 870-2100 |

| Area | Telephone Numbers |
| --- | --- |
| Austria | Microsoft Ges.m.b.H.<br>Phone: 0222 - 68 76 07<br>Fax: 0222 - 68 16 2710<br>Information: 0660 - 6520<br>    Prices, updates, etc.: 0660 - 6520<br>CompuServe: GO MSEURO (Microsoft Central Europe)<br>Technical support:<br>    MS-DOS, MS-DOS Lernprogramm: 0660 - 6517 |
| Belgium | Microsoft NV<br>Phone: 02-7303911<br>Customer Service: 02-7303922<br>CompuServe: 02-2150530 (GO MSBEN)<br>Bulletin Board Service: 02-7350045 (1200/2400/9600 baud, 8 bits, no parity, 1 stop bit, ANSI terminal emulation)<br>Technical Support:<br>(Dutch speaking): 02-5133274<br>(English speaking): 02-5023432<br>(French speaking): 02-5132268 |
| Bolivia | See Argentina |
| Brazil | Microsoft Informatica Ltda.<br>Phone: (55) (11) 530-4455<br>Fax: (55) (11) 240-2205<br>Technical Support Phone: (55) (11) 533-2922<br>Technical Support Fax: (55) (11) 241-1157<br>Technical Support Bulletin Board Service:<br>    (55) (11) 65-8564 |
| Canada | Microsoft Canada Inc.<br>Phone: 1 (905) 568-0434<br>Technical Support Phone: 1 (905) 568-3503<br>Technical Support Bulletin Board Service:<br>    1 (905) 507-3022<br><br>Text Telephone (TT/TDD) 1 (905) 568-9641 |
| Chile | Microsoft Chile S.A.<br>Tel: 56 2 218 5771, 56 2 218 5711, 56 2 218 7524<br>Fax: 56 2 218 5747 |
| Colombia | Microsoft Colombia<br>Tel: (571) 618 2245 Soporte Tecnico: (571) 618 2255<br>Fax:(571) 618 2269 |

| Area | Telephone Numbers |
| --- | --- |
| Denmark | Microsoft Denmark AS<br>Phone: (45) (44) 89 01 00<br>Fax: (45) (44) 68 55 10 |
| Dubai | Microsoft Middle East<br>Phone: (971) 4 513 888<br>Fax: (971) 4 527 444 |
| England | Microsoft Limited<br>Phone: (44) (734) 270000<br>Fax: (44) (734) 270002<br>Upgrades: (44) (81) 614 8000<br>Technical Support:<br>    Main Line (All Products): (44) (734) 271000<br>    Database Direct Support Line: (44) (734) 271126<br>    MS-DOS  Warranty Support: (44) (734) 271900<br>    MS-DOS  Fee Support Line: (44) (891) 315500<br>    Bulletin Board Service: (44) (734) 270065 (2400 Baud)<br>    Fax Information Service: (44) (734) 270080 |
| Finland | Microsoft OY<br>Phone: (358) (0) 525 501<br>Fax: (358) (0) 522 955 |
| France | Microsoft France<br>Phone: (33) (1) 69-86-46-46<br>Telex: MSPARIS 604322F<br>Fax: (33) (1) 64-46-06-60<br>Technical Support Phone: (33) (1) 69-86-10-20<br>Technical Support Fax: (33) (1) 69-28-00-28 |
| French Polynesia | See France |
| Germany | Microsoft GmbH<br>Phone: 089 - 3176-0<br>Telex: (17) 89 83 28 MS GMBH D<br>Fax: 089 - 3176-1000<br>Information: 089 - 3176 1199<br>    Prices, updates, etc.: 089 - 3176 1199<br>Bulletin board, device drivers, tech notes : Btx: microsoft#<br>or *610808000#<br>CompuServe: GO MSEURO (Microsoft Central<br>    Europe)<br>Technical support:<br>    MS-DOS, MS-DOS Lernprogramm: 089 - 3176 - 1152 |

| Area | Telephone Numbers |
| --- | --- |
| Greece | Microsoft Hellas, S.A.<br>Phone: (30) (1) 6893 635<br>Fax: (30) (1) 6893 636 |
| Hong Kong | Microsoft Hong Kong Limited<br>Technical Support: (852) 804-4222<br>Fax: (852) 560-2217 |
| Ireland | See England |
| Israel | Microsoft Israel  Ltd.<br>Phone: 972-3-575-7034<br>Fax: 972-3-575-7065 |
| Italy | Microsoft SpA<br>Phone: (39) (2) 269121<br>Telex: 340321 I<br>Fax: (39) (2) 21072020<br>Customer Service (Prices, new product info, product literature): (39) (2) 26901359<br>Bulletin Board: (39) (2) 21072051<br>Technical Support:<br>    MS-DOS Update: (39) (2) 26901363 |
| Japan | Microsoft Company Ltd.<br>Tokyo Japan<br>Phone: (81) (3) 5454-8025<br>Fax: (81) (3) 5454-7972<br>PSS Technical Support Fax: (81) (3) 5454-7955<br>Customer Service Phone (Version upgrade/Registration)<br>Phone: (81) (3) 5454 2305 Fax: (81) (3) 5454-7952<br>Channel Marketing (Pre-sales Product Support)<br>Information Center Phone: (81) (3) 5454-2300<br>Fax: (81) (3) 5454 7951 |
| Korea | Microsoft CH<br>Phone: (82) (2) 552-9505<br>Fax: (82) (2) 555-1724<br>Technical Support: (82) (2) 563-9230<br>Technical Support Fax : (82) (2) 563-5194<br>Technical Support Bulletin Board Service :<br>    (82) (2) 538-3256 |
| Liechtenstein | See Switzerland (German speaking) |

| Area | Telephone Numbers |
| --- | --- |
| Luxembourg | Microsoft NV<br>Phone: (32) 2-7303911<br>Customer Service: (32) 2-7303922<br>CompuServe: (32) 2-2150530 (GO MSBEN)<br>Bulletin Board Service: (32) 2-7350045 (1200/2400/9600 baud, 8 bits, No parity, 1 stop bit, ANSI terminal emulation)<br>Technical Support:<br>(Dutch speaking): (32) 2-5133274<br>(English speaking): (32) 2-5023432<br>(French speaking): (32) 2-5132268 |
| México | Microsoft México, S.A. de C.V.<br>Phone: (52) (5) 325-0910<br>Customer Service: (52) (5) 325-0911<br>Bulletin Board Service: (52) (5) 590-5988 (1200/2400 baud, 8 bits, No parity, 1 stop bit, ANSI terminal emulation)<br>Fax: (52) (5) 280-7940<br>Technical Support: (52) (5) 325-0912 |
| Netherlands | Microsoft BV<br>Phone: 02503-89189<br>Customer Service: 02503-77700<br>CompuServe: 020-6880085 (GO MSBEN)<br>Bulletin Board Service: 02503-34221 (1200/2400/9600 baud, 8 bits, No parity, 1 stop bit, ANSI terminal emulation)<br>Technical Support:<br>(Dutch speaking) Technical Support: 02503-77877<br>(English speaking) Technical Support: 02503-77853 |
| New Zealand | Technology Link Centre<br>Phone: 64 (9) 358-3724<br>Fax: 64 (9) 358-3726<br>Technical Support Applications: 64 (9) 357-5575 |
| Northern Ireland | See England |
| Norway | Microsoft Norway AS<br>Phone: (47) (22) 18 35 00<br>Fax: (47) (22) 95 06 64<br>Technical Support: (47) (22) 02 25 50 |
| Papua New Guinea | See Australia |

| Area | Telephone Numbers |
| --- | --- |
| Paraguay | See Argentina |
| Portugal | MSFT, Lda.<br>Phone: (351) 1 4412205<br>Fax: (351) 1 4412101 |
| Republic of China | Microsoft Taiwan Corp.<br>Phone: (886) (2) 504-3122<br>Fax: (886) (2) 504-3121<br>Technical Support : (886) (2) 508-9501 |
| Republic of Ireland | See England |
| Scotland | See England |
| South Africa | Phone: (27) 11 444 0520<br>Fax: (27) 11 444 0536 |
| Spain | Microsoft Iberica SRL<br>Phone: (34) (1) 804-0000<br>Fax: (34) (1) 803-8310<br>Technical Support: (34) (1) 803-9960 |
| Sweden | Microsoft AB<br>Phone: (46) (8) 752 56 00<br>Fax: (46) (8) 750 51 58<br>Technical Support:<br>    MS-DOS: (46) (071) 21 05 15 (SEK 4.55/min)<br>Sales Support: (46) (8) 752 56 30<br>Bulletin Board Service: (46) (8) 750 47 42<br>Fax Information Service: (46) (8) 752 29 00 |
| Switzerland | Microsoft AG<br>Phone: 01 - 839 61 11<br>Fax: 01 - 831 08 69<br>Documentation: Phone: 155 59 00 Fax: 064 - 224294,<br>Microsoft Info-Service, Postfach, 8099 Zürich<br>    Prices, updates, etc.: 01/839 61 11<br>    CompuServe: GO MSEURO(Microsoft Central Europe)<br>    Technical support: (German speaking)<br>    MS-DOS, MS-DOS Lernprogramm: 01 - 342 - 2152<br>Technical support: (French speaking) 022 - 738 96 88 |
| Uruguay | See Argentina |

| Area | Telephone Numbers |
|------|-------------------|
| Venezuela | Corporation MS 90 de Venezuela S.A.<br>Technical Support: 58.2.910046, 58.2.910510<br>Other information: 58.2.910008, 58.2.914739, 58.2.913342<br><br>Fax: 58.2.923835 |
| Wales | See England |

C H A P T E R   1

# Getting Started

This chapter describes how to set up the MS-DOS 6 operating system on a computer that has a previous version of DOS or OS/2 installed on its hard disk.

Before you can use MS-DOS 6, you must run the Setup program. The Setup program detects the type of hardware and software you have and notifies you if your computer does not meet the minimum requirements. Setup also notifies you if it detects system features that are incompatible with MS-DOS 6. It is recommended that you back up your hard disk before you run Setup.

The files on the Setup disks are compressed. The Setup program decompresses these files and copies them to your hard disk. You can begin using MS-DOS 6 as soon as Setup is complete.

**Note**  If you can use only 360 kilobyte (K) or 720K disks in your disk drives, use the coupon in the back of this guide to order 360K or 720K Setup disks.

## Upgrading from an Earlier Version of DOS to MS-DOS 6

This section describes how to set up MS-DOS 6 on a computer that already has an earlier version of DOS installed on its hard disk.

**Note**  If you have OS/2 on your computer, see "Upgrading from OS/2 to MS-DOS 6" later in this chapter.

## Before You Upgrade to MS-DOS 6

Before you start the Setup program, read the following three sections. You must carry out the procedure in "Prepare the Uninstall Disk." Carry out the remaining two procedures only if they apply to your system.

## Prepare the Uninstall Disk

Write "Uninstall #1" on the label of one unformatted or newly formatted floppy disk that is compatible with drive A. (If you are using 360K disks, you might need two floppy disks. If this is the case, label the disks "Uninstall #1" and "Uninstall #2.") You will need to use the Uninstall disk in drive A during Setup.

The purpose of the Uninstall disk is to safeguard the files on your computer while you are installing MS-DOS 6. The Uninstall disk protects the files if Setup cannot finish installing MS-DOS or if you encounter problems with MS-DOS 6 after Setup. By using the Uninstall disk, you can restore your previous version of DOS if you need to. For more information about the Uninstall disk, see "Using the Uninstall Disk" in the chapter "Diagnosing and Solving Problems."

## Disable Automatic Message Services

Before you run Setup, disable any automatic message service, such as a network popup or a printing notification, that prints directly to your screen. These message services are incompatible with Setup.

## Disable Disk-Caching, Delete-Protection, and Anti-Virus Programs

Some disk-caching, delete-protection, and anti-virus programs conflict with Setup. If programs such as these are loaded each time you start your computer, you might want to edit your AUTOEXEC.BAT and CONFIG.SYS files and disable or remove the startup commands for these programs. To do this, carry out the following procedure.

---

**Note**   You do not need to disable the startup command for the MS-DOS SMARTDrive program.

---

▶  **To disable disk-caching, delete-protection, or anti-virus programs**

1. Open your AUTOEXEC.BAT file by using any text editor.

2. Type **rem** and a space at the beginning of each command line that starts a disk-caching, delete-protection, or anti-virus program. For example, suppose the following command appears in your AUTOEXEC.BAT file:

   ```
   c:\dos\vsafe.com
   ```

   To disable this command, you would change it to the following:

   ```
   rem c:\dos\vsafe.com
   ```

   If you don't know the names of the commands that load your disk-caching, delete-protection, or anti-virus programs, see the documentation that came with the programs.

3. Save your AUTOEXEC.BAT file.

4. Open your CONFIG.SYS file, and disable any disk-caching, delete-protection, or anti-virus programs (as described in step 2).

5. Save your CONFIG.SYS file, and then quit the text editor.

6. Restart your computer by pressing CTRL+ALT+DEL. Then run Setup.

7. After you set up MS-DOS, open your CONFIG.SYS and AUTOEXEC.BAT files, delete the **rem** commands that you added, and then save the files.

8. Restart your computer by pressing CTRL+ALT+DEL.

# Running Setup

To set up MS-DOS 6, you need the Setup disks included with this product. You'll also need to supply the unformatted or newly formatted Uninstall disk described earlier in this chapter.

---

**Important**　Do not run Setup while Microsoft Windows or MS-DOS Shell is running.

---

▶ **To set up MS-DOS**

1. Start your computer.

2. Insert Setup Disk 1 in drive A or B.

3. Type the following at the command prompt:

   **a:setup**

   or

   **b:setup**

4. Follow the instructions on your screen.

   If you have questions about any of the procedures or options you encounter during Setup, press F1 for Help.

5. When Setup prompts you for the Uninstall disk(s), insert the disk(s) in drive A.

   You must use drive A because Setup copies files to the Uninstall disk that MS-DOS needs to start your computer.

---

**Note**　Setup places your previous DOS files in a directory named OLD_DOS.*x*. If you are sure you do not want to restore your previous version of DOS, you can delete the OLD_DOS.*x* directory and its contents by typing **deloldos** at the command prompt.

---

During Setup, a screen will prompt you to specify whether you want to install Microsoft Anti-Virus, Backup, and Undelete.

If you choose to install Anti-Virus, Backup, or Undelete for Windows, Setup automatically creates a Microsoft Tools group in Program Manager and adds icons for these programs to the group.

**Note**  If you do not have Windows installed on your computer, you cannot set up these programs for Windows.

If you are running Windows version 3.1 and you install Undelete for Windows, Setup adds an Undelete command to the File menu in File Manager. If you install Anti-Virus and Backup for Windows, Setup creates a Tools menu in File Manager and adds commands for these programs to it.

If you have problems running Setup, see "Troubleshooting During Setup" in the chapter "Diagnosing and Solving Problems."

# Installing Anti-Virus, Backup, and Undelete After Setup

If you didn't install Anti-Virus, Backup, or Undelete during Setup, you can run Setup again to install the programs. For example, if you install Windows after setting up MS-DOS 6, you can run MS-DOS 6 Setup again to install Anti-Virus, Backup, and Undelete for Windows.

**Note**  If you installed MS-DOS 6 by inserting Setup Disk 1 in drive A and restarting your computer, Anti-Virus, Backup, and Undelete for MS-DOS are already installed. However, you need to run Setup again to configure Anti-Virus, Backup, and Undelete for Windows.

Carry out the following procedure to set up the Anti-Virus, Backup, and Undelete programs. If you want to install the Windows versions of these programs, make sure Windows is installed on your computer first.

▶  **To set up Anti-Virus, Backup, or Undelete if you have already run Setup**

1. If you originally started Setup by typing **setup** at the command prompt, insert Setup Disk 1 in drive A or B, and then type the following at the command prompt:

   **a:setup /e**

   or

   **b:setup /e**

If you originally started Setup by inserting Setup Disk 1 in drive A and restarting your computer, insert Setup Disk 1 in drive A, and then type the following at the command prompt:

**a:busetup /e**

2. Follow the instructions on your screen.

# Upgrading from OS/2 to MS-DOS 6

This section describes how to set up MS-DOS 6 on a computer that has the OS/2 operating system installed on its hard disk. (If you have only DOS on your computer, see the previous section, "Upgrading from an Earlier Version of DOS to MS-DOS 6.")

This section contains information about setting up MS-DOS if you:

- Have neither OS/2 Dual Boot nor OS/2 Boot Manager on your computer.
- Have OS/2 Dual Boot with DOS or OS/2 Boot Manager with DOS on your computer.
- Have OS/2 Boot Manager without DOS on your computer.

# If You Have Neither OS/2 Dual Boot Nor OS/2 Boot Manager

This section describes how to set up MS-DOS 6 on a computer that has the OS/2 operating system, but has neither OS/2 Dual Boot nor OS/2 Boot Manager.

## Running Setup

To set up MS-DOS 6, you need the Setup disks included with this product.

▶ **To set up MS-DOS 6 if you have neither OS/2 Dual Boot nor OS/2 Boot Manager**

1. Insert Setup Disk 1 in drive A (the startup drive).

2. Restart your computer by pressing CTRL+ALT+DEL.

3. If you want to remove OS/2 from your computer without saving the data on your hard disk, choose to remove it when Setup prompts you to do so.

   If you want to remove OS/2 from your computer but want to save the data on your hard disk first, skip to the following section, "Removing OS/2 and Saving the Data on Your Hard Disk."

4. Follow the instructions on your screen.

   If you have questions about any of the procedures or options you encounter during Setup, press F1 for Help.

If you have problems running Setup, see "Troubleshooting During Setup" in the chapter "Diagnosing and Solving Problems."

## Removing OS/2 and Saving the Data on Your Hard Disk

If you want to remove OS/2 from your computer but want to save the data on your hard disk first, quit Setup, and then view the OS2.TXT file for instructions. To view the OS2.TXT file, open it by using any text editor. The file is located on Setup Disk 1.

# If You Have OS/2 Dual Boot with DOS or OS/2 Boot Manager with DOS

This section describes how to set up MS-DOS if you have OS/2 Dual Boot or OS/2 Boot Manager and one of your operating systems is DOS.

## Before You Upgrade to MS-DOS 6

Prepare your computer for the MS-DOS Setup program by doing the following:

- Prepare the Uninstall disk(s). For instructions, see the section "Prepare the Uninstall Disk" earlier in this chapter.
- Disable automatic message services. For more information, see "Disable Automatic Message Services" earlier in this chapter.
- Disable disk-caching, delete-protection, and anti-virus programs. For more information, see "Disable Disk-Caching, Delete-Protection, and Anti-Virus Programs" earlier in this chapter.

## Running Setup

To set up MS-DOS 6, you need the Setup disks included with this product. You will also need the Uninstall disk(s) mentioned in the previous section.

▶ **To set up MS-DOS 6 if you have OS/2 Dual Boot or OS/2 Boot Manager, and one of your operating systems is DOS**

1. Start your computer with your current version of DOS.

2. Insert Setup Disk 1 in drive A or B.

3. Type the following at the command prompt:

   **a:setup**

   or

   **b:setup**

4. If you want to keep OS/2 on your computer, choose the "Continue Setup" option when Setup displays the "Non–MS-DOS Partition Detected" or "OS/2 Files Detected" screen. Then proceed to step 5.

   If you want to remove OS/2 from your computer but want to save the data on your hard disk first, skip to the following section, "Removing OS/2 and Saving the Data on Your Hard Disk."

   ---
   **Note**  If you have a version of OS/2 Dual Boot that prompts you to select an operating system each time you start your computer and you want to keep OS/2, you must reinstall OS/2 after you install MS-DOS 6.

   ---

5. Follow the instructions on your screen.

   If you have questions about any of the procedures or options you encounter during Setup, press F1 for Help.

6. When Setup prompts you for the Uninstall disk, insert the disk(s) in drive A.

   You must use drive A because Setup copies files to the Uninstall disk that MS-DOS needs to start your computer.

   ---
   **Note**  Setup places your previous DOS files in a directory named OLD_DOS.*x*. If you are sure you do not want to restore your previous version of DOS, you can delete the OLD_DOS.*x* directory and its contents by typing **deloldos** at the command prompt.

   ---

7. If you are using OS/2 Boot Manager, make the Boot Manager partition active after Setup is complete and your computer restarts. To make the Boot Manager partition active, carry out the following procedure.

▶ **To make the Boot Manager partition active**

1. Type **fdisk** at the command prompt.

   The Fdisk Options screen appears.

2. Choose 2, and then press ENTER.

   The Set Active Partition screen appears.

   The Boot Manager partition appears as a 1-MB non–MS-DOS partition.

3. Choose the number that corresponds with the Boot Manager partition, and then press ENTER.

4. When the confirmation screen appears, press ESC.

   The Fdisk Options screen appears.

5. Press ESC to exit Fdisk.

   Your computer restarts.

If you install Anti-Virus, Backup, or Undelete for Windows during Setup, Setup automatically creates a Microsoft Tools group in Program Manager and adds their icons to the group. In addition, if you install Undelete for Windows, Setup adds an Undelete command to the File menu in File Manager. If you install Anti-Virus and Backup for Windows, Setup adds commands for these programs to a Tools menu.

---

**Note**  If you do not have Windows installed on your computer, you cannot set up the optional programs for Windows.

---

If you have problems running Setup, see "Troubleshooting During Setup" in the chapter "Diagnosing and Solving Problems."

## Removing OS/2 and Saving the Data on Your Hard Disk

When Setup detects OS/2, it displays a "Non–MS-DOS Partition Detected" or an "OS/2 Files Detected" screen. Make a note of which screen Setup displays; the procedure you use to remove OS/2 and save data on your computer depends on which screen Setup displays. For instructions on removing OS/2 and saving data on your computer, quit Setup and view the OS2.TXT file. To view the OS2.TXT file, open it by using any text editor. The file is located on Setup Disk 1.

# If You Have OS/2 Boot Manager Without DOS

This section describes how to set up MS-DOS on a computer that has OS/2 Boot Manager and does not have DOS.

## Running Setup

To set up MS-DOS 6, you need the Setup disks included with this product.

▶ **To set up MS-DOS 6 if you have OS/2  Boot Manager without DOS**

1. Insert Setup Disk 1 in drive A (the startup drive).

2. Restart your computer by pressing CTRL+ALT+DEL.

3. If you want to remove OS/2 from your computer without saving the data on your hard disk, choose to remove the data when Setup prompts you to do so. Then proceed to step 4.

If you want to remove OS/2 from your computer but want to save the data on your hard disk first, skip to the following section, "Removing OS/2 and Saving the Data on Your Hard Disk."

If you want to keep OS/2, see your OS/2 documentation for information about setting up OS/2 and MS-DOS on the same computer. In general, you will first need to install MS-DOS on drive C.

4.  Follow the instructions on your screen.

If you have questions about any of the procedures or options you encounter during Setup, press F1 for Help.

If you have problems running Setup, see "Troubleshooting During Setup" in the chapter "Diagnosing and Solving Problems."

## Removing OS/2 and Saving the Data on Your Hard Disk

If you want to remove OS/2 from your computer but want to save the data on your hard disk first, quit Setup. Then view the OS2.TXT file for instructions on how to remove OS/2 and save the data on your hard disk. To view the OS2.TXT file, open it by using any text editor. The file is located on Setup Disk 1.

C H A P T E R  2

# MS-DOS Basics

This chapter explains the basics of using MS-DOS 6. The first section of this chapter is a tutorial. You can use the tutorial to learn and practice some of the most common MS-DOS commands. The second section of this chapter explains in more detail some of the concepts described in the tutorial and provides more information about using MS-DOS and MS-DOS Help.

## Learning MS-DOS Basics—A Tutorial

This tutorial gives you an opportunity to try basic MS-DOS commands. By following the procedures in this section, you will learn to:

- View the contents of a directory
- Change from one directory to another
- Create and delete directories
- Change from one drive to another
- Copy files
- Rename files
- Delete files
- Format a floppy disk

# The Command Prompt

When you first turn on your computer, you will see some cryptic information flash by. MS-DOS displays this information to let you know how it is configuring your computer. You can ignore it for now. When the information stops scrolling past, you'll see the following:

```
C:\>
```

This is called the *command prompt*. The flashing underscore next to the command prompt is called the *cursor*. The cursor shows where the command you type will appear.

If your command prompt looks like the sample command prompt earlier in this section, skip to the following section, "Typing a Command."

If your command prompt does not look like the example, type the following at the command prompt, and then press ENTER:

**cd \**

Note that the slash leans backward, not forward. You will learn more about the **cd** command later in the tutorial. If your command prompt still doesn't look like the example, type the following at the command prompt, and then press ENTER:

**prompt $p$g**

Your command prompt should now look like the example.

# Typing a Command

This section explains how to type a command at the command prompt and demonstrates the "Bad command or file name" message.

▶ **To type a command at the command prompt**

1. Type the following at the command prompt (you can type the command in either uppercase or lowercase letters):

   **nul**

   If you make a typing mistake, press the BACKSPACE key to erase the mistake, and then try again.

2. Press ENTER.

   You must press ENTER after every command you type.

The following message appears:

```
Bad command or file name
```

The "Bad command or file name" message appears when you type something that MS-DOS does not recognize. Because **nul** is not a valid MS-DOS command, MS-DOS displays the "Bad command or file name" message.

3. Now, type the following command at the command prompt:

**ver**

The following message appears on your screen:

```
MS-DOS version 6.00
```

The **ver** command displays the version number of MS-DOS.

Continue to the next section, where you will use the **dir** command to view the contents of a directory.

# Viewing the Contents of a Directory

In this section, you will view the contents of a directory by using the **dir** command. The **dir** command stands for "directory."

▶   **To view the contents of a directory**

●   Type the following at the command prompt:

**dir**

A list similar to the following appears:

```
Volume in drive C is MS-DOS_6
Volume Serial Number is 1E49-15E2
Directory of C:\

WINDOWS      <DIR>        09-08-92  10:27p
TEMP         <DIR>        05-15-92  12:09p
CONFIG   SYS         278  09-23-92  10:50a
COMMAND  COM       53014  09-18-92   6:00a
WINA20   386        9349  11-11-91   5:00a
DOS          <DIR>        09-02-92   4:23p
AUTOEXEC BAT         290  09-23-92  10:54a
        7 file(s)       62931 bytes
                      8732672 bytes free
```

This is called a *directory list*. A directory list is a list of all the files and subdirectories that a directory contains. In this case, you see all the files and directories in the main or *root* directory of your drive. All the files and directories on your drive are stored in the root directory.

# Changing Directories

Look at the list on your screen. All the names that have <DIR> beside them are directories. You can see a list of the files in another directory by changing to that directory, and then using the **dir** command again. In this case, you will change to the DOS directory.

Before you begin this section, make sure you have a directory named DOS by carrying out the following procedure.

▶ **To make sure you have a directory named DOS**

1. Look through the directory list on your screen for a line that looks similar to the following:

   ```
   DOS          <DIR>       09-02-92    4:23p
   ```

2. If you see a line like this, you have a directory named DOS. Skip to the next procedure, "To change from the root directory to the DOS directory."

   If you do not see a line in the directory list indicating that you have a directory named DOS, type the following at the command prompt:

   **dir /s memmaker.exe**

   You will see a message that includes a line such as the following:

   ```
   Directory of C:\DIRNAME
   ```

   If the name that appears in place of DIRNAME is DOS, you have a DOS directory. Skip to the next procedure.

   If the name that appears in place of DIRNAME is not DOS, substitute the name that appears for DOS throughout this tutorial. For example, if the name that appears in place of DIRNAME is MSDOS, type **msdos** whenever you are instructed to type **dos**.

▶ **To change from the root directory to the DOS directory**

To change directories, you will use the **cd** command. The **cd** command stands for "change directory."

• Type the following at the command prompt:

   **cd dos**

   The command prompt changes. It should now look like the following:

   ```
   C:\DOS>
   ```

The command prompt shows which directory you are in. In this case, you know you successfully changed to the DOS directory because the command prompt displays the directory's name. Now the *current directory* is DOS.

Next, you will use the **dir** command to view a list of the files in the DOS directory.

▶ **To view a list of the files in the DOS directory**

- Type the following at the command prompt:

   **dir**

A list of the files in the DOS directory appears, but scrolls by too quickly to read. You can modify the **dir** command so that it displays only one screen of information at a time.

▶ **To view the contents of a directory one screen at a time**

1. Type the following at the command prompt:

   **dir /p**

   One screen of information appears. At the bottom of the screen, you will see the following message:

   `Press any key to continue . . .`

2. To view the next screen of information, press any key on your keyboard. Repeat this step until the command prompt appears at the bottom of your screen.

When you typed the **dir** command this time, you included the **/p** switch after the command. A *switch* modifies the way MS-DOS carries out a command. Generally, a switch consists of a forward slash (/) that is followed by one or more letters or numbers. When you used the **/p** switch with the **dir** command, you specified that MS-DOS should pause after it displays each screen of directory list information.

Another helpful switch you can use with the **dir** command is the **/w** switch. The **/w** switch indicates that MS-DOS should show a wide version of the directory list.

▶ **To view the contents of a directory in wide format**

1. Type the following at the command prompt:

   **dir /w**

   The directory list appears, with the filenames listed in wide format. Note that only filenames are listed. No information about the files' size or date and time of creation appears.

2. If the directory contains more files than will fit on one screen, you can combine the **/p** and **/w** switches as follows:

   **dir /w /p**

# Changing Back to the Root Directory

Next, you will change from the DOS directory to the root directory. The root directory is the directory you were in before you changed to the DOS directory. Before you begin this section, make sure your command prompt looks like the following:

```
C:\DOS>
```

▶ **To change to the root directory**

- Type the following at the command prompt:

  **cd \\**

  Note that the slash you type in this command is a backslash (\\), not a forward slash (/).

  No matter which directory you are in, this command always returns you to the root directory of a drive. The root directory does not have a name. It is simply referred to by a backslash (\\).

  The command prompt should now look like the following:

  ```
  C:\>
  ```

When your command prompt appears similar to this—that is, when it does not contain the name of a directory—you are in the root directory.

# Creating a Directory

In this section, you will create two directories. Creating a directory is helpful if you want to organize related files into groups to make them easy to find. Before you begin this section, make sure the command prompt looks like the following:

```
C:\>
```

To create a directory, you will use the **md** command. The **md** command stands for "make directory."

▶ **To create and change to a directory named FRUIT**

1. Type the following at the command prompt:

   **md fruit**

   You have now created a directory named FRUIT. You won't see the new FRUIT directory until you carry out the **dir** command in the next step.

2.  To confirm that you successfully created the FRUIT directory, type the following at the command prompt:

**dir**

or

**dir /p**

Look through the directory list. A new entry somewhere in the list should look similar to the following:

```
FRUIT        <DIR>      09-25-93  12:09p
```

3.  To change to the new FRUIT directory, type the following at the command prompt:

**cd fruit**

The command prompt should now look like the following:

```
C:\FRUIT>
```

You will now create a directory within the FRUIT directory, named GRAPES.

▶  **To create and work with a directory named GRAPES**

1.  Type the following at the command prompt:

**md grapes**

You will not see the new GRAPES directory until you carry out the **dir** command in the next step.

2.  To confirm that you successfully created the GRAPES directory, type the following at the command prompt:

**dir**

A list similar to the following appears:

```
Volume in drive C is MS-DOS_6
Volume Serial Number is 1E49-15E2
Directory of C:\FRUIT

    .        <DIR>      09-25-93  12:08p
    ..       <DIR>      09-25-93  12:08p
GRAPES     <DIR>      09-25-93  12:10p
        3 file(s)            0 bytes
                    11534336 bytes free
```

Note that there are three entries in the FRUIT directory. One is the GRAPES directory that you just created. There are two other entries—one looks like a single period (.) and the other looks like a double period (..). These directory entries are important to MS-DOS, but you can ignore them. They appear in every directory.

The GRAPES directory is a *subdirectory* of the FRUIT directory. A subdirectory is a directory within another directory. Subdirectories are useful if you want to further subdivide information.

3. To change to the GRAPES directory, type the following at the command prompt:

**cd grapes**

The command prompt should now look like the following:

```
C:\FRUIT\GRAPES>
```

4. To switch back to the FRUIT directory, type the following:

**cd ..**

The command prompt should now look like the following:

```
C:\FRUIT>
```

When the **cd** command is followed by two periods (..), MS-DOS moves up one level in the directory structure. In this case, you moved up one level from the GRAPES directory to the FRUIT directory.

# Deleting a Directory

If you no longer use a particular directory, you may want to delete it to simplify your directory structure. Deleting a directory is also useful if you type the wrong name when you are creating a directory and you want to delete the incorrect directory before creating a new one.

In this section, you will delete the GRAPES directory. Before you begin this section, make sure the command prompt looks like the following:

```
C:\FRUIT>
```

To delete a directory, use the **rd** command. The **rd** command stands for "remove directory."

▶  **To delete the GRAPES directory**

1. Type the following at the command prompt:

**rd grapes**

2. To confirm that you successfully deleted the GRAPES directory, type the following at the command prompt:

**dir**

The GRAPES directory should no longer appear in the directory list.

**Note**  You cannot delete a directory if you are in it. Before you can delete a directory, you must make the directory that is one level higher the current directory. To do this, type **cd..** at the command prompt.

# Changing Drives

This section describes how to change drives. Changing drives is useful if you want to work with files that are on a different drive.

So far, you have been working with drive C. You have other drives you can use to store information. For example, drive A is your first floppy disk drive. The files and directories on drive A are located on the floppy disk in the drive. (You might also have a drive B, which contains the files and directories stored on the floppy disk in that drive.)

Before you begin this section, make sure your command prompt looks like the following:

```
C:\FRUIT>
```

▶ **To change to and view files on a different drive**

1. Insert Setup Disk 1 (included with your copy of MS-DOS 6) in drive A label-side up. Then close the drive door or make sure the disk clicks into the drive.

2. Type the following at the command prompt:

   **a:**

   Note that the command prompt changed to the following:

   ```
   A:\>
   ```

   This message may appear:

   ```
   Not ready reading drive A
   Abort, Retry, Fail?
   ```

   If you see this message, the drive door may not be closed properly. Place the disk label-side up in the disk drive, and then close the drive door or make sure the disk clicks into the disk drive. Then, type **r** for Retry. If this message appears again, press F for Fail, and then type **b:** at the command prompt. If you no longer see this message, type **b:** instead of **a:** throughout the rest of the tutorial.

   There must be a floppy disk in the drive that you want to change to.

3. To view a list of the files on the floppy disk in drive A, type the following at the command prompt:

   **dir**

   A list of the files on the disk appears.

4. Change back to drive C by typing the following at the command prompt:

   **c:**

   Your command prompt should return to the following:

   C:\FRUIT>

When you type a drive letter followed by a colon, you change to that drive. The drive letter that appears in the command prompt shows which drive is the *current drive*. Unless you specify otherwise, any commands you type are carried out on the current drive and in the current directory.

So far, all the commands you typed were carried out on the current drive and in the current directory. You can also carry out a command on a drive that isn't current. For example, you can view the files on a disk in drive A without switching to drive A by following this procedure.

▶  **To view files on drive A when drive C is current**

- Type the following at the command prompt:

  **dir a:**

  If your MS-DOS Setup disk is in drive B, type **dir b**: instead.

  A list of the files on the floppy disk in drive A appears, even though your command prompt indicates that drive C is current.

By specifying **a:** after the **dir** command, you are giving MS-DOS additional information. You are indicating that you want the **dir** command to show the list of files and directories on drive A instead of drive C. The **a:** you typed after the **dir** command is called a *parameter*. A parameter specifies what a command should act on. In the previous example, the parameter you used indicated which directory list you want to view.

The following procedure presents another example of using a parameter.

▶  **To view the contents of the DOS directory on drive C**

- Type the following at the command prompt:

  **dir c:\dos**

  A list of the files in the DOS directory on drive C should scroll past on your screen.

The **c:\dos** parameter specifies that you want MS-DOS to display the contents of the DOS directory on drive C, even though your command prompt indicates that the FRUIT directory is current.

# Copying Files

This section describes how to copy a single file and a group of files. Copying files creates a duplicate of the original file and does not remove the original file. This is useful for many reasons. For example, if you want to work on a document at home, you can copy it from your computer at work to a floppy disk and then take the floppy disk home.

To copy a file, you will use the **copy** command. When you use the **copy** command, you must include two parameters. The first is the location and name of the file you want to copy, or the *source*. The second is the location to which you want to copy the file, or the *destination*. You separate the source and destination with a space. The **copy** command follows this pattern:

**copy** *source destination*

## Copying a Single File

In this section, you will copy the EDIT.HLP and EDIT.COM files from the DOS directory to the FRUIT directory. You will specify the source and destination of these files in two different ways. The difference between the two methods is explained at the end of this section.

Before you begin this section, make sure the command prompt looks like the following:

`C:\FRUIT>`

▶   **To copy the EDIT.HLP and EDIT.COM files from the DOS directory to the FRUIT directory**

1.  Return to the root directory by typing the following at the command prompt:

    **cd \**

    The command prompt should now look like the following:

    `C:\>`

2.  Change to the DOS directory by typing the following at the command prompt:

    **cd dos**

    The command prompt should now look like the following:

    `C:\DOS>`

3.  Make sure the file you are going to copy, EDIT.COM, is located in the DOS directory by using the **dir** command followed by a filename.

To see if the EDIT.COM file is in the DOS directory, type the following at the command prompt:

**dir edit.com**

A list similar to the following appears:

```
Volume in drive C is MS-DOS_6
Volume Serial Number is 1E49-15E2
Directory of C:\DOS

EDIT     COM      413 03-25-93    5:00a
        1 file(s)          413 bytes
                     11999232 bytes free
```

This shows that the EDIT.COM file is located in the DOS directory. You just specified another parameter with the **dir** command, one that directs MS-DOS to list only the files that match the filename you specified in the command. Since only one file in the DOS directory can be named EDIT.COM, the directory list includes only that file.

4. To copy the EDIT.COM file from the DOS directory to the FRUIT directory, type the following at the command prompt:

**copy c:\dos\edit.com c:\fruit**

The following message appears:

```
1 file(s) copied
```

The command you just typed copied the file from its source to its destination. By specifying C:\DOS\EDIT.COM as the source, you indicated that MS-DOS would find the source file EDIT.COM on drive C in the DOS directory. By specifying C:\FRUIT as the destination, you indicated that MS-DOS should place the copy of EDIT.COM on drive C in the FRUIT directory.

5. Next, you will copy the EDIT.HLP file to the FRUIT directory. To confirm that the EDIT.HLP file is in the DOS directory, type the following at the command prompt:

**dir edit.hlp**

6. To copy the EDIT.HLP file from the DOS directory to the FRUIT directory, type the following at the command prompt:

**copy edit.hlp \fruit**

The following message appears:

```
1 file(s) copied
```

If you forgot to leave a space before typing **\fruit**, the following message will appear:

```
Access denied
```

If this message appears, type the command again and leave a space before **\fruit**.

7. To confirm that you copied the files successfully, view the contents of the FRUIT directory by typing the following at the command prompt:

   **dir \fruit**

   You should see the two files listed in the FRUIT directory.

Note that you specified the source and destination in the two **copy** commands differently. In the command you typed in step 4, you specified the source file as C:\DOS\EDIT.COM and the destination directory as C:\FRUIT. Both C:\DOS\EDIT.COM and C:\FRUIT are called *full paths* because you specified the drive and directory where these files are located. Specifying the full path is the safest way to copy files, because you provide all the information about which file you want to copy and which directory you want to copy it to.

In the **copy** command you typed in step 6, you specified EDIT.HLP for the source file and \FRUIT for the destination directory. These are *relative paths*. A relative path specifies only the difference between the current drive and directory and the destination of the files you are copying. The following illustration shows how the DOS directory and the FRUIT directory are related:

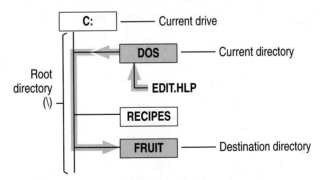

When you typed the second **copy** command, you specified the source filename as EDIT.HLP instead of C:\DOS\EDIT.HLP. This is because drive C is the current drive, so you did not have to repeat C: in the path. The DOS directory is the current directory, so you did not have to repeat DOS in the path. You had to specify only the filename.

For the destination directory, you specified the relative path as \FRUIT instead of C:\FRUIT. Again, you did not need to specify drive C, because drive C is current. However, the FRUIT directory is not current. To access the FRUIT directory from the current directory, DOS, MS-DOS must first return to the root directory (\), and then switch to the FRUIT directory, before copying the file to its new location. Therefore, you typed the path MS-DOS must take to switch between the current directory and the FRUIT directory, or \FRUIT.

## Copying a Group of Files

In this section, you will use *wildcards* to copy a group of files from the DOS directory to the FRUIT directory. In a card game, a wildcard matches any card in the deck. In MS-DOS, the asterisk (*) wildcard matches any character in that position and all the other positions that follow it. If you want to copy a group of files with similar names, using wildcards is easier than copying each file individually.

In this section, you will first view a group of files by using wildcards, and then copy the files using wildcards. Before you begin this section, make sure your command prompt looks like the following:

```
C:\DOS>
```

▶  **To list all files ending with the extension .TXT and copy them from the DOS directory to the FRUIT directory by using wildcards**

1. View all the files in the DOS directory that end with the extension .TXT by typing the following at the command prompt:

   **dir *.txt**

   Note that there is a space before the asterisk (*), but not after it.

   This command directs MS-DOS to list all files and subdirectories in the current directory that end with the extension .TXT. The asterisk matches the first character of the filename and all other characters that follow it, up to the period (.) that separates the name from the .TXT extension.

   A list similar to the following appears:

   ```
   Volume in drive C is MS-DOS_6
   Volume Serial Number is 1E49-15E2
   Directory of C:\DOS

   NETWORKS TXT     8369  11-11-93    5:00a
   OS2      TXT     4587  11-11-93    5:00a
   README   TXT    10858  11-11-93    5:00a
            3 file(s)      23814 bytes
   ```

MS-DOS lists all the files that end with a .TXT extension. The wildcard in your command specified that MS-DOS should ignore the very different beginnings of the files and focus only on the extensions.

Next, you will copy all the files with a .TXT extension to the FRUIT directory by using wildcards.

2. To copy the files with a .TXT extension to the FRUIT directory, type the following at the command prompt:

**copy \*.txt \fruit**

This command copies all the files that have the .TXT extension from the current directory (DOS) to the FRUIT directory.

3. To confirm that you copied the files successfully, change to the FRUIT directory by typing the following at the command prompt:

**cd \fruit**

4. To view a list of all the files in the FRUIT directory, type the following at the command prompt:

**dir**

A list similar to the following appears:

```
Volume in drive C is MS-DOS_6
Volume Serial Number is 1E49-15E2
Directory of C:\FRUIT

.              <DIR>       09-27-93   11:11p
..             <DIR>       09-27-93   11:11p
EDIT    COM        413 11-11-93    5:00a
EDIT    HLP      17898 11-11-93    5:00a
NETWORKS TXT      8369 11-11-93    5:00a
OS2     TXT       4587 11-11-93    5:00a
README  TXT      10858 11-11-93    5:00a

     7 file(s)      42125 bytes
                 40652800 bytes free
```

The EDIT.COM and EDIT.HLP files are the files you copied by following the procedure in the previous section. The files with .TXT extensions are the ones you just copied by using wildcards.

# Renaming Files

This section explains how to rename files. You may want to rename a file if the information in it changes or if you decide you prefer another name.

To rename a file, you will use the **ren** command. The **ren** command stands for "rename." When you use the **ren** command, you must include two parameters.

The first is the file you want to rename, and the second is the new name for the file. You separate the two names with a space. The **ren** command follows this pattern:

**ren** *oldname newname*

## Renaming a File

In this section, you will rename the README.TXT file.

Before you begin this section, make sure your command prompt looks like the following:

```
C:\FRUIT>
```

▶  **To rename the README.TXT file to PEACH.TXT**

1. Type the following at the command prompt:

   **ren readme.txt peach.txt**

2. To confirm that you renamed the file successfully, type the following at the command prompt:

   **dir**

   The name PEACH.TXT should appear instead of the name README.TXT. It is the same file, but now has a different name.

## Renaming a Group of Files

You also can use wildcards to rename a group of files. If you want to rename a group of files that have similar names, using wildcards is easier than renaming the files individually. In this section, you will rename a group of files by using wildcards.

Before beginning this section, make sure your command prompt looks like the following:

```
C:\FRUIT>
```

▶  **To rename the files whose names begin with EDIT by using wildcards**

1. List the files in the FRUIT directory that begin with EDIT by typing the following at the command prompt:

   **dir edit.***

   A list of the files in the FRUIT directory that begin with EDIT appears.

2. To rename the files that begin with EDIT to the new name PEAR, type the following command:

**ren edit.\* pear.\***

This command specifies that all the files that begin with EDIT should be renamed PEAR, but should keep their original extensions.

3. To confirm that you renamed the files successfully, type the following at the command prompt:

**dir pear.\***

When the files were renamed, their extensions remained the same. For example, EDIT.COM became PEAR.COM, and EDIT.HLP became PEAR.HLP.

You can also rename extensions this way. For example, suppose you want to indicate that a group of files ending with a .TXT extension are old. You can use wildcards to rename the files so they have the extension .OLD.

▶ **To rename all the files in the current directory whose names end with the extension .TXT**

1. View a list of all the files in the current directory with the extension .TXT by typing the following command:

**dir \*.txt**

2. To rename all files in the current directory that end with the extension .TXT to end with the extension .OLD, type the following command:

**ren \*.txt \*.old**

3. To confirm that you renamed the files successfully, type the following at the command prompt:

**dir**

The files that had the extension .TXT now have the extension .OLD.

# Deleting Files

This section explains how to delete, or remove, a file that you no longer want on your disk. If you don't have very much disk space, deleting files you no longer use is essential.

To delete a file, you will use the **del** command. The **del** command stands for "delete."

## Deleting a File

In this section, you will delete two files using the **del** command.

Before you begin, make sure your command prompt looks like the following:

`C:\FRUIT>`

▶ **To delete the PEAR.COM and PEAR.HLP files**

1. Delete the PEAR.COM file by typing the following at the command prompt:

   **del pear.com**

2. Delete the PEAR.HLP file by typing the following at the command prompt:

   **del pear.hlp**

3. To confirm that you deleted the files successfully, type the following at the command prompt:

   **dir**

   The PEAR.COM and PEAR.HLP files should no longer appear in the list.

## Deleting a Group of Files

In this section, you will use wildcards to delete a group of files.

Before you begin this section, make sure your command prompt looks like the following:

`C:\FRUIT>`

▶ **To delete files in the current directory that end with the extension .OLD by using wildcards**

1. View all files that end with the extension .OLD by typing the following at the command prompt:

   **dir *.old**

   A list of all the files that end with the extension .OLD appears. Make sure that these are the files you want to delete. When you are deleting files by using wildcards, this step is very important. It will prevent you from deleting files accidentally.

2. Delete all files ending with .OLD by typing the following at the command prompt:

   **del *.old**

3. To confirm that all the files with the extension .OLD have been deleted, type the following at the command prompt:

   **dir**

The FRUIT directory should contain no files.

Now that the FRUIT directory is empty, you can delete it by using the **rd** (remove directory) command that you learned to use in "Deleting a Directory" earlier in this chapter.

▶   **To delete the FRUIT directory**

1. Return to the root directory by typing the following at the command prompt:

   **cd \**

2. You can see the FRUIT directory in the directory list by typing the following at the command prompt:

   **dir**

   or

   **dir /p**

3. Remove the FRUIT directory by typing the following at the command prompt:

   **rd fruit**

4. To verify that the FRUIT directory has been removed, type the following at the command prompt:

   **dir**

   or

   **dir /p**

   The FRUIT directory should not appear in the directory list.

# Formatting a Floppy Disk

When you purchase new floppy disks, you must generally format them before you can use them. Practice formatting a floppy disk now.

Caution   The data on the disk you format will be erased, so make sure you select a disk that does not contain information you may need later.

▶   **To format a floppy disk**

1. Type the following at the command prompt:

   **format a:**

   If you want to format a disk that fits only in drive B, type **format b:** at the command prompt and insert a disk in drive B when MS-DOS prompts you to do so.

This command specifies that you want to format the disk in drive A. When you press ENTER, the following message appears:

```
Insert new diskette for drive A:
and press ENTER when ready...
```

2. Insert the disk you want to format in drive A label-side up. Then close the drive door or make sure the disk clicks into the drive. When you are ready, press ENTER. The following message appears:

```
Checking existing disk format
Saving UNFORMAT information
```

As it formats the disk, MS-DOS displays the percentage of the disk that has been formatted. When the format is complete, the following message appears.

```
Volume label (11 characters, ENTER for none)?
```

3. A volume label is a name for your disk. You can give your disk any name you like, as long as it has 11 or fewer characters. For this exercise, type **practice** and then press ENTER. Information similar to the following appears:

```
    1213952 bytes total disk space
    1213952 bytes available on disk

        512 bytes in each allocation unit.
       2371 allocation units available on disk.

Volume Serial Number is 1E49-15E2

Format another (Y/N)?
```

4. If you have another disk to format, press Y. If not, press N.

# Summary

This concludes the MS-DOS tutorial. During this tutorial, you learned how to:

- View the contents of a directory by using the **dir** command.
- Change directories by using the **cd** command.
- Create directories by using the **md** command.
- Delete directories by using the **rd** command.
- Change drives by specifying the drive letter followed by a colon.
- Copy files by using the **copy** command.
- Rename files by using the **ren** command.
- Delete files by using the **del** command.
- Format a floppy disk by using the **format** command.

For more information about files, directories, drives, and paths, see the following sections. For more information about the commands discussed in this tutorial, use MS-DOS Help. Instructions for using MS-DOS Help are in the section "Getting Help" later in this chapter.

# How MS-DOS Organizes Information

The preceding tutorial introduced the commands you will most often use to find and move information. It also introduces some important terms—*file*, *directory*, and *drive*—that you need to understand to use MS-DOS effectively. This section provides more information about these terms and explains how MS-DOS organizes information.

## Files

A file is the primary unit of storage on your computer. A file enables MS-DOS to distinguish one collection of information from another. For example, when you use a word-processing program to write a letter, you store the letter in its own file. Every file has a name, which generally indicates what type of information the file contains.

The files on your computer come from various sources; not all of them are created by you. Some files come with MS-DOS, while others come with applications such as a word processor. These files contain code and other information that is necessary to make your computer and applications run. For example, each of the files that comes with MS-DOS contains information about a specific subject. Many of these files contain the code for MS-DOS commands. Like the files you create, each file in your DOS directory has a name that reflects the contents of the file.

Before long, there will be hundreds or even thousands of files on your computer. This can make it difficult to locate specific files—just as it would be difficult to find a particular knife if you stored all the items in your kitchen in one large box.

## Directories

Storing groups of files in different directories makes files easier to find. For example, all the files that come with MS-DOS are stored in a single directory that is usually named DOS. If you ever need to locate an MS-DOS file, you know where to look. Like files, directories can be created by you or by an application. For example, if you use your computer to store files that contain recipes, you might want to create a directory called RECIPES, so these files will be easier to find.

# The Current Directory

Directories would be hard to use if you didn't know which one you were in. How, you might ask, can you be "in" a directory? Think of your computer as a store. When your computer is off, you are outside the store. When you turn your computer on, you step into the store. As long as you are in the store, you are in one of its aisles and can easily find the goods on that aisle. In the same sense, as long as your computer is on, you are in a directory and can easily find the files in that directory. MS-DOS indicates which directory you are in by displaying the directory's name in the command prompt. For example, the following command prompt indicates that you are in the DOS directory:

```
C:\DOS>
```

The following command prompt indicates that you are in the RECIPES directory:

```
C:\RECIPES>
```

The directory you are in is called the *current directory*. Knowing which directory is current helps you find files and helps you move from one directory to another more easily.

You do not have to be in the directory that contains the files you want to use, but the commands you type will be shorter if you are. When you become comfortable with typing longer commands, you might rely less on being in the directory that contains the files you want to work with.

# Subdirectories

Directories can contain other directories. A directory within another directory is called a *subdirectory*. By creating subdirectories, you can better categorize your files. For example, suppose you have 75 recipe files in your RECIPES directory. If you are looking for a particular file and cannot remember the name of it, you would have to search through the names of all 75 files. You can avoid this problem by creating subdirectories in the RECIPES directory and storing the files in the appropriate subdirectory. For example, you could create subdirectories called BREADS, ENTREES, and DESSERTS, each of which might contain about 25 files.

# The Root Directory

Strictly speaking, all directories are subdirectories, except for one, which is called the *root directory*. In this guide, the term *subdirectory* is used only to emphasize the relationship between two directories. The root directory is the starting point from which all other directories branch out. The root directory does not have a name. Instead, it is represented by a backslash (\). When the root directory is the current directory, the command prompt appears similar to the following:

```
C:\>
```

This prompt indicates that you are in the root directory of drive C. For more information about drives, see the following section.

Because the root directory is the basis for all other directories, you cannot delete it. Avoid unnecessarily storing files in the root directory. There is a limit to the number of files and directories the root directory can hold. Besides, it's a good idea to get into the habit of using directories to organize files.

# Drives

Just as a directory is a group of files, a drive, which is always represented by a drive letter, is a group of directories. Drives are usually associated with a piece of hardware called a disk. A *disk* is a flat piece of metal or plastic on which data is stored. The most common types of disks are the *hard disk*, which is inside your computer, and the *floppy disk* and *compact disc*, which you insert into a slot either in or next to your computer.

In most cases, a drive is a grouping of all the directories on a disk. A drive is named with a single letter. Your first floppy disk drive is drive A. Your second floppy disk drive, if you have one, is drive B. Your hard disk, or at least part of it, is called drive C.

The following command prompt indicates that drive C is the current drive and that the root directory, represented by a backslash (\), is the current directory.

```
C:\>
```

If the current drive is drive A and the current directory on that drive is SAMPLES, the command prompt would appear similar to the following:

```
A:\SAMPLES>
```

For information about changing the current drive, see the tutorial earlier in this chapter.

If you have more than one hard disk or you use compact (CD-ROM) discs or a network, you will have additional drive letters (D, E, and so on). Every drive, no matter what type it is, has one root directory.

# Using Paths to Specify the Location of Files

A *path* is the course that leads from the root directory of a drive to the file you want to use. For example, suppose that drive C has the following directory structure:

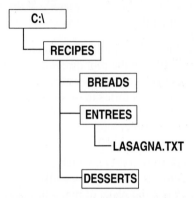

To access the LASAGNA.TXT file in the ENTREES directory, MS-DOS must go from the root directory through the RECIPES directory to the ENTREES directory, as shown in the following illustration:

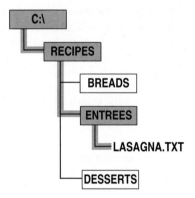

To specify the same path at the command prompt, you would type it as shown in the following illustration:

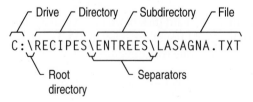

This is the path to the LASAGNA.TXT file. The first letter and colon (C:) represent the drive the file is on. The first backslash (\) represents the root directory. The second backslash separates the RECIPES directory from the ENTREES subdirectory. The third backslash separates the ENTREES subdirectory from the filename, LASAGNA.TXT. This path is called a *full path* because it contains all the available information about the location of the LASAGNA.TXT file.

To delete the LASAGNA.TXT file by specifying the full path, you would type the following at the command prompt:

**del c:\recipes\entrees\lasagna.txt**

Another kind of path is a *relative path.* The relative path of a file depends on which directory is current. For example, suppose your current directory is RECIPES. Your command prompt would look like the following:

```
C:\RECIPES>
```

To delete the LASAGNA.TXT file from the ENTREES directory by specifying the relative path, you would type the following at the command prompt:

**del entrees\lasagna.txt**

This command does exactly the same thing that the previous **del** command does —it deletes the LASAGNA.TXT file. However, the path shown in this command specifies the location of the LASAGNA.TXT file relative to the current directory, RECIPES. You don't have to include the drive letter and colon (C:) in the command because drive C is the current drive. You don't have to include the RECIPES directory in the command because it is the current directory.

MS-DOS recognizes paths up to 67 characters long (including the drive letter, colon, and backslashes).

# Naming Files and Directories

Every file and directory, except for the root directory on each drive, must have a name. The following list summarizes the rules for naming files and directories. File and directory names:

- Can be up to eight characters long. In addition, you can include an extension up to three characters long. For more information about extensions, see the following section, "Using Extensions."

- Are not case-sensitive. It does not matter whether you use uppercase or lowercase letters when you type them.

- Can contain only the letters A through Z, the numbers 0 through 9, and the following special characters: underscore (_), caret (^), dollar sign ($), tilde (~), exclamation point (!), number sign (#), percent sign (%), ampersand (&), hyphen (-), braces ({}), at sign (@), single quotation mark (`), apostrophe ('), and parentheses (). No other special characters are acceptable.

- Cannot contain spaces, commas, backslashes, or periods (except the period that separates the name from the extension).

- Cannot be identical to the name of another file or subdirectory in the same directory.

# Using Extensions

Most filenames have two parts: the name and the extension. These parts are separated by a period. For example, LETTERS.TXT is a valid filename. The name (before the period) can be up to eight characters long and should reflect the contents of the file. The extension (after the period) can be up to three characters long and indicates what type of information the file contains. Extensions can also be used in directory names, but are not commonly used for that purpose.

The following are examples of commonly used extensions for filenames:

- .EXE, .COM, or .BAT

  These extensions are used for files that contain programs. If you type the name of a file containing one of these extensions at the command prompt, MS-DOS will run the program that the file contains.

- .TXT

  This extension is commonly used for unformatted text files.

- .SYS

  This extension is commonly used for device drivers, which are files that enable your computer to communicate with hardware devices.

Many applications name files using an extension that is unique to that application. It is generally best to use the extension that an application specifies, because the extension helps the application identify the files that it created.

# Using Wildcards

If you want to carry out a task for a group of files whose names have something in common, you don't have to use the same command repeatedly for each filename in the group. You can use one or more *wildcards* to specify groups of files. A wildcard is a character that can represent one or more characters in a filename.

MS-DOS recognizes two wildcards:

- The asterisk (*) represents one or more characters that a group of files has in common.
- The question mark (?) represents a single character that a group of files has in common.

You can use wildcards to replace all or part of a file's name or extension. The following table shows examples of wildcards.

| Wildcard | What it represents | Examples |
|---|---|---|
| *.TXT | All files with a .TXT extension | JULY93.TXT, LASAGNA.TXT |
| REPORT.* | All files named REPORT with any extension | REPORT.TXT, REPORT.WRI |
| M*.* | All files beginning with the letter M, regardless of their extension | MEMO.TXT, MARCH.XLS |
| ???.* | All files having 3-letter names, with any or no extension | SUN.BMP, WIN.INI, AUG |

You can include multiple wildcards in a command. For example, the following command lists all the files from the current directory:

**dir *.***

---

**Note**  If you use the asterisk (*) wildcard when you specify a filename, MS-DOS ignores letters that come after the asterisk up to the period. For example, typing **\*m.exe** would have the same result as typing **\*.exe**. If you use the asterisk in the extension, MS-DOS ignores the letters that appear afterward. For example, typing **myapp.\*xe** would have the same result as typing **myapp.\***.

---

# Getting Help

There are two types of online help for MS-DOS commands:

- MS-DOS Help, which is a complete online reference for MS-DOS commands, including syntax, notes, and examples
- Command Line Help, which displays the syntax of a command without leaving the command line

This section explains how to use both types of help.

# Using MS-DOS Help

MS-DOS Help provides a complete online reference to MS-DOS commands. You can start MS-DOS Help in two ways: you can display the table of contents and choose a topic from it, or you can bypass the table of contents and display information about a specific command.

▶ **To start MS-DOS Help and choose a topic from the table of contents**

1. Type the following at the command prompt:

   **help**

   The MS-DOS Help table of contents appears.

2. If you are using a mouse, click the name of the command you want information about. If the command does not appear on your screen, click the arrow at the bottom of the scroll bar on the right side of your screen until the command comes into view.

If you are using a keyboard, press the key that represents the first letter of the command you want information about. The first command beginning with that letter is selected. If this is not the command you want, continue pressing the key until the command you want is selected, and then press ENTER. You can also use the TAB, UP ARROW, DOWN ARROW, PAGE UP, and PAGE DOWN keys to move between topics in the table of contents.

▶ **To start MS-DOS Help and display information about a specific command**

- At the command prompt, type **help** followed by a space and the name of the command you want information about.

  For example, for help with the **copy** command, type the following at the command prompt:

  **help copy**

Most commands have three associated topics: Syntax, Notes, and Examples. When you choose a command from the table of contents or type **help** followed by a command name at the command prompt, the Syntax topic appears first. If the topic has associated Notes or Examples topics, you can choose those topics by carrying out the following procedure.

▶ **To choose Notes or Examples**

- If you are using a mouse, click the Notes or Examples button at the top of the help screen.

  If you are using a keyboard, press N for Notes or E for Examples. When the cursor is on the Notes or Examples button, press ENTER.

When you are in a Notes or Examples topic, you can return to the Syntax topic in two ways:

▶ **To choose Syntax**

- If you are using a mouse, click the Syntax button at the top of the help screen.

  If you are using a keyboard, press s for Syntax. When the cursor is on the Syntax button, press ENTER.

The status bar at the bottom of the MS-DOS Help screen can help you navigate through the Help system.

- To return to the MS-DOS Help table of contents, press ALT+C, or choose the <ALT+C=Contents> button with your mouse.

- To view the next topic in MS-DOS Help, press ALT+N, or choose the <ALT+N=Next> button with your mouse.

- To view topics that were displayed previously, press ALT+B, or choose the <ALT+B=Back> button with your mouse.

For more information about using MS-DOS Help, press F1.

You can search for a specific string of text in MS-DOS Help by using the Find command on the Search menu. The Find command conducts a full-text search—that is, it searches through all the topics in MS-DOS Help.

▶ **To search for text**

1. From the Search menu, choose Find.

   The Find dialog box appears.

2. In the Find What box, specify the text you want to search for.

   If you want to make the search case sensitive, select the Match Upper/Lowercase check box.

   If you want to find only whole-word occurrences of the search text, select the Whole Word check box.

3. Choose the OK button.

   MS-DOS Help searches forward from the cursor position for the first occurrence of the text you specify. When it finds an occurrence of the text, it displays the topic in which the text was found.

4. To find the next occurrence of the search text, press F3.

▶ **To quit MS-DOS Help**

- If you are using a mouse, open the File menu by clicking its name in the menu bar. Then, choose the Exit command by clicking its name on the File menu.

  If you are using a keyboard, press ALT, F, X.

## Using Command Line Help

You can get information about the syntax of a command without starting MS-DOS Help. This information is less detailed than MS-DOS Help, and appears directly at the command prompt.

▶ **To display the syntax of a command**

- At the command prompt, type the name of the command followed by a space and the **/?** switch.

  For example, to view the syntax of the **dir** command, type the following at the command prompt:

  **dir /?**

# MS-DOS Shell

MS-DOS Shell provides a visual alternative to the MS-DOS command prompt. On a single screen, it can display the drives, directories, files, and applications that are available for you to use.

▶ **To start MS-DOS Shell**

- Type the following at the command prompt.

  **dosshell**

  A screen similar to the following will appear:

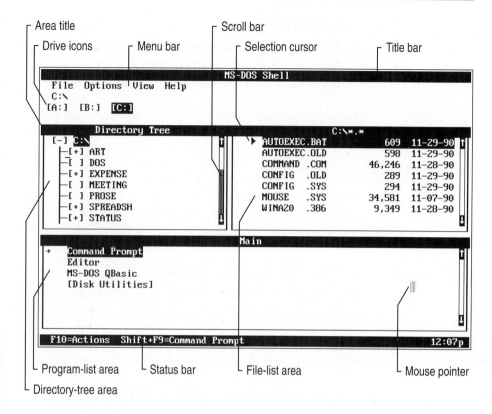

Area title

Drive icons    Menu bar

Scroll bar

Selection cursor

Title bar

Program-list area     Status bar     File-list area     Mouse pointer

Directory-tree area

The commands in MS-DOS Shell are listed on menus. The names of these menus are located in the menu bar at the top of the screen.

▶  **To choose MS-DOS Shell commands by using your mouse**

1.  In the menu bar, click the name of the menu that contains the command you want to use. The menu opens.

2.  Click the name of the command or task you want to carry out.

▶  **To choose MS-DOS Shell commands by using your keyboard**

1.  Press the ALT key.

2.  Press the first letter in the name of the menu that you want to open. For example, to open the View menu, press V.

3.  Press the DOWN ARROW key until the command or task you want to carry out is selected, and then press ENTER.

    Or press the highlighted letter that appears in the name of the command or task.

▶ **To quit MS-DOS Shell**

- If you are using a mouse, open the File menu by clicking its name in the menu bar. Then, choose the Exit command.

  If you are using a keyboard, press ALT, F, X.

For more information about using MS-DOS Shell, use MS-DOS Shell Help. For more information about MS-DOS Shell Help, see the following section.

# Using MS-DOS Shell Help

MS-DOS Shell Help provides a quick way to get information about MS-DOS Shell basics and about using menus, commands, dialog boxes, dialog box options, and procedures. When you are using MS-DOS Shell, you can get help in three ways:

- Press F1 for context-sensitive help.
- Select the Help button that appears in most dialog boxes.
- Use the Help menu.

If you haven't used MS-DOS Shell before, you can get information about MS-DOS Shell Basics by carrying out the following procedure:

▶ **For information about MS-DOS Shell Basics**

- If you are using a mouse, choose Shell Basics from the Help menu.

  If you are using a keyboard, press ALT, H, S.

A Help window containing information about the basics of using MS-DOS Shell appears. To scroll through the Help window, use the PAGE UP or PAGE DOWN key.

If you haven't used MS-DOS Shell Help before, you can get information about using it by carrying out the following procedure.

▶ **For information about using MS-DOS Shell Help**

- If you are using a mouse, choose Using Help from the Help menu.

  If you are using a keyboard, press ALT, H, U.

A Help window containing information about using MS-DOS Shell Help appears. To scroll through the Help window, use the PAGE UP or PAGE DOWN key.

▶ **To close MS-DOS Shell Help**

- If you are using a mouse, click the Close button at the bottom of the Help window.

  If you are using a keyboard, press ESC.

C H A P T E R   3

# Managing Your System

MS-DOS 6 includes several programs that you can use to manage and protect your data and improve the performance of your computer. Microsoft Backup helps you increase available hard disk space and protect your data. Microsoft Anti-Virus minimizes the possibility that your data will be damaged by a computer virus. The Microsoft Defragmenter and SMARTDrive programs minimize the time it takes your computer to access files on your hard disk. Microsoft Undelete recovers files you may have accidentally deleted.

To keep your computer in top working order, use these programs on a regular basis. When you determine which tasks are necessary to manage your computer, consider the following.

| To ensure that | Do this | For details, see |
|---|---|---|
| You maximize free space on your hard disk | Run DoubleSpace or delete unnecessary files. | The chapter "Freeing Disk Space." |
| Lost allocation units aren't taking up space on your hard disk | Use the **chkdsk** command. | The chapter "Freeing Disk Space." |
| You minimize the time your computer spends reading data from your hard disk | Use the SMARTDrive program. | "Using SMARTDrive" later in this chapter. |
| Disk space is freed and files aren't damaged if your hard disk fails | Run Backup. | "Backing Up Your Files" later in this chapter. |
| Viruses don't damage data | Run Anti-Virus. | "Protecting Your Computer from Viruses" later in this chapter. |
| Your computer can access files quickly and efficiently | Defragment your hard disk. | "Using the Defragmenter" later in this chapter. |
| You can recover files that you accidentally delete | Set up Undelete. | "Recovering Deleted Files" later in this chapter. |

Managing your computer need not be complicated or time-consuming. It can be as simple as automatically searching for viruses when you start your computer, backing up your files once a week, and occasionally using the Defragmenter to defragment your hard disk. No matter what your computer management plan, carry it out at regular intervals.

# Backing Up Your Files

Backing up your files safeguards them against loss if your hard disk fails or you accidentally overwrite or delete data. Using Backup, you can return to older file versions, move backed up files off your hard disk, and transfer files easily from one computer to another.

Hard disk failure can render all your data inaccessible. It takes an average of 2,000 hours of work to replace the data on the average hard disk. Backup helps you protect your data and your investment of time and effort. Within minutes, you can restore a hard disk you've backed up.

# Overview of Backup

MS-DOS 6 includes two backup programs: Backup for MS-DOS, a program you can run from the MS-DOS command prompt, and Backup for Windows, a program you can run from Microsoft Windows. For instructions on starting these programs, see "Using Backup" later in this chapter.

## Backup Help

Backup includes extensive online help for commands, procedures, and dialog boxes. Online help also includes instructions for using the help system.

▶ **To get help**

- Press F1 when Backup displays the screen, window, or dialog box you want more information about.

## Backup Media

You can back up your files to the following types of media:

- Floppy disks

  Backup can back up files to floppy disks in standard MS-DOS format or in Backup format. Backup format stores more data faster and in less space.

- MS-DOS devices

  If you can copy files to a device by using MS-DOS commands, Backup supports that device. For example, Backup supports network drives and removable drives such as Bernoulli ™ drives.

# Types of Backup

You can back up your data in three ways.

A *full backup* backs up all the files that you select before starting the backup. A full backup can include all the files on your hard disk, but more commonly includes all files of one type, all files on a particular drive, or all files in one or more directories.

An *incremental backup* backs up only files that have changed since your last full or incremental backup. Because an incremental backup backs up only files that have changed, it quickly and fully protects you against data loss.

A *differential backup* backs up only the files that have changed since your last full backup. A differential backup may take a little longer to complete than an incremental backup. On the other hand, you need to keep only the last full and the last differential backup sets to restore files.

The following table describes the purpose, advantages, and disadvantages of each type of backup:

| Backup Type | Purpose | Advantages | Disadvantages |
|---|---|---|---|
| Full | Ensures that you have a copy of every file that you might need to restore. | Can restore any file easily. | Backing up a large amount of data can be time-consuming and require more space on backup media than other methods. |
| Incremental | Records changes since the last full or incremental backup. Preserves multiple versions of a file. | Is fastest if you work with many different files. Requires less space on your backup media. | You need to keep each incremental backup (between full backups) because the backups build on each other. |
| Differential | Records changes since the last full backup. Maintains the latest version of your files. | Is fastest if you work with the same set of files each day. Requires less space on your backup media. In the event of hard disk failure, you'll have fewer backups to restore. | Can become large if you work with many different files. Cannot retrieve previous versions of a file. |

For a backup strategy to be effective, you should back up your data in regular cycles. A *backup cycle* begins when you fully back up your files and includes all subsequent incremental or differential backups. A new backup cycle begins when you perform the next full backup of the same set of files. Backup cycles for different groups of files may be of different durations, depending on the types of files you back up and how you use them.

## Backup Strategies

To establish an effective backup strategy, decide how you want to implement a backup cycle. Your strategy will depend largely on how you work with files.

### If You Work with the Same Files Repeatedly

If you work with the same files each day, you may want to combine full backups with differential backups. The differential backup is ideal if you work with the same database or spreadsheet files each day and don't need to keep old versions of your files.

Begin your backup cycle by fully backing up your files. Then, at regular intervals, make differential backups of your files. Each differential backup records only the changes that have occurred since your last full backup. You keep only the last differential backup.

Although you can copy new backup files over old ones each time you perform a differential backup, it's best to alternate between two sets of disks or other backup media. If a backup fails, you would still have a complete copy of the previous backup. Even if you use two sets of floppy disks, this strategy minimizes the number of disks required to implement your backup strategy.

### If You Work with Different Files

If you work with different files each day, you may want to combine full backups with incremental backups. The incremental backup works best if you create new files, such as correspondence, every day.

Begin your backup cycle by fully backing up your files. Then, at regular intervals, make incremental backups of your files. Each time you back up your files incrementally, Backup records any changes that were made since your last incremental backup. Save the floppy disks from each incremental backup until you complete the cycle by performing another full backup.

### If You Need to Keep Older Versions of Files

If you need access to older versions of your files, combine full backups with incremental backups, as described in the previous section, "If You Work with Different Files." With Backup, you can easily choose which version you want to restore. For information about selecting which files to restore, see "Restoring Files" later in this chapter.

For more information about backup strategies, carry out one of the following procedures:

- If you are using Backup for Windows, choose Index from the Help menu. When the index of help topics appears, press the PAGE DOWN key. Under the Automating Backups section, choose Designing Backup Routines.

- If you are using Backup for MS-DOS, choose Backup from the Help menu. Press the DOWN ARROW key until the words Backup Type are highlighted, and then press ENTER.

## Using Setup Files

Before you begin a backup, you must select files, settings, and options. You can store these selections in *setup files*. Setup files simplify the backup process by providing a standard set of options that reflect all the selections you made for a particular backup, including:

- Which drives to back up
- What type of media to back up to
- Which files to back up
- What type of backup to perform
- Which options you selected in the options dialog box

You can create up to 50 setup files and save them with different names. By using setup files, you can perform backups routinely with a minimum of time and effort. By distributing carefully prepared setup files to other Backup users in your organization, others can benefit from a comprehensive backup strategy you've developed.

Backup uses setup files to identify which files to back up and what type of backup to perform. If you have not created a setup file, you can use the DEFAULT.SET file to control your backups.

The DEFAULT.SET file contains the default settings that appear in the main screen when you start Backup. The file also contains information that Backup gathered during the compatibility test, such as the size of the disks used in your floppy disk drive(s).

If you have not created setup files or you don't specify a setup file, the DEFAULT.SET file is selected in the Setup File text box when you open the Backup dialog box.

---

**Note**  To change the contents of a setup file, carry out the procedure described in the Setup Files topic in Backup Help.

---

For instructions on using setup files, carry out one of the following procedures:

- If you are using Backup for Windows, choose Index from the Help menu. When the index of help topics appears, press the PAGE DOWN key. Under the Miscellaneous section, choose Setup Files.

- If you are using Backup for MS-DOS, choose Index from the Help menu. When the Backup Help Topics screen appears, press the PAGE DOWN key until the Backing Up section comes into view. Under Backing Up, choose Backup Commands and Options. When the Backup Commands and Options screen appears, choose any of the first three topics.

## Backup Sets

Every full, incremental, or differential backup results in a *backup set*, which Backup creates and writes to floppy disks or other storage media. You can create any number of backup sets during a backup cycle. A backup set also includes a backup catalog, which is described in the following section.

## Backup Catalogs

As part of the backup process, Backup creates a *backup catalog* that contains information about the files you backed up. When you need to restore one or more files, you can load the backup catalog and easily select specific files from a backup set. The backup catalog includes the following information:

- The backed-up disk's directory structure
- The names, sizes, and attributes of the directories or files you selected
- The total number of files you backed up
- The total size of the backup
- The name of the setup file you used
- The date the backup was made

Backup gives each backup catalog a unique filename that helps you identify a backup set. Each character in the catalog's filename contains information about a particular backup set. For example, consider a typical catalog filename such as CD20823A.FUL. Reading from left to right, the characters in the filename mean the following.

| Character | Meaning |
| --- | --- |
| C | The first drive backed up in this set. |
| D | The last drive backed up in this set. (If only one drive was backed up, this letter will be the same as the first.) |
| 2 | The last digit of the year, as determined by your computer's date setting. In this example, the year is 1992. |

| Character | Meaning |
| --- | --- |
| 08 | The month the backup set was created, as determined by your computer's date setting. |
| 23 | The day of the month the backup set was created, as determined by your computer's date setting. |
| A | The position of this backup in a sequence of backups. If you perform more than one backup of the same drive(s) on the same day and you set the Keep Old Backup Catalogs option to On, Backup assigns a letter from A to Z to indicate the order in which the backups were performed. If you set the Keep Old Backup Catalogs option to Off, this letter alternates between A and B. |
| FUL | The backup type—FUL indicates a full backup, INC indicates an incremental backup, and DIF indicates a differential backup. |

You can easily locate the catalog for a specific backup set by using the information contained in the catalog filenames, even if your directory contains many catalog files.

Each time you perform a full backup using a specific setup file, Backup creates a *master catalog*. The master catalog keeps track of all the backup catalogs that were created during the backup cycle. When you begin a new backup cycle by performing the next full backup, Backup creates a new master catalog.

You use the master catalog if you need to restore a complete backup cycle. When you load the master catalog, Backup automatically merges the catalogs of all the backups that you performed during the backup cycle. Then you can choose to restore the latest version or an earlier version of each backed-up file.

You can also choose whether you want to keep all the old catalogs or only the current catalogs on your hard disk. The catalogs you choose to keep remain part of your backup sets.

When you back up files, Backup places one copy of the backup catalog on your hard disk and a second copy on the medium that contains your backup set. If you delete the catalog from your hard disk or the catalog on your hard disk is damaged, you can retrieve the catalog from the backup set you created.

You may have to rebuild a catalog if the catalog on your hard disk is unusable and one of the following has happened:

- The backup medium that contains the copy of the catalog is no longer available.
- The catalog file on the backup medium is damaged.
- Part of the backup set is damaged or missing.

For instructions on retrieving or rebuilding a backup catalog, carry out one of the following procedures:

- If you are using Backup for Windows, choose Index from the Help menu. When the index of help topics appears, press the PAGE DOWN key. Under the Menus section, choose Catalog Menu.

- If you are using Backup for MS-DOS, choose the Restore button in the main screen. In the Restore screen, choose the Catalog button. The Select Catalog screen appears. Choose the Retrieve or Rebuild button, and then press F1.

# Ensuring a Reliable Backup

The first time you run Backup, you are prompted to carry out a compatibility test, which verifies that Backup is configured correctly for your computer. The compatibility test is Backup's primary means of ensuring that your backups will be reliable. However, Backup also offers the following options to further ensure reliable backups:

- Verify Backup Data
- Use Error Correction
- Compare

For instructions on running the compatibility test, see "Running the Compatibility Test" later in this chapter.

## Verify Backup Data

If you choose the Verify Backup Data option when you back up your files, Backup writes data to the backup medium, compares it to the data in the source file, and then verifies the data by reading it back from the backup medium. Because data verification dramatically slows performance, you might want to make sure Verify Backup Data is turned off. However, it is recommended that you use some level of data verification, such as Compare, to help ensure the reliability of your backups. For instructions on using the Verify Backup Data option, see "Selecting Backup Options" later in this chapter.

## Use Error Correction

If you choose the Use Error Correction option when you back up your files, Backup adds coding information to the backup media to improve your chances of restoring the data if the backup set is damaged. An error correction code (ECC) is created during the backup and is used only if necessary while the files are being restored. For example, if a floppy disk is damaged by a scratch or thumbprint but the backup set was made with Use Error Correction on, there is a good chance that Backup will be able to restore the data. For instructions on using the Use Error Correction option, see "Selecting Backup Options" later in this chapter.

## Compare

After you have created a backup set, you can use the Compare command to verify that the information contained in your backup set is identical to the data on your hard disk and that the data can be restored. Compare provides maximum data security by checking the data in the backup set against the source data on the hard disk. For instructions on using Compare, choose the Compare button from the main screen or window, and then press F1.

# Using Backup

This section describes how to start a backup, use setup files, select which files to back up, and select Backup options.

**Note**  If you want to share backup sets between Norton Backup™ and Microsoft Backup, contact Symantec™ for an updated version of Norton Backup.

## Starting a Backup

The first time you start Backup, you will receive a message about running a compatibility test. Backup uses the test to adjust its configuration to your computer's hardware. This ensures that your backups will be reliable. You should run the compatibility test before you back up files for the first time or whenever you change your computer's hardware configuration. For more information, see "Running the Compatibility Test" later in this chapter.

If you are using Backup for MS-DOS, carry out the following procedure. If you are using Backup for Windows, skip to the next procedure.

**Note**  Backup program files must be located on your hard disk. You cannot start Backup from a floppy disk.

▶ **To start a backup by using Backup for MS-DOS**

   1. To start Backup, type the following at the command prompt:

      **msbackup**

      If a message about running the compatibility test appears when you start
Backup, see "Running the Compatibility Test" later in this chapter. If you
choose not to run the compatibility test the first time you start Backup, you
will receive this message each time you start Backup until you run the test.

   2. Choose the Backup button.

      The following screen appears:

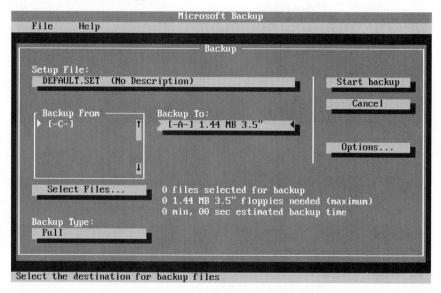

   3. For an overview of Backup, press F1. After the Backup screen appears, press
PAGE DOWN until "Overview of Backup" appears. Press TAB until the topic is
selected, and then press ENTER.

If you are using Backup for Windows, carry out the following procedure.

▶ **To start a backup by using Backup for Windows**

   1. Choose the Backup icon from the Microsoft Tools group in Program Manager.

      Or choose the Backup command from the Tools menu in File Manager.

      The following screen appears:

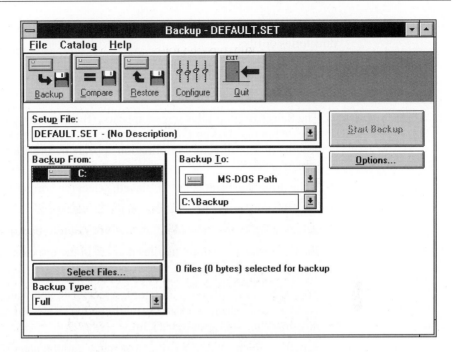

2.  For an overview of Backup, press F1.

**Note**  If a message about running the compatibility test appears when you start Backup,  see "Running the Compatibility Test" later in this chapter.

## Selecting Which Files to Back Up

You can specify which files Backup should back up by selecting one or more drives and indicating which files on those drives to include or exclude from a backup. You can select your hard disk(s) or network drives.

▶ **To back up all the files on a drive**

1.  In the Backup From box, select the drive that contains the files you want to back up, and then press the SPACEBAR.

    A message appears stating that Backup is reading disk or directory information.

    When Backup has completed reading the disk, "All Files" appears next to the drive letter you selected.

2.  Repeat step 1 for each drive you want to back up.

Instead of backing up entire drives, you can use Backup to back up selected directories or files.

▶ **To back up selected directories or files**

1. Choose the Select Files button.

   The Select Backup Files screen appears. (Backup may not have read the disk selected in the Backup From list. If it hasn't, a message stating that Backup is reading disk or directory information appears before the Select Backup Files screen appears.)

2. If the drive you want is not displayed, select the correct drive.

   The directory structure and files on the drive appear.

3. Select the directory that contains files you want to back up.

   Backup displays a list of the files that are in the directory you selected.

4. To select all the files in the selected directory, press the SPACEBAR.

   To specify some files in a directory, select a file you want to back up, and then press the SPACEBAR. Repeat this until you have selected all the files in the directory that you want to back up.

   A mark appears next to the directory name and the names of all the files in the directory that you selected.

   ---

   **Note**  If all the files are already selected, you can cancel the selection by pressing the SPACEBAR, or you can return to the previous screen by pressing ESC. The message "All Files" appears after the selected drive letter. Press the SPACEBAR to clear the selection, and then select individual files as described in the previous procedure. You can also clear selected files individually or by directory by pressing the SPACEBAR.

   ---

5. Repeat steps 2 through 4, as appropriate, until you have selected all the files you want to back up.

6. When you finish selecting files, choose the OK button.

   ---

   **Note**  If you select individual files, and later run an incremental or differential backup, Backup will back up only the files you selected, even if other files have been added or changed. If you want Backup to include new files or files that have changed but were not originally selected, make sure you select the entire directory.

   ---

Instead of selecting individual files or directories of files to back up, you can select groups of files by using the Include, Exclude, and Special buttons on the Select Backup Files screen. With these buttons, you can:

- Include or exclude files with identical filenames or extensions.
- Back up files that were created within the time period you specify.
- Exclude files from a backup based on their attributes.

For instructions on selecting groups of files, carry out one of the following procedures:

- If you are using Backup for Windows, choose the Select Files button in the main window, and then press F1.
- If you are using Backup for MS-DOS, choose the Backup button from the main screen; the Backup screen appears. Choose the Select Files button, and then press F1.

## Selecting Backup Options

You can change the settings that Backup uses by carrying out the following procedure.

▶ **To select backup options**

1. In the Backup dialog box, choose the Options button.

   A Backup options dialog box appears.

2. Select the option you want, and then press the SPACEBAR. Repeat this until you have selected all the options you want.

   A mark appears in the check box beside each option you selected.

3. When you finish selecting Backup options, choose the OK button.

For information about Backup options, press F1 when a Backup options dialog box is displayed.

# Running the Compatibility Test

Before you back up files for the first time, Backup prompts you to:

- Run a compatibility test to ensure that Backup is configured correctly for your system's hardware.
- Accept the default backup configuration or modify it to meet your needs. For more information about modifying the default configuration, see "Configuring Backup" later in this chapter.

Running the compatibility test ensures that Backup is configured to work reliably with your hardware. You should run this test before you perform your first backup and again whenever you install new hardware or change your existing hardware configuration.

---

**Note**  If your computer does not pass the compatibility test, backups you make may not be reliable.

---

The compatibility test consists of a small backup to a device you select. The test verifies that Backup is correctly installed and that it can back up and restore files properly. It also checks for hardware incompatibilities.

Before you start the test, make sure you have two floppy disks available. The disks must be the correct size and capacity for the floppy disk drive you intend to use, but do not have to be formatted.

If you use Backup for MS-DOS, carry out the following procedure to run the compatibility test the first time you use it.

If you use Backup for Windows, carry out the procedure that follows this one.

▶ **To run the compatibility test the first time you use Backup for MS-DOS**

1. Start Backup by typing the following at the command prompt:

    **msbackup**

    The following dialog box appears:

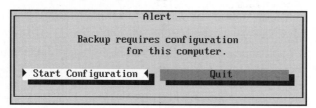

2. To start the compatibility test, press ENTER.

    Follow the instructions on your screen.

If you use Backup for Windows, carry out the following procedure to run the compatibility test.

▶ **To run the compatibility test the first time you use Backup for Windows**

1. Start Backup by choosing the Backup icon from the Microsoft Tools group in Program Manager.

   A dialog box appears, informing you that the compatibility test has not been performed.

2. To start the compatibility test, choose the OK button.

   The following dialog box appears:

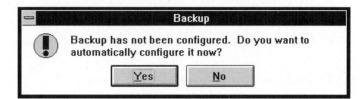

3. To configure Backup, choose the Yes button.

   A dialog box appears, prompting you to remove all disks from your drives.

4. Remove any floppy disks from your drives, and choose the OK button.

5. Select the drive you will use to create backup disks, and then choose the Start button.

   Backup performs a small backup during the first phase of the compatibility test. During the test, Backup prompts you to insert disks into the drive you chose in step 5. After the test is complete, Backup compares the files it backed up to the files on your hard disk.

# Configuring Backup

If you change your hardware configuration by adding a new video display adapter, mouse, or disk drive to your computer, you may need to change the configuration of Backup. This section describes how to change the configuration of Backup for MS-DOS and Backup for Windows.

## Configuring Backup for MS-DOS

If you use Backup for MS-DOS, you can choose video options, mouse options, and backup devices from the Configure dialog box. You can also run the compatibility test to ensure that Backup is compatible with your hardware. For more information about the compatibility test, see the previous section, "Running the Compatibility Test."

## Configuring the Video Display and Mouse

You can change the following video display and mouse settings:

- The video display adapter and color scheme
- The number of lines displayed on your screen
- Whether the mouse pointer and other screen elements are displayed in text or graphics mode
- The display speed for CGA video adapters
- Whether dialog boxes expand when they appear on the screen
- How the movement of a mouse and its buttons are interpreted

▶ **To configure your video display and mouse**

1. From the main screen, choose the Configure button.

   The Configure dialog box appears.

2. In the Configure dialog box, choose the Video And Mouse button.

   The Video And Mouse Configuration dialog box appears.

3. Change the configuration of your video display and mouse, as necessary.

4. Choose the OK button.

5. To save your configuration changes so they can be used for later backup sessions, choose the Save button in the Configure dialog box. To apply your configuration changes only to your current backup session, choose the OK button.

For more information about a dialog box and its options, press F1.

## Configuring Backup Devices

You can have Backup automatically configure the drives you use to back up your files or you can configure the drives yourself. Configuring drives is necessary when you install a new drive or use disks that do not match the default size of a drive.

When you specify that your drives should be configured automatically, Backup checks each drive to determine the default size of the disks it supports. Backup also determines if the drive detects whether the drive door is closed.

▶ **To configure backup devices**

1. From the main screen, choose the Configure button.

2. From the Configure dialog box, choose the Backup Devices button.

   The Backup Devices dialog box appears.

3. Change the configuration of your backup devices, as necessary.

   To configure your backup devices automatically, choose the Auto Config button.

4. After you finish configuring your backup devices, choose the OK button.

5. To save your configuration changes so they can be used for later backup sessions, choose the Save button in the Configure dialog box. To apply your configuration changes only to your current backup session, choose the OK button.

For more information about the options in each dialog box, press F1.

# Configuring Backup for Windows

If you use Backup for Windows, you can specify the types of floppy disk drives installed on your computer.

The changes you make take effect immediately and remain in effect until you quit Backup.

You can also run the compatibility test again to ensure that any configuration changes you make to Backup are compatible with your hardware. For more information about the test, see "Running the Compatibility Test" earlier in this chapter.

## Configuring Drives

You can have Backup automatically configure the drives you use to back up your files or you can configure the drives yourself. Configuring drives is necessary when you install a new drive or use disks that do not match the default size of a drive.

When you specify that your drives should be configured automatically, Backup checks each drive to determine the default size of the disks it supports. Backup also determines if the drive detects whether the drive door is closed. The ability to detect the state of the drive door is called *disk-change detection*.

▶ **To configure drives**

1. From the main Backup window, choose the Configure button.

   A screen similar to the following appears:

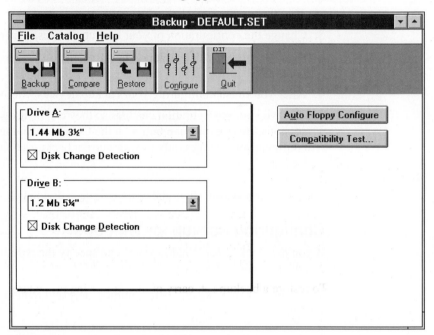

2. If you want Backup to configure your drives automatically, choose the Auto Floppy Configure button. Do not carry out the remaining steps in this procedure.

   If you want to configure drives yourself, select the first drive you want to configure.

3. Open the list box containing drive configurations, and select the configuration you want.

4. If you want to configure another drive, repeat the second half of step 2, and then repeat step 3.

5. To save the configuration for later backup sessions, quit Backup.

   The Exit Backup dialog box appears.

6. Select the Save Configuration check box.

7. Choose the OK button.

# Comparing Files

After you back up files, you can use the Compare command to verify that the backup set contains exact copies of the original files on your hard disk.

Comparing files confirms that the files you've backed up can be restored by the same disk drive that was used to create the backup set. Comparing files also provides a method for determining which files on the hard disk have changed since the backup set was made. You can compare one file, selected files, or all files in a backup set.

It's important to use the Compare command to verify backup sets even if you selected the Verify Backup Data option. By comparing files, you are more likely to detect slight mechanical variations in a disk drive that can affect the reliability of a backup.

For instructions on using Compare, choose the Compare button from the main screen or window, and then press F1.

# Restoring Files

You can easily restore files that you've backed up using Backup. Restoring files transfers them from a backup set to the location you specify. If your hard disk fails, you'll probably want to restore the files to their original location. However, you can also restore files to an alternate location—for example, you could use the Restore command to transfer a backup set to another computer.

To restore a backup set, carry out the following procedure.

▶ **To restore a backup set**

1. In the main Backup screen, choose the Restore button.

   If you use Backup for MS-DOS, the following screen appears:

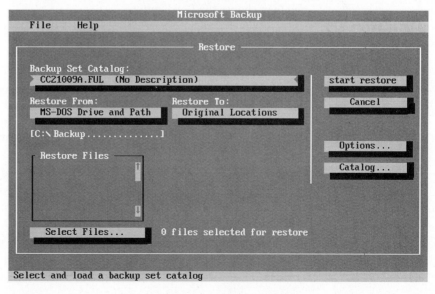

If you use Backup for Windows, the following screen appears:

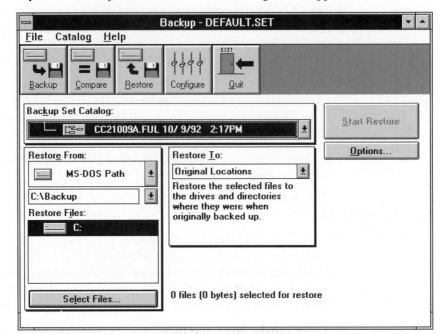

2. To specify the catalog that identifies the backup set you want to restore, open the Backup Set Catalog list box.

   If you use Backup for MS-DOS, the Backup Set Catalog dialog box appears. Use the arrow keys and the SPACEBAR to select the catalog you want to use, and then choose the Load button.

   If you use Backup for Windows, a list of available catalogs appears. Select the catalog you want to use and then press the TAB key.

3. Open the Restore From list box.

   If you use Backup for MS-DOS, the Restore From dialog box appears. Select the drive that contains the files you want to restore, and then choose the OK button. If you select MS-DOS Drive And Path, a text box appears in the main Restore screen. Type the path of the files you want to restore, and then press TAB.

   If you use Backup for Windows, a list of drives appears. Select the drive that contains the files you want to restore, and then press TAB. If you select MS-DOS Path, a text box appears under the Restore From list box. Type the path of the files you want to restore, and then press TAB.

4. In the Restore Files box, choose the drive that contains the files you want to restore.

5. If you want to restore all files on the drive, press the SPACEBAR.

   The words "All Files" appear next to the drive letter.

   If you want to restore selected files on the drive, press ENTER.

   The Select Restore Files screen appears.

   Select the directory that contains the files you want to restore.

   Backup displays a list of the files that are in the directory you selected.

   Select a file you want to restore, and then press the SPACEBAR. Repeat this until you have selected all the files in the directory that you want to restore.

6. To specify the destination for the files you want to restore, open the Restore To list box.

   If you use Backup for MS-DOS, the Restore To dialog box appears. Select the destination for the files you want to restore, and then choose the OK button.

   If you use Backup for Windows, a list of locations appears. Select the destination for the files you want to restore, and then press TAB.

7. If you want to change Restore options, choose the Options button. Select or clear the options you want to change, and then choose the OK button.

8. To start restoring your files, choose the Start Restore button.

   Backup displays status information while it restores the files.

For instructions on using Restore, choose the Restore button from the main screen or window, and then press F1.

# If the "DMA buffer size too small" Message Appears

If you have installed Windows or the EMM386 device driver on your computer, Backup for MS-DOS may display the following message when you run the compatibility test or start a backup:

```
DMA buffer size too small. You cannot back up,
compare, or restore files until you increase
the DMA buffer size.
```

If you receive this message while you are running Backup for MS-DOS from within Windows, carry out the following procedure:

▶ **To increase the size of the DMA buffer if you use Windows**

1. Open your SYSTEM.INI file, which is located in your Windows directory, by using any text editor.

2. Find the [386Enh] section of the file, and then add the following line:

   **dmabuffersize=32**

3. Save the changes to your SYSTEM.INI file, and then quit the text editor.

4. If you are running Windows, quit Windows.

5. Restart Windows.

# Protecting Your Computer from Viruses

Anti-Virus can protect your data by detecting more than 800 different viruses and removing them from your computer. MS-DOS 6 includes two versions of Anti-Virus: Anti-Virus for MS-DOS and Anti-Virus for Windows.

MS-DOS also includes VSafe, a memory-resident program that monitors your computer and warns of changes that might have been caused by a virus. For more information about VSafe, see "Using VSafe" later in this chapter.

If a virus infects your computer, you might need a startup disk to restart your computer. It's important to make the disk before your computer is infected by a virus. To create a startup disk, carry out the following procedure.

▶ **To create a startup disk**

1. Insert an unformatted floppy disk in drive A, and then type the following at the command prompt:

   **format a: /s**

2. Copy the Anti-Virus files to your startup disk by typing the following at the command prompt:

   **copy msav*.* a:**

   The Anti-Virus files are located in the same directory as your MS-DOS files.

# What Are Computer Viruses?

Computer viruses are programs designed to replicate and spread, sometimes without indicating that they exist. Computer viruses can produce a variety of symptoms on your computer. Some viruses multiply without causing obvious changes. More malicious strains can issue random sounds or greet you with unexpected screen messages. In extreme cases, viruses can damage files and hard disks.

Computer viruses can be classified by how they infect system.

| Type | Characteristics |
|---|---|
| Boot sector virus | The *boot sector* is the portion of a hard disk that controls how your operating system starts when you turn on your computer. A boot sector virus replaces the disk's original boot sector with its own, and loads the virus into memory. Once in memory, the virus can spread to other disks. |
| File infector | A file infector virus adds virus code to files that run programs, so the virus is activated whenever you run the program. When the virus is activated, it spreads to other program files. |
| Trojan horse | A Trojan horse virus is disguised as a legitimate program. When you run a program infected with a Trojan horse virus, your computer may be damaged. Trojan horse viruses are much more likely to destroy files or damage disks than other viruses. Files or disks infected with a Trojan horse virus may not be recoverable. |

For information about specific viruses and how they work, see "Getting Information About Viruses" later in this chapter.

# Anti-Virus Help

Anti-Virus includes comprehensive help on dialog boxes, options, and tasks.

▶ **To get help**

- When an Anti-Virus screen, window, or dialog box appears, press F1.

# Scanning for Viruses

Anti-Virus protects your computer from viruses by scanning your computer's memory and disk drives. Anti-Virus offers the following methods of detecting computer viruses:

- Detect—Scans for viruses and displays information about each virus it finds. This method does not automatically remove viruses from your computer.

- Detect and Clean—Scans for viruses and removes any that it finds.

If you are using Anti-Virus for MS-DOS, carry out the following procedure. If you are using Anti-Virus for Windows, skip to the next procedure.

When you start Anti-Virus for MS-DOS, it reads file information on the drive you used to start the program. If you want to search for viruses on a different drive, you must select the drive before scanning for viruses.

▶ **To scan for viruses using Anti-Virus for MS-DOS**

1. Type the following at the command prompt:

   **msav**

   The Main Menu appears:

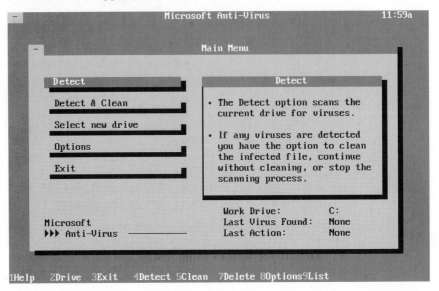

2. To scan the drive from which you started Anti-Virus, skip to step 5. To scan a different drive, proceed to step 3.

3. Choose the Select New Drive button.

   Drive letters appear in the upper-left area of your screen.

4. Select the drive you want to scan.

   Anti-Virus reads file information on the drive you selected.

5. To detect viruses and remove them from your computer, choose the Detect & Clean button.

   To detect viruses and have Anti-Virus prompt you if it finds one, choose the Detect button.

   If you choose the Detect button and Anti-Virus finds a virus, a screen similar to the following appears:

Choose the action you want to take.

6. A status screen similar to the following appears after Anti-Virus has finished scanning your computer's memory and the drive you selected. Choose the OK button.

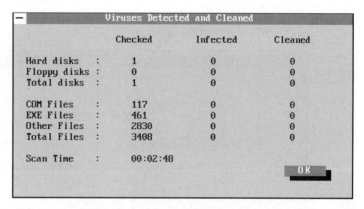

| Viruses Detected and Cleaned | | | |
|---|---|---|---|
| | Checked | Infected | Cleaned |
| Hard disks : | 1 | 0 | 0 |
| Floppy disks : | 0 | 0 | 0 |
| Total disks : | 1 | 0 | 0 |
| COM Files : | 117 | 0 | 0 |
| EXE Files : | 461 | 0 | 0 |
| Other Files : | 2830 | 0 | 0 |
| Total Files : | 3408 | 0 | 0 |
| Scan Time : | 00:02:48 | | |

Using Anti-Virus for Windows, you can scan one or more drives at a time. To scan for viruses, carry out the following procedure.

▶ **To scan for viruses using Anti-Virus for Windows**

1. From the Microsoft Tools group, choose the Anti-Virus icon.

   Or, from the Tools menu in File Manager, choose Anti-Virus.

   A screen similar to the following appears:

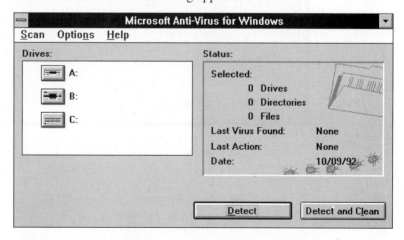

2. In the Drives box, choose the drive you want to scan by clicking it with your mouse or by selecting it with the arrow keys and then pressing the SPACEBAR.

   Anti-Virus reads file information on the drive you chose.

3. Repeat step 2 for each drive you want to scan.

4. To detect viruses and remove them from your computer, choose the Detect And Clean button.

   To detect viruses and have Anti-Virus prompt you if it finds one, choose the Detect button.

   If you choose the Detect button and Anti-Virus detects a virus, a dialog box similar to the following appears:

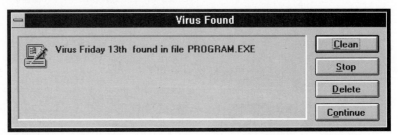

   Choose the action you want to take.

5. When Anti-Virus completes scanning your computer's memory and the drives you selected, a status screen similar to the following appears:

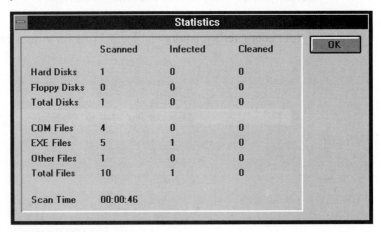

   Choose the OK button.

# Automatically Scanning for Viruses

You can configure Anti-Virus to check for viruses automatically. If you are using Anti-Virus for MS-DOS, you can automatically scan your memory and disk drives for viruses each time you turn on your computer. If you are using Anti-Virus for Windows, you can automatically scan a drive you specify each time you start Anti-Virus.

If you are using Anti-Virus for MS-DOS, carry out the following procedure. If you are using Anti-Virus for Windows, skip to the next procedure.

▶ **To scan automatically using Anti-Virus for MS-DOS**

- To specify that Anti-Virus should scan your computer's memory and drives each time you start your computer, add the following command to your AUTOEXEC.BAT file:

  **msav /p**

  If you use network drives, use the following command to limit scanning to local drives:

  **msav /p /l**

  If your AUTOEXEC.BAT file includes this command, Anti-Virus searches your computer's memory and local drives for viruses each time you start your computer.

If you are using Anti-Virus for Windows, you can specify which drive should be scanned automatically whenever you choose the Anti-Virus icon in the Microsoft Tools group.

▶ **To specify a startup command for Anti-Virus for Windows**

1. From the Microsoft Tools group, select (but do not choose) the Anti-Virus icon.

2. From the File menu in Program Manager, choose Properties.

   The Program Item Properties dialog box appears.

3. In the Command Line box, specify the drive you want Anti-Virus to scan automatically. The drive letter should follow the MWAV.EXE command that is already in the Command Line box.

   For example, to specify that Anti-Virus should scan drive C, make sure the text in the Command Line box looks like the following:

   ```
   mwav.exe c:
   ```

4. Choose the OK button.

# Setting Anti-Virus Options

You can choose which drives Anti-Virus scans, set options to control how the program checks for viruses, and obtain information about viruses known to infect computers.

▶ **To set Anti-Virus options**

1. If you are using Anti-Virus for MS-DOS, choose the Options button from the Main Menu.

   If you are using Anti-Virus for Windows, choose the Set Options command from the Options menu.

   An Options dialog box appears.

2. Move to the check box you want to select or clear by pressing TAB.

3. To select or clear the box, press the SPACEBAR.

4. When you have finished setting options, choose the OK button.

For more information about Anti-Virus options, carry out one of the following procedures:

- If you are using Anti-Virus for MS-DOS, press F1 when the Options dialog box is on your screen.

- If you are using Anti-Virus for Windows, choose Index from the Help menu. The Anti-Virus Help screen appears. Choose Commands. The Commands screen appears. Under the Option Menu section, choose Set Options.

# Getting Information About Viruses

Anti-Virus includes a list of all the viruses it can recognize. Each virus is listed by its most common name, with known aliases indented under the name. The virus list also specifies the type of virus, the size of the virus code, and the number of known strains, or variants, of the virus.

▶ **To get information about a virus**

1. If you are using Anti-Virus for MS-DOS, press F9.

   The Virus List appears:

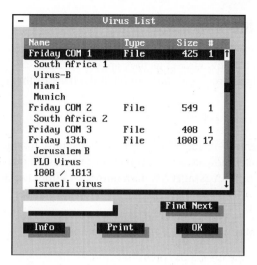

If you are using Anti-Virus for Windows, choose Virus List from the Scan menu.

The Virus List appears:

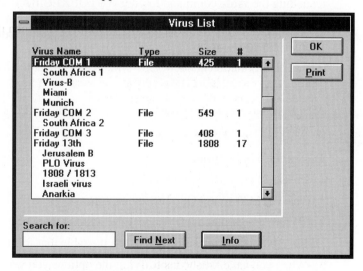

2. Select the virus you want information about.

Or type the name, type, or size of the virus you want information about in the text box below the list.

3. Choose the Info button.

Information about the virus you selected appears.

## Updating the Virus List

New viruses are discovered regularly. For information about protecting your computer against new viruses as they are discovered, see Appendix D, "Obtaining New Virus Signatures" and the coupon at the back of this guide.

# Using VSafe

VSafe is a memory-resident program that constantly monitors your computer for activity that may indicate a virus infection. If VSafe detects suspicious activity, it displays a warning message. VSafe requires 44 kilobytes (K) of memory.

▶ **To start VSafe**

- Type the following at the command prompt:

  **vsafe**

  This command loads VSafe into memory using default settings. For a list of VSafe settings, see the table later in this section.

  You can load VSafe into memory every time you start your computer by adding the **vsafe** command to your AUTOEXEC.BAT file. For information about changing your AUTOEXEC.BAT file, see "Editing Your AUTOEXEC.BAT File" in the chapter "Configuring Your System."

For more information about VSafe, type **help vsafe** at the MS-DOS command prompt.

After you start VSafe, you can change options that control how VSafe monitors your computer.

▶ **To change VSafe options**

1. Press ALT+V.

   The VSafe Warning Options screen appears.

2. To turn an option on or off, press the number that corresponds to the option.

   For a description of each option, see the table that follows this procedure.

3. When you have finished specifying the options you want, press ESC.

   VSafe saves the options you specified.

The following table describes VSafe options and their default values.

| Number | Name | Description | Default |
|--------|------|-------------|---------|
| 1 | HD low-level format | Warns of formatting that could completely erase your hard disk. | On |
| 2 | Resident | Warns of any attempt by a program to use standard MS-DOS methods of staying resident in memory. Warnings do not necessarily indicate the presence of a virus. | Off |
| 3 | General write protect | Prevents programs from writing to the disk. This option is useful if you suspect that a virus has infected a program. | Off |
| 4 | Check executable files | Checks programs opened by MS-DOS. | On |
| 5 | Boot sector viruses | Checks disks for boot sector viruses. | On |
| 6 | Protect HD boot sector | Warns of attempts to write to the hard disk boot sector and partition table. | On |
| 7 | Protect FD boot sector | Warns of attempts to write to the floppy disk boot sector. | Off |
| 8 | Protect executable files | Warns of attempts to modify executable files. | Off |

If VSafe is loaded, you can unload it from memory by carrying out the following procedure.

▶ **To unload VSafe from memory**

1. Press ALT+V.

   The VSafe Warning Options screen appears.

2. To unload VSafe from memory, press ALT+U.

   MS-DOS unloads VSafe from memory.

If you use Windows, you must load the VSafe Manager program to ensure that Windows displays VSafe messages. Carry out the following procedure to make sure that VSafe is loaded into memory each time you start your computer and that the VSafe Manager is loaded into memory each time you start Windows.

▶ **To set up VSafe and VSafe Manager for Windows**

1. From the File menu in Program Manager, choose Run.

2. In the Command Line box, type the following:

   **sysedit**

3. Choose the OK button.

   The System Configuration Editor appears, with the following files open:

   AUTOEXEC.BAT
   CONFIG.SYS
   WIN.INI
   SYSTEM.INI

4. Add the following command to your AUTOEXEC.BAT file:

   **vsafe**

5. Add the following command to the **load=** line in the [Windows] section of your WIN.INI file:

   **mwavtsr.exe**

6. From the File menu, choose Exit.

   The System Configuration Editor prompts you to save your changes.

7. Choose the Yes button.

8. Quit Windows, and then restart your computer by pressing CTRL+ALT+DEL.

When you add the **vsafe** command to your AUTOEXEC.BAT file, you can include one or more switches that control how VSafe monitors your computer. For more information, type **help vsafe** at the MS-DOS command prompt.

If you use Windows 3.1, you can add VSafe Manager to the StartUp group instead of adding the **mwavtsr.exe** command to the **load=** line in your WIN.INI file. To do this, carry out the following procedure.

▶ **To add VSafe Manager to your Startup group if you use Windows 3.1**

1. Open the Startup group.

2. From the File menu in Program Manager, choose New.

3. The New Program Object dialog box appears. Choose the OK button.

   The Program Item Properties dialog box appears.

4. In the Description box, type **VSafe Manager**.

5. In the Command Line box, type **mwavtsr.exe**, and then choose the OK button.

6. Quit Windows, and then restart you computer by pressing CTRL+ALT+DEL.

---

**Caution**  Do not run the MS-DOS 6 or Windows Setup program again unless you unload VSafe from memory.

# Troubleshooting Anti-Virus

This section explains messages that Anti-Virus displays and provides instructions for correcting problems.

## Messages

Anti-Virus displays messages that offer choices for correcting specific conditions. For help, press F1.

After you upgrade software, Anti-Virus might display messages warning about a possible virus infection. To reduce unwanted messages after upgrades, carry out the following procedure.

▶ **To reduce Anti-Virus messages after you upgrade software**

1. Use Anti-Virus to scan the manufacturer's disks before you install the software.

2. Write-protect the installation disks.

3. Install the software.

4. Scan the drive on which you installed the software. Doing so automatically updates Anti-Virus files.

### "Virus Found" Message

If Anti-Virus for MS-DOS finds a virus, it displays a Virus Found dialog box such as the following:

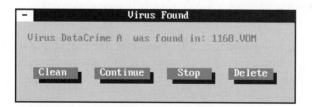

If Anti-Virus for Windows finds a virus, it displays a Virus Found dialog box such as the following:

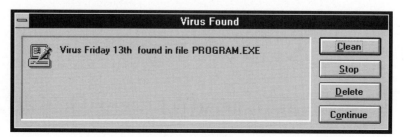

When a Virus Found dialog box appears, you have the following options:

- You can remove the virus from the file and restore the file to its original condition by choosing the Clean button. This minimizes the possibility of the virus infecting other files on your computer.

- You can ignore the virus and continue scanning the remaining files by choosing the Continue button.

- You can stop the scan and return to the Anti-Virus program by choosing the Stop button.

- You can erase the infected file from your computer by choosing the Delete button.

### "Verify Error" Message

If you selected the Verify Integrity and Prompt While Detect options, Anti-Virus alerts you when an executable file changes by displaying a dialog box similar to the following:

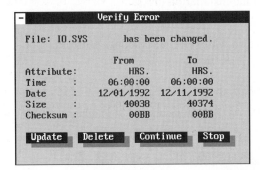

The dialog box provides information about the executable file that changed. The dialog box might appear as a result of an intentional change you made (such as upgrading a software program). If you know you changed the file, you can choose the Update button to register the change.

Microsoft Anti-Virus displays information about the following:

- *Attribute* indicates the file's attribute. Available attributes are:

  R        Read-Only

  H        Hidden

  S        System

  A        Archive

- *Time, Date,* and *Size* indicate the time and date the file was last modified and the size of the file in bytes. Most likely, this information indicates changes that you made intentionally. Although some viruses modify this information when they infect a file, you will be notified of any behind-the-scenes activity if VSafe is installed.

- *Checksum* provides information retrieved from the CHKLIST.MS file, which stores the checksum, MS-DOS attributes, size, date, and time of executable and system files. If this information no longer matches, the file may have been altered by a virus.

Anti-Virus offers you the following options:

- If you know the change is legitimate, choose the Update button to avoid receiving this message during subsequent scans.

- If the file size or checksum changed, choose the Delete button to delete the infected file.

- If you know about the change but don't want to update Anti-Virus, choose the Continue button.

- If you want to cancel the scan and return to the Anti-Virus screen, choose the Stop button.

### "File was destroyed by the virus" Message

If a virus damaged a file, Anti-Virus displays the following dialog box:

```
File was destroyed by the virus!!!
Recovery for this file is impossible.
Delete this file in order to prevent further
infection and damage?
```

If a file is destroyed by a virus, you have the following options:

- You can delete the infected file by choosing the Delete button.

- You can ignore the infected file and continue scanning for viruses by choosing the Continue button.

- You can stop the scanning process and return to the Anti-Virus screen by choosing the Stop button.

### "Invalid Signature – Checksum does not match" Message

A *signature* is a series of 37 two-character, hexadecimal (hex) codes that uniquely identify a virus. If a virus signature has an error in it, Anti-Virus displays an invalid signature message. If you receive this message, fill out and mail the coupon in the back of this guide.

### "Program is trying to modify system memory" Message

If VSafe detects a program that is trying to modify your computer's memory without using standard MS-DOS calls for memory-resident programs, Anti-Virus displays this warning.

Modifying system memory in this way generally indicates that a virus is attempting to infect your computer. However, some network drivers may cause VSafe to display this message when they load.

▶ **If a program is modifying system memory**

1. If you know that a network driver is being loaded after VSafe was loaded, choose the Continue button.

2. If you do not know what may be causing the memory modification, choose the Stop button.

3. Run Anti-Virus to check for viruses.

### "Program is trying to stay resident in memory" Message

If you have selected the Resident option in VSafe and VSafe detects another program trying to load into memory, VSafe displays this warning.

▶ **If a program tries to stay resident in memory**

1. If you are aware that a memory-resident program is being loaded into memory after VSafe was loaded, choose the Continue button.

   If you do not think a memory-resident program should be loading into memory, choose the Stop button.

2. Run Anti-Virus to check for viruses.

### "Program is trying to write to disk" Message

If you select the General Write Protect option in VSafe and a program tries to write to a disk, VSafe displays this warning.

▶ **If a program tries to write to a disk**

1. If you expected the program to write to a disk, choose the Continue button.

   If you do not think a program should be writing to a disk, choose the Stop button.

2. Run Anti-Virus to ensure that the program trying to write to the disk is not infected.

## "Resident programs were loaded after VSafe" Message

If one or more memory-resident programs were loaded after VSafe and you try to remove VSafe from memory, this message appears.

▶ **To remove other memory-resident programs from memory**

1. Choose the Stop button to leave VSafe resident in memory.

2. If possible, remove other memory-resident programs from memory in reverse order of their installation.

3. Remove VSafe from memory.

4. If you can't remove a program from memory, disable the command in your AUTOEXEC.BAT file that loads the program. Then, restart your computer by pressing CTRL+ALT+DEL.

For information about how to disable commands, type **help rem** at the command prompt.

## "Since a virus was detected..." Message

When you quit Anti-Virus after it has detected a virus, the following message appears:

```
Since a virus was detected, rebooting is recommended
to minimize the possibility of further infection.
```

▶ **To quit Anti-Virus after a virus is detected**

• When Anti-Virus displays this warning message, choose the Reboot button to restart your system.

## "The xxxxxx virus is known to infect DATA files..." Message

If you have not selected the Check All Files option and Anti-Virus detects a virus, the the following message appears:

```
The xxxxxx virus is known to infect DATA files as well as
executable files. As a result you should check all of the
files on this disk. For your convenience, the Check All
Files option will be automatically turned on when you leave
this message. When this option is on, Microsoft Anti-Virus will
scan every file on the disk, including data files.
```

## Miscellaneous Problems

The following section provides instructions for resolving other problems that might occur when you are using Anti-Virus.

### A program doesn't run correctly after a virus has been removed

If a program doesn't run correctly after you remove a virus from it, carry out the following procedure.

▶ **To restore a file that doesn't run after a virus is removed**

1. Delete the program file from your computer.

2. Restore a non-infected backup copy of the program file to your computer.

   Or install a new file that you've obtained from your software vendor.

### Windows does not start

Windows may not start if system files are infected.

To detect and remove viruses from Windows system files, run Anti-Virus for MS-DOS.

To set up Anti-Virus for MS-DOS, see "Installing Anti-Virus, Backup, and Undelete After Setup" in the chapter "Getting Started."

### Pressing ALT+V does not display the VSafe Warning Options screen

The ALT+V key combination works only if you are using Anti-Virus for MS-DOS and VSafe has been loaded into memory. If these conditions are met and you still cannot use the ALT+V key combination, another memory-resident program is probably using it.

You can change the key combination that VSafe uses by specifying the **/a** switch and the letter you want to use with the ALT key after the **vsafe** command. For example, to change the key combination to ALT+Q, type the following at the command prompt or add it to your AUTOEXEC.BAT file:

**vsafe /aq**

This command will cause the VSafe Warning Options screen to appear when you press ALT+Q.

For more information about adding commands to your AUTOEXEC.BAT file, see "Editing Your AUTOEXEC.BAT File" in the chapter "Configuring Your System."

For more information, type **help vsafe** at the command prompt.

### Your computer stops responding when you are using Anti-Virus

If the directory structure on your hard disk is damaged, your computer may stop responding when you use Anti-Virus.

▶ **To repair the directory structure of your hard disk**

1. Quit Anti-Virus.

   If you cannot quit, restart your computer by pressing CTRL+ALT+DEL. (If you are running Windows, quit Windows.)

2. To repair the directory structure, type the following at the command prompt:

   **chkdsk /f**

3. Run Anti-Virus again.

# Using SMARTDrive

SMARTDrive is a program that decreases the time your computer spends reading data from your hard disk. Use SMARTDrive if your computer has a hard disk and extended memory.

SMARTDrive reserves an area in extended memory in which it stores information that it reads from your hard disk. An application can access this information in memory faster than it can access the same information on a hard disk. When system resources are in demand, SMARTDrive can also temporarily store information to be written to your hard disk and write it to the disk when resources become available.

If your computer can use SMARTDrive, MS-DOS Setup adds the **smartdrv** command to your AUTOEXEC.BAT file when you install MS-DOS. After you run Setup, SMARTDrive starts automatically when you start your computer.

For more information about SMARTDrive, type **help smartdrv** at the MS-DOS command prompt.

# Using the Defragmenter

Over time, as programs read from and write to your hard disk, information that is stored on the disk can become *fragmented*. Fragmentation occurs when a file is broken into fragments that are stored in different locations on the disk. Fragmentation doesn't affect the validity of the information—your files are still complete when they are opened. But it takes much longer for your computer to read and write fragmented files than it does to read and write unfragmented files.

▶ **To defragment the files on your hard disk**

1. Delete any unnecessary files from your hard disk. For more information, see the chapter "Freeing Disk Space."

2. Quit all programs that are running, including Windows.

   You cannot run the Defragmenter from an MS-DOS prompt within Windows.

3. Check for lost allocation units on your hard disk by typing the following at the command prompt:

   **chkdsk /f**

   If MS-DOS detects lost allocation units, a prompt similar to the following appears:

   ```
   10 lost allocation units found in 3 chains.
   Convert lost chains to files?
   ```

   Press Y to save the information in the lost allocation units.

   For information about the **chkdsk** command, type **help chkdsk** at the command prompt.

4. Start the Defragmenter by typing the following at the command prompt:

   **defrag**

   The Defragmenter displays a list of the disk drives on your computer.

5. To select the drive you want to defragment, use the UP ARROW or DOWN ARROW key and then press ENTER.

   The Defragmenter analyzes the data on that drive and recommends a defragmentation option.

6. To begin defragmentation, press ENTER.

   If you want to change defragmentation settings or want more information about the current defragmentation settings before you begin, press TAB to select the Configure button, and then press ENTER. The Optimize menu appears.

For more information about the Defragmenter, type **help defrag** at the command prompt.

# Recovering Deleted Files

Undelete includes two undelete programs: Undelete for MS-DOS, a program you can run from the command prompt, and Undelete for Windows, a program you can run from Windows.

Undelete enables you to choose one of three levels of protection: Delete Sentry, Delete Tracker, and standard. For more information about specifying a level of protection, see the following section.

For instructions on recovering a file that was accidentally deleted, see "Undelete for Windows" or "Undelete for MS-DOS" later in this chapter.

# Configuring Delete Protection

Undelete offers three levels of protection: Delete Sentry, Delete Tracker, and standard. Of these, Delete Sentry provides the highest level of protection. It requires a small amount of memory and disk space. Delete Tracker, the next level of protection, requires the same amount of memory, but minimal disk space. The lowest level of protection, standard, requires neither memory nor disk space, but still makes it possible to recover many deleted files. For more information about each level of protection, type **help undelete** at the command prompt.

By default, MS-DOS 6 configures your computer for the standard level of delete protection. Using this level of protection, you can recover a deleted file unless MS-DOS has placed another file in the deleted file's location.

If you use Undelete for MS-DOS and want a higher level of delete protection, carry out the following procedure. If you use Undelete for Windows and want a higher level of delete protection, skip to the following procedure.

▶ **To choose a level of delete protection using Undelete for MS-DOS**

- To choose the Delete Sentry level of protection on your current drive, type the following at the command prompt:

  **undelete /s**

  To choose the Delete Tracker level of protection, include the **/t** switch and the drive you want to protect with the **undelete** command. For example, to enable Delete Tracker on drive C, include the following command in your AUTOEXEC.BAT file or type it at the command prompt:

  **undelete /tc**

  For information about how to include a command in your AUTOEXEC.BAT file, see the chapter "Configuring Your System."

  For more information about configuring Undelete for MS-DOS, type **help undelete** at the command prompt.

If you use Undelete for Windows and want a higher level of protection, carry out the following procedure.

▶  **To choose a level of delete protection using Undelete for Windows**

1. Start Undelete by choosing the Undelete icon from the Microsoft Tools group in Program Manager.

    Or choose the Undelete command from the File menu in File Manager.

2. From the Options menu in Undelete, choose Configure Delete Protection.

    The Configure Delete Protection dialog box appears.

3. Select a delete-protection method, and then choose the OK button.

    For more information about delete-protection methods, press F1.

4. If you choose Delete Sentry, a dialog box appears. Choose the Drives button. Select the drive(s) you want to protect, and then choose the OK button. For information about changing options in the Configure Delete Sentry dialog box, press F1. When you finish changing options, choose the OK button.

    If you choose Delete Tracker, select the drives you want to protect, and then choose the OK button. For help with the Configure Delete Tracker dialog box, press F1.

    The Update AUTOEXEC.BAT dialog box appears.

5. To implement the delete-protection method you selected, choose OK.

    Before the method you selected can take effect, you must quit Windows and restart your computer by pressing CTRL+ALT+DEL.

# Undelete for Windows

This section explains how to use Undelete for Windows to recover files you have accidentally deleted.

If you cannot find information about an Undelete feature in this section, press F1 when an Undelete window or dialog box appears on your screen.

# Recovering a File

The successful recovery of deleted files depends on their condition. Files can be in Perfect, Excellent, Good, Poor, or Destroyed condition. For more information about each condition, see the following table.

| This condition | Indicates that the file |
|---|---|
| Perfect | Was protected by the Delete Sentry method of delete protection and can be recovered without difficulty. |
| Excellent | Was protected by the Delete Tracker method of delete protection. This file may be partially overwritten by other data. |
| Good | Is fragmented on the disk. Some of the data in this file may be lost. |
| Poor | Cannot be recovered by using Undelete for Windows. You might be able to recover some data by using Undelete for MS-DOS. |
| Destroyed | Cannot be recovered. |

▶ **To recover a file**

1. Start Undelete by choosing the Undelete icon from the Microsoft Tools group in Program Manager.

   Or choose the Undelete command from the File menu in File Manager. A screen such as the following appears:

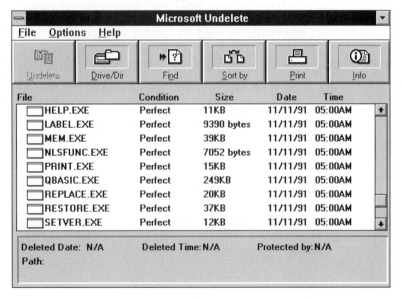

2. If the file you want to recover does not appear in the list, choose the Drive/Dir button. Then choose the drive and directory that contained the deleted file.

   The Undelete screen displays files that were deleted from the directory you chose. If the condition of the file you want to recover is Excellent or Perfect, you can easily recover it.

   If the file is in Good condition, see the following section, "Recovering a File in Good Condition," before carrying out the rest of this procedure.

   If the file is in Poor condition, you cannot recover it by using Undelete for Windows. However, you might be able to recover some of the data in the file by using Undelete for MS-DOS.

   If the file is in Destroyed condition, you cannot recover it.

   For more information about the condition of deleted files, choose the File Info command from the File menu, and then press F1.

3. Select the file you want to recover.

4. Choose the Undelete button.

   If the first letter of the deleted file is a question mark (?), Undelete displays a dialog box prompting you to substitute the correct letter for the question mark. If this dialog box appears, type the missing letter, and then choose the OK button.

   The file is listed as Recovered in the Undelete screen.

## Recovering a File in Good Condition

If a file is in Good instead of Perfect or Excellent condition, the file's data is fragmented and may be overwritten by other data. To maximize your chances of recovering the file, recover it to a drive other than its original drive.

▶ **To recover a file in Good condition**

1. From the Microsoft Tools group, choose the Undelete icon.

   The main Undelete screen appears.

2. To select the directory from which you want to recover a deleted file, choose the Drive/Dir button.

   Select the directory you want by using the arrow keys, and then choose the OK button.

3. Select the file you want to recover.

4. From the File menu, choose Undelete To.

   The Undelete To dialog box appears.

5. Select the drive and directory to which you want to recover the file, and then choose the OK button.

# Recovering a File on a Network Drive

You can recover files on a network drive that is protected by Delete Sentry. For more information, see "Configuring Delete Protection" earlier in this chapter.

To recover a file on a network drive, carry out the procedure in "Recovering a File" earlier in this section.

# Recovering a Directory and Its Files

If you accidentally delete a directory and its contents, you might be able to recover it by using Undelete for Windows. You must recover a directory before you can recover any of the files in it.

Caution   Undelete for Windows uses the standard level of delete protection for directories. You must specify the first letter of the name of the directory you want to recover. If a program is using the disk space formerly used by the directory, you may not be able to recover the directory and its contents.

▶ **To recover a directory**

1. Start Undelete by choosing the Undelete icon from the Microsoft Tools group in Program Manager.

   Or choose the Undelete command from the File menu in File Manager.

2. If Undelete does not list the directory you want to recover, choose the Drive/Dir button. Then choose the drive and directory that contained the directory you want to recover.

   The deleted directory appears with its file size listed as *dir*.

3. Select the directory you want to recover, and then choose the Undelete button.

   If Undelete can find all the parts of the directory, the directory is recovered and appears as Recovered in the Undelete window.

4. If the directory contains the group of files you want to recover, choose the Add button. If not, choose the Skip button.

   Undelete displays another group of files.

5. Repeat step 4 until you have identified all the groups of files contained in the deleted directory. Then choose the Undelete button.

   The directory is recovered and is listed as Recovered in the Undelete screen.

# Finding Deleted Files

If you cannot find deleted files by using the Change Drive And Directory dialog box, you can search for them by choosing the Find button. For help with the Find Deleted Files dialog box, press F1.

### Purging Files Protected by Delete Sentry

When you select the Delete Sentry method of delete protection, you can specify how many days to save deleted files and a maximum percentage of disk space to allow for Delete Sentry's hidden directory. Delete Sentry files are purged automatically when these limits are reached or when the disk space they occupy is needed by MS-DOS.

When Delete Sentry purges files, it removes the oldest deleted files first. You can also purge deleted files yourself by using Undelete. Purging deleted files creates more room for protecting files, especially when disk space is at a premium.

▶ **To purge files protected by Delete Sentry**

1. From the Microsoft Tools group, choose the Undelete icon.

   The main Undelete screen appears.

2. To select the directory from which you want to purge files, choose the Drive/Dir button.

   Select the directory you want by using the arrow keys, and then choose the OK button.

3. In the Undelete screen, select the files you want to purge.

   Files protected by Delete Sentry are in Perfect condition.

4. From the File menu, choose Purge Delete Sentry File.

   A dialog box appears, prompting you to confirm the deletion.

5. Choose the OK button.

   The selected files disappear from the Undelete screen.

## Undelete for MS-DOS

Use Undelete for MS-DOS if you are not running Windows or haven't installed Undelete for Windows.

If you want to use Undelete for MS-DOS and didn't install it during Setup, see "Installing Anti-Virus, Backup, and Undelete After Setup" in the chapter "Getting Started."

### Recovering Files

You can recover deleted files by making the directory that contained the files current, and then using the **undelete** command.

▶ **To recover files**

1. Make the directory that contained the deleted files current. For example, if the deleted files were in the DOS directory, type the following at the command prompt:

   **cd \dos**

2. To recover the files, type the following at the command prompt:

   **undelete**

3. One by one, MS-DOS lists the deleted files it has found and prompts you to specify whether it should recover them. To recover a file, press Y. MS-DOS may also prompt you to type the initial letter of a filename.

## Using Advanced Undelete Methods

For information about using advanced methods of recovering files or about using **undelete** syntax, type the following at the command prompt:

**help undelete**

C H A P T E R   4

# Configuring Your System

When you configure your system, you set it up so that MS-DOS, your hardware, and your applications work the way you want them to. This can be as simple as customizing the appearance of your command prompt or as complex as setting up a new hardware component. Most of your system's configuration information is stored in two files:

- Your CONFIG.SYS file is a text file that contains commands that configure your computer's hardware components (memory, keyboard, mouse, printer, and so on) so MS-DOS and your applications can use them. When MS-DOS starts, it carries out the commands in your CONFIG.SYS file first.

- Your AUTOEXEC.BAT file is a batch program that MS-DOS runs immediately after carrying out the commands in your CONFIG.SYS file. Your AUTOEXEC.BAT file can contain any commands you want carried out when you start your system—for example, commands that define the port your printer is connected to, clear your screen of startup messages, or run your favorite menu program.

These files are typically located in the root directory of your startup disk (usually drive C).

Unless you specify otherwise, MS-DOS carries out the commands in both your CONFIG.SYS and AUTOEXEC.BAT files each time you start your computer. You can instruct MS-DOS to bypass the commands in these files if you need to. For more information, see "Bypassing CONFIG.SYS and AUTOEXEC.BAT Commands" later in this chapter.

When you install MS-DOS 6, MS-DOS Setup creates a basic system configuration that works for most computers. However, you might want to change this configuration to:

- Customize the way MS-DOS uses hardware, memory, and files. For more information about changing your MS-DOS configuration, see the following section.

- Add a new hardware component or reconfigure an existing component. For more information about adding or changing hardware devices, see "Configuring Hardware Devices" later in this chapter.

- Specify commands you want MS-DOS to carry out each time your computer starts. For more information, see "Specifying Startup Commands in Your AUTOEXEC.BAT File" later in this chapter.

- Define more than one system configuration. For example, if two different people use the same computer, each person can specify a separate configuration. This is an advanced use of CONFIG.SYS commands and is explained in "Using Multiple Configurations" later in this chapter.

The rest of this chapter explains how to configure your system by using commands in your CONFIG.SYS and AUTOEXEC.BAT files.

# Using CONFIG.SYS Commands to Configure Your System

When your computer starts, MS-DOS carries out commands that configure your hardware and reserve space in memory for information processing. The file that contains these commands is named CONFIG.SYS. MS-DOS Setup creates a CONFIG.SYS file and stores it in the root directory of your startup disk. (If you already have a CONFIG.SYS file, Setup modifies your existing file as necessary.)

You can edit your CONFIG.SYS file to add and change commands that configure your system.

## Editing Your CONFIG.SYS File

To edit your CONFIG.SYS file, use a text editor that saves files as unformatted (ASCII) text (for example, MS-DOS Editor).

**Caution**  Do not edit your CONFIG.SYS file by using a word processor that saves files only in a special document format. If you save your CONFIG. SYS file as a formatted file, your computer might not start correctly.

MS-DOS reads your CONFIG.SYS file only when you start your computer. Therefore, any time you change your CONFIG.SYS file, you must restart your computer for your changes to take effect.

▶ **To make changes to your CONFIG.SYS file**

1. Create a startup disk by inserting an unformatted floppy disk in drive A, and then typing the following at the command prompt:

   **format a: /s**

2. Copy your CONFIG.SYS file to the startup disk you just created by typing the following at the command prompt:

   **copy c:\config.sys a:**

3. Open the CONFIG.SYS file on your hard disk by using a text editor such as MS-DOS Editor. (To open the file by using MS-DOS Editor, type **edit c:\config.sys** at the command prompt.)

4. Add or change CONFIG.SYS commands as necessary. Each CONFIG.SYS command must begin on a separate line. For a list of the commands you can use in your CONFIG.SYS file, see the following section.

5. When you finish editing your CONFIG.SYS file, save your changes, and then quit the text editor.

6. Remove any disks from your floppy disk drives, and then restart your computer by pressing CTRL+ALT+DEL.

---

**Note**   The settings in your CONFIG.SYS file control basic components of your system, such as memory and other hardware devices. If you change your CONFIG.SYS file and the new settings are incorrect, your system might be unable to start correctly. If this happens, restart your computer by inserting the startup disk you created in drive A and pressing CTRL+ALT+DEL. Or, follow the procedures in "Bypassing CONFIG.SYS and AUTOEXEC.BAT Commands" later in this chapter.

---

# CONFIG.SYS Commands

The commands in your CONFIG.SYS file load special programs or determine how your hardware should work. Most CONFIG.SYS commands can be used only in your CONFIG.SYS file; the only exceptions are the **break**, **rem**, and **set** commands, which you can also use in your AUTOEXEC.BAT file or type at the command prompt. A typical CONFIG.SYS file contains some, but not all, of these commands. The following table briefly describes the purpose of each CONFIG.SYS command.

| Command | Purpose |
|---------|---------|
| **break** | Specifies whether MS-DOS should check periodically for the CTRL+C or CTRL+BREAK key combination. For more information, type **help break** at the command prompt. |
| **buffers** | Specifies how much memory MS-DOS reserves for transferring information to and from disks. For more information, type **help buffers** at the command prompt. |
| **country** | Sets the language conventions for your system. For more information, see the chapter "Customizing for International Use" or type **help country** at the command prompt. |
| **device** | Loads an installable device driver—a program that controls a hardware component, such as a mouse or memory board. For more information, see "Configuring Hardware Devices" later in this chapter or type **help device** at the command prompt. |
| **devicehigh** | Loads an installable device driver into the upper memory area. For more information, see the chapter "Making More Memory Available" or type **help devicehigh** at the command prompt. |
| **dos** | Specifies whether MS-DOS will use the high memory area (HMA) and whether it will provide access to upper memory blocks (UMBs). For more information, see the chapter "Making More Memory Available" or type **help dos** at the command prompt. |
| **drivparm** | Sets the characteristics of a disk drive. For more information, type **help drivparm** at the command prompt. |
| **files** | Specifies how many files can be open at a time. For more information, type **help files** at the command prompt. |
| **install** | Loads a memory-resident program (also called a terminate-and-stay-resident program, or TSR). For more information, type **help install** at the command prompt. |
| **lastdrive** | Sets the number of valid drive letters. For more information, type **help lastdrive** at the command prompt. |
| **numlock** | Specifies whether the NUM LOCK setting of the numeric keypad is initially on or off. For more information, type **help numlock** at the command prompt. |
| **rem** | Indicates that the text that follows is a descriptive remark, not a command. Can also be used to disable a command. For more information, type **help rem** at the command prompt. |
| **set** | Sets the value of environment variables such as PROMPT or TEMP. For more information, see "Using Multiple Configurations" later in this chapter or type **help set** at the command prompt. |
| **shell** | Configures COMMAND.COM or specifies that a command interpreter other than COMMAND.COM should be used. For more information, type **help shell** or **help command** at the command prompt. |

| Command | Purpose |
| --- | --- |
| **stacks** | Specifies how much memory to reserve for processing hardware interrupts. For more information, type **help stacks** at the command prompt. |
| **switches** | Specifies special options in MS-DOS. For more information, type **help switches** at the command prompt. |

Your CONFIG.SYS file can also contain the **include**, **menucolor**, **menudefault**, **menuitem**, and **submenu** commands. For more information, see "Using Multiple Configurations" later in this chapter.

---

**Note**  Most CONFIG.SYS commands can appear in your CONFIG.SYS file in any order. For example, the **dos**, **files**, or **buffers** commands can appear anywhere in the file. However, the relative order of the **device** and **devicehigh** commands is important. For more information, see "Determining the Order of CONFIG.SYS Commands" later in this chapter.

---

# Configuring Hardware Devices

Each of your computer's hardware components is called a *device*. Your computer's keyboard, mouse, monitor, printer, disk drives, and memory boards are all devices. Each device has characteristics that can be customized.

MS-DOS uses a program called a *device driver* to control each device. For example, MS-DOS uses a built-in device driver to control how information is read from and written to a floppy disk drive. MS-DOS has built-in device drivers for your keyboard, monitor, hard and floppy disk drives, and communication ports. Because these device drivers are built in, you do not have to do anything special to use them. However, you can customize certain features of these device drivers by using CONFIG.SYS commands. For a list of these commands, see "CONFIG.SYS Commands" earlier in this chapter.

Other devices, such as a memory board or a mouse, come with their own device drivers. Such a device driver is called an *installable* device driver because you install it by adding a command to your CONFIG.SYS file. MS-DOS includes several installable device drivers.

To use an installable device driver, add a **device** command for that driver to your CONFIG.SYS file. When MS-DOS starts, it loads the device driver into memory. For example, to load the MOUSE.SYS device driver located in the C:\MOUSE directory, you would add the following command to your CONFIG.SYS file:

**device=c:\mouse\mouse.sys**

When MS-DOS receives this command, it loads the MOUSE.SYS device driver into memory. The mouse device driver remains in memory and provides access to your mouse.

---

**Note**  Many hardware devices come with installation programs that automatically add the necessary commands to your CONFIG.SYS file.

---

MS-DOS comes with the following installable device drivers.

| Driver | Purpose |
|---|---|
| ANSI.SYS | Supports American National Standards Institute (ANSI) terminal emulation. For more information, type **help ansi.sys** at the command prompt. |
| DISPLAY.SYS | Supports code-page switching for monitors. For more information, type **help display.sys** at the command prompt. |
| DBLSPACE.SYS | Causes MS-DOS to move DBLSPACE.BIN its final location in memory. (DBLSPACE.BIN is the part of MS-DOS that provides access to drives compressed by using DoubleSpace.) For more information, type **help dblspace.sys** at the command prompt. |
| DRIVER.SYS | Creates a logical drive that you can use to refer to a physical floppy disk drive. For more information, type **help driver.sys** at the command prompt. |
| EGA.SYS | Saves and restores the display when MS-DOS Shell Task Swapper or Windows is used with an EGA monitor. For more information, type **help ega.sys** at the command prompt. |
| EMM386.EXE | Simulates expanded memory and provides access to the upper memory area on a computer with an 80386 or higher processor with extended memory. (The first time you use the Microsoft MemMaker memory-optimization program, it installs this device driver automatically.) For more information, type **help emm386.exe** at the command prompt. |
| HIMEM.SYS | Manages the use of extended memory on a computer with an 80286 or higher processor and extended memory. (MS-DOS Setup installs this device driver automatically on such systems.) For more information, type **help himem.sys** at the command prompt. |
| RAMDRIVE.SYS | Simulates a hard disk drive by creating a virtual disk drive in your system's random-access memory (RAM). For more information, type **help ramdrive.sys** at the command prompt. |

| Driver | Purpose |
|--------|---------|
| SETVER.EXE | Loads the MS-DOS version table into memory. For more information, type **help setver.exe** at the command prompt. |
| SMARTDRV.EXE | Performs double buffering, which provides compatibility for hard-disk controllers that cannot work with memory provided by EMM386 or Windows running in 386 enhanced mode. For more information, type **help smartdrv.exe** at the command prompt. |

# Determining the Order of CONFIG.SYS Commands

Most CONFIG.SYS commands can appear in your CONFIG.SYS file in any order. For example, the **dos**, **files**, or **buffers** commands can appear anywhere in the file.

The order of the **device** and **devicehigh** commands is important, however, because some device drivers enable devices that are needed by other drivers. For example, the HIMEM.SYS extended-memory driver must be loaded before any drivers that use extended memory.

The following list shows the order in which device drivers should appear in your CONFIG.SYS file:

1.  HIMEM.SYS, if your computer has extended memory.
2.  Your expanded-memory manager, if your computer has an expanded-memory board.
3.  EMM386.EXE, if your computer has an 80386 processor and extended memory. (If your CONFIG.SYS file includes commands that load both an expanded-memory manager and EMM386, the EMM386.EXE command line should include the **noems** switch.)

    The EMM386 memory manager can provide access to the upper memory area. EMM386 can also use extended memory to simulate expanded memory on computers that do not have expanded memory. For more information, see the chapter "Making More Memory Available."

4.  Any other device drivers.

**Note**  This list shows only the recommended order for device drivers. It is not intended to be a list of the commands that your CONFIG.SYS file should contain. The contents of your CONFIG.SYS file depend on the type of computer, amount and type of memory, hardware configuration, and programs you have.

# Sample CONFIG.SYS Files

The following is a typical CONFIG.SYS file for an 80386 computer with 2 or more megabytes (MB) of extended memory:

```
device=c:\dos\setver.exe
device=c:\dos\himem.sys
device=c:\dos\emm386.exe ram
devicehigh=c:\mouse\mouse.sys
buffers=20
files=40
break=on
dos=high,umb
```

In this example:

- The **device** commands load the SETVER.EXE, HIMEM.SYS, and EMM386.EXE device drivers. The SETVER.EXE driver manages the MS-DOS version table. The HIMEM.SYS driver manages extended memory. The **ram** switch directs the EMM386.EXE driver to provide access to upper memory and simulate expanded memory.

- The **devicehigh** command loads the MOUSE.SYS device driver, which provides access to the mouse, into upper memory.

- The **buffers** command reserves 20 buffers for transferring information to and from disks.

- The **files** command gives MS-DOS access to 40 files at one time.

- The **break** command checks frequently for the CTRL+C or CTRL+BREAK key combination.

- The **dos=high, umb** command runs MS-DOS in the high memory area and gives programs access to the upper memory area. (For more information about the upper memory area, see the chapter "Making More Memory Available.")

If you use a network and your computer has an 80286 processor and expanded memory, your CONFIG.SYS file might look similar to the following:

```
device=c:\emsdrv\emsdrv.sys
device=c:\mouse\mouse.sys
device=c:\net\network.sys
device=c:\dos\ramdrive.sys 256 /a
lastdrive=z
buffers=20
files=30
break=on
```

In this example:

- The first three **device** commands load device drivers for an expanded memory board, a mouse, and a network.

- The **device** command for RAMDRIVE.SYS starts RAMDrive and creates a 256-kilobyte (K) RAM drive; the **/a** switch instructs RAMDrive to create the RAM drive in expanded memory.

- The **lastdrive** command reserves space for 26 logical drives, so that letters from A through Z can be assigned as drive letters.

# Specifying Startup Commands in Your AUTOEXEC.BAT File

Each time you start your computer, MS-DOS first carries out the commands in your CONFIG.SYS file, then it carries out the commands in your AUTOEXEC.BAT file. This file is located in the root directory of your startup disk (usually drive C). The commands in your AUTOEXEC.BAT file set the characteristics of your devices, customize the information that MS-DOS displays, and start memory-resident programs and other applications.

You can customize your system by adding commands to your AUTOEXEC.BAT file. You can include any commands you would usually type at the command prompt.

## Editing Your AUTOEXEC.BAT File

To edit your AUTOEXEC.BAT file, use a text editor that saves files as unformatted (ASCII) text.

Caution  Do not edit your AUTOEXEC.BAT file by using a word processor that saves files only in a special document format. If you save your AUTOEXEC.BAT file as a formatted file, your computer might not start correctly.

MS-DOS carries out the commands in your AUTOEXEC.BAT file when you start your computer. After changing your AUTOEXEC.BAT file, restart your computer so your changes can take effect.

▶ **To make changes to your AUTOEXEC.BAT file**

1. Create a startup disk by inserting an unformatted floppy disk in drive A and then typing the following at the command prompt:

   **format a: /s**

2. Copy your AUTOEXEC.BAT file to the startup disk you just created by typing the following at the command prompt:

   **copy c:\autoexec.bat a:**

3. Open the AUTOEXEC.BAT file on your hard disk by using a text editor such as MS-DOS Editor. (To open the file by using MS-DOS Editor, type **edit c:\autoexec.bat** at the command prompt.)

4. Add or change AUTOEXEC.BAT commands as necessary. Each command must begin on a separate line. For more information, see the following section, "AUTOEXEC.BAT Commands."

5. When you finish editing your AUTOEXEC.BAT file, save your changes, and then quit the text editor.

6. Remove any disks from your floppy disk drives, and then restart your computer by pressing CTRL+ALT+DEL.

---

**Note**  If you change your AUTOEXEC.BAT file and the new settings are incorrect, your system might not be able to start correctly. If this happens, restart your computer by inserting the startup disk you created in drive A and pressing CTRL+ALT+DEL. Or, follow the procedures in "Bypassing CONFIG.SYS and AUTOEXEC.BAT Commands" later in this chapter.

---

# AUTOEXEC.BAT Commands

A *batch program* is a text file that contains a series of commands that MS-DOS carries out when you type its name at the command prompt. Your AUTOEXEC.BAT file is a special batch program that runs every time you start your computer.

Batch commands can be used in all batch programs, including your AUTOEXEC.BAT file. The following batch commands are commonly used in an AUTOEXEC.BAT file:

| Command | Purpose |
|---------|---------|
| **prompt** | Sets the appearance of your command prompt. For more information, type **help prompt** at the command prompt. |
| **mode** | Sets the characteristics of your keyboard, monitor, and printer and communication ports. For more information, type **help mode** at the command prompt. |
| **path** | Specifies the directories that MS-DOS should search for executable files (files with a .COM, .EXE, or .BAT filename extension) and the order in which the directories should be searched. For more information, type **help path** at the command prompt. |

| Command | Purpose |
|---------|---------|
| **echo off** | Directs MS-DOS not to display the commands in your AUTOEXEC.BAT file as they run. (You can also prevent a command from appearing by inserting an at sign [@] before the command.) For more information, type **help echo** at the command prompt. |
| **set** | Creates an environment variable that programs can use. (You can also use the **set** command in your CONFIG.SYS file.) For more information, type **help set** at the command prompt. |

For more information about creating batch files, type **help batch** at the command prompt.

Another common use of the AUTOEXEC.BAT file is to start *memory-resident programs*—programs that load into memory and generally stay there until you turn your computer off. These are also called terminate-and-stay-resident (TSR) programs. MS-DOS includes several memory-resident programs that are commonly started from the AUTOEXEC.BAT file.

| Command | Purpose |
|---------|---------|
| **doskey** | Provides keyboard shortcuts you can use at the command prompt. For example, you can use **doskey** to recall and edit commands you entered previously. For more information, type **help doskey** at the command prompt. |
| **vsafe** | Monitors your system for the presence of viruses. For more information, type **help vsafe** at the command prompt. |
| **smartdrv** | Speeds up access to your hard disk. For more information, type **help smartdrv** at the command prompt. |

After MS-DOS finishes running all the commands in your AUTOEXEC.BAT file, it displays the command prompt. (If your AUTOEXEC.BAT file starts MS-DOS Shell, Microsoft Windows, or another program, you will see that program's interface instead.)

# Sample AUTOEXEC.BAT Files

The following sample AUTOEXEC.BAT file contains some of the most commonly used commands:

```
path c:\;c:\dos;c:\utility;c:\batch
prompt $t$_$p$g
set temp=c:\temp
doskey
smartdrv
```

In this example:

- The **path** command directs MS-DOS to search for program files in the current directory and then in the following directories: the root directory of drive C and the C:\DOS, C:\UTILITY, and C:\BATCH directories. A semicolon (;) separates the names of the directories.

- The **prompt** command sets the command prompt so that it shows the current time, drive, and directory, followed by a greater-than sign (>).

- The **set temp** command creates an environment variable named TEMP and sets it equal to the directory C:\TEMP. (The name you specify must be the name of an existing directory.) Many programs, including MS-DOS, use this variable when storing temporary files.

- The **doskey** command loads the Doskey program into memory.

- The **smartdrv** command loads the SMARTDrive program into memory.

Suppose your system has a hard disk drive and a printer connected to port COM1, and you want Microsoft Windows to start automatically each time you start your computer. In this case, your AUTOEXEC.BAT file might include the following commands:

```
@echo off
path c:\;c:\dos;c:\windows
mode lpt1=com1
set temp=c:\temp
smartdrv
doskey
win
```

In this example:

- The **echo off** command prevents AUTOEXEC.BAT commands from being displayed as MS-DOS carries them out. (The @ sign at the beginning of the line prevents the **echo off** command from being displayed.)

- The **mode** command redirects printer output from parallel port LPT1 (the default port) to serial port COM1.

- The **smartdrv** command loads the SMARTDrive program into memory.

- The **doskey** command loads the Doskey program, which provides keyboard shortcuts at the command prompt.

- The last command, **win**, starts Microsoft Windows.

# Bypassing CONFIG.SYS and AUTOEXEC.BAT Commands

If you need to, you can start your computer without running the commands in your CONFIG.SYS and AUTOEXEC.BAT files. This is most useful when you are experiencing problems that might be related to the settings in those files. You can bypass startup commands in the following ways:

- You can bypass all the commands in both your CONFIG.SYS and AUTOEXEC.BAT files. For more information, see the following section.

- You can prevent MS-DOS from carrying out specific CONFIG.SYS commands and specify whether or not MS-DOS should run the AUTOEXEC.BAT file. For more information, see "Confirming Each CONFIG.SYS Command" later in this chapter.

- You can have MS-DOS prompt you to confirm a particular CONFIG.SYS command every time your computer starts. To do this, insert a question mark (?) after the command name but before the equal sign (=). For example, your CONFIG.SYS file might contain the **device=c:\dos\ramdrive.sys** command line. To have MS-DOS prompt you to confirm that command each time your computer starts, change the command line to **device?=c:\dos\ramdrive.sys**.

---

**Note**   For security purposes, you can prevent yourself or others from bypassing startup commands when your computer starts. To do this, add the **switches /n** command to your CONFIG.SYS file. For more information, type **help switches** at the command prompt.

---

## Completely Bypassing Your Startup Files

If you are having problems that you suspect are related to commands in your CONFIG.SYS or AUTOEXEC.BAT files, you might want to temporarily bypass both files.

▶ **To bypass your CONFIG.SYS and AUTOEXEC.BAT files**

1. Start or restart your computer. After your computer starts, MS-DOS displays the following text:

   ```
   Starting MS-DOS...
   ```

2. While the text is on your screen, press and release the F5 key or press and hold down the SHIFT key.

MS-DOS displays the following text:

```
MS-DOS is bypassing your CONFIG.SYS and AUTOEXEC.BAT files.
```

Your computer will start with a basic configuration instead of your usual configuration. Therefore, some parts of your system might not work as they usually do. For example:

- MS-DOS might be unable to find the COMMAND.COM file. If this happens, MS-DOS displays the message "Bad or missing command interpreter" when you start your computer and prompts you to specify the path to the COMMAND.COM file. Type the full path to the file (for example, C:\DOS\COMMAND.COM), and then press ENTER.

- MS-DOS will not load installable device drivers. As a result, any device that requires an installable device driver will not work. For example, your mouse will not work. Also, programs that require expanded or extended memory will be unable to run because MS-DOS will not load expanded- or extended-memory managers.

- MS-DOS will set environment variables to their default values. The command prompt might not appear the way it usually does; it will display the current drive and directory. The search path will be set to the directory that contains your MS-DOS files (usually C:\DOS). You will have to type the complete path and filename of any commands or files that are not located in this directory.

# Confirming Each CONFIG.SYS Command

If you are having problems that you suspect are related to a specific CONFIG.SYS command, you might want to have MS-DOS prompt you to confirm each command when your computer starts.

▶ **To confirm each CONFIG.SYS command**

1. Start or restart your computer. After your computer starts, MS-DOS displays the following text:

```
Starting MS-DOS...
```

2. While the text is on your screen, press and release the F8 key.

MS-DOS displays the following text:

```
MS-DOS will prompt you to confirm each CONFIG.SYS command.
```

One at a time, MS-DOS displays each command in your CONFIG.SYS file followed by a prompt. For example, when MS-DOS reaches the **dos=high** command, it displays the following prompt:

```
DOS=HIGH [Y,N]?
```

To carry out the current command, press Y for Yes. To bypass that command, press N for No. To carry out all remaining startup commands, press ESC. To bypass all remaining startup commands, press F5.

3. When MS-DOS finishes processing the CONFIG.SYS file, the following prompt appears:

```
Process AUTOEXEC.BAT [Y,N]?
```

To carry out all the commands in your AUTOEXEC.BAT file, press Y for Yes. To bypass your AUTOEXEC.BAT file completely, press N for No.

# Using Multiple Configurations

A single CONFIG.SYS file can define several different system configurations. This can be useful if several people share a single computer or if you want to be able to start your own computer with a choice of configurations.

# Overview of Procedures

This section provides an overview of the procedures for defining multiple configurations.

1. Define a startup menu in your CONFIG.SYS file.

   Each time your computer starts, the startup menu appears and lists the available configurations; you choose the configuration you want from the menu. For information about creating a startup menu, see the following section.

2. Create a *configuration block* in your CONFIG.SYS file for each configuration you want.

   A configuration block begins with a *block header*—a name surrounded by square brackets. Each block contains the CONFIG.SYS commands that you want MS-DOS to carry out when that configuration is selected from the startup menu. For information about creating configuration blocks, see "Defining Configuration Blocks" later in this chapter.

3. If you want, you can have MS-DOS carry out different AUTOEXEC.BAT commands for each startup configuration. To do this, you can use batch commands such as **if** and **goto** to create conditional branches in your AUTOEXEC.BAT file. For more information, see "Modifying Your AUTOEXEC.BAT File for Multiple Configurations" later in this chapter.

## Example: Defining Multiple Configurations

The following example shows the basic structure of a CONFIG.SYS file that defines a startup menu and two different configurations.

```
[menu]
menuitem=Green
menuitem=Purple

[green]
files=40
device=c:\device1.sys

[purple]
files=10
device=c:\device2.sys
```

In this example:

- The first configuration block defines the choices that will appear on the startup menu. This startup menu contains two items, Green and Purple. Each menu item refers to a different configuration block.

- The [green] configuration block contains the commands that will be carried out when Green is chosen from the startup menu. When the computer starts with the Green configuration, MS-DOS sets the value for **files** to 40 and loads the DEVICE1.SYS device driver.

- The [purple] configuration block contains the commands for the Purple configuration. When the computer starts with the Purple configuration, MS-DOS sets the value for **files** to 10 and loads the DEVICE2.SYS device driver.

When the computer starts with this CONFIG.SYS file, the following menu appears:

```
MS-DOS 6 Startup Menu
---------------------

    1. Green
    2. Purple

Enter a choice: 1
```

If you choose Green from this menu, MS-DOS runs the commands in the [green] configuration block; if you choose Purple, MS-DOS runs the commands in the [purple] configuration block.

The sections in the rest of this chapter explain how to carry out each of the procedures that were introduced in this overview.

# Defining a Startup Menu

To use multiple configurations, you must define a startup menu. To do this, create a configuration block with the block heading **[menu]**. The following table lists the commands a menu block can contain.

| Command | Purpose |
| --- | --- |
| **menuitem** | Defines a menu item. The command specifies the configuration block associated with that item and, optionally, the menu text for that item. For more information, type **help menuitem** at the command prompt. |
| **menudefault** | Specifies the default menu item. This command is optional; if the **[menu]** block does not contain a **menudefault** command, the default is set to item 1. The **menudefault** command can include an optional time-out value; if you don't select an item within the specified time, MS-DOS starts your computer using the default configuration. For more information, type **help menudefault** at the command prompt. |
| **menucolor** | Sets the text and background colors for the menu. (For more information, including the list of color values, type **help menucolor** at the command prompt.) |
| **submenu** | Specifies a menu item that displays another set of choices. The command specifies another menu block that defines the choices on the submenu. For more information, type **help submenu** at the command prompt. |
| **numlock** | Specifies whether the NUM LOCK key should be on or off when you start your computer. For more information, type **help numlock** at the command prompt. |

## Example: Defining a Sample [Menu] Block

The following is a sample **[menu]** block:

```
[menu]
menuitem=Net, Start the network
menuitem=No_Net, Do not start the network
menucolor=15,1
menudefault=Net, 20
```

In this example:

- The two **menuitem** commands define the items that will appear on the menu. The first **menuitem** value, "Net," specifies the name of the associated configuration block. The second value, which is optional, specifies the text you want to display on the menu ("Start the network"). If you don't specify any menu text, MS-DOS uses the name of the configuration block.

In this example, the first **menuitem** command is associated with the [net] block; the menu text is "Start the network." The second **menuitem** command is associated with the [no_net] block; the menu text is "Do not start the network."

- The **menucolor** command sets the text color to 15 (bright white) and the background color to 1 (blue).

- The **menudefault** command specifies [net] as the default configuration and sets a time-out value of 20 seconds. If no item is selected within the specified time, MS-DOS starts the computer with the default configuration.

# Defining Configuration Blocks

A configuration block is a set of CONFIG.SYS commands that you want MS-DOS to run when a particular configuration is chosen from the startup menu. A configuration block begins with a block header—the block name surrounded by brackets. The block name must be a single word, but can be as long as you want. When MS-DOS starts with a particular configuration, it carries out all the commands between the block header for that configuration and the next block header.

A configuration block can contain any CONFIG.SYS command. The following commands can be particularly useful in configuration blocks:

- The **set** command sets the value of an environment variable. You can use this command in your CONFIG.SYS file to set unique values for each configuration. For more information about the **set** command, type **help set** at the command prompt.

- The **include** command directs MS-DOS to carry out the commands in another configuration block in addition to the commands in the current block. For more information, see "Example: Using the Include Command" later in this chapter, or type **help include** at the command prompt.

Commands common to all configuration blocks can be placed in a block named **[common]**. MS-DOS carries out the commands in a **[common]** block for every configuration. You can have as many **[common]** blocks as you want; MS-DOS runs **[common]** commands in the order in which they appear.

You might want to place a **[common]** block at the end of your CONFIG.SYS file, even if the block doesn't contain any commands. Some applications append commands to your CONFIG.SYS file when you install them. If your CONFIG.SYS file ends with a **[common]** block, an application can append commands to the file and MS-DOS will carry out those commands for all your configurations.

---

**Note**  If you plan to optimize your CONFIG.SYS file by using the MemMaker program, you might want to avoid using the **include** command or [**common**] blocks, since these can complicate the optimization process. For instructions on using MemMaker with multiple configurations, see the chapter "Making More Memory Available."

---

## Example: Using [Common] Blocks

The following CONFIG.SYS file defines two configurations and includes several commands that are common to both:

```
[menu]
menuitem=Steve
menuitem=Lisa

[common]
dos=high
buffers=15
device=c:\dos\himem.sys

[steve]
files=20
device=c:\dos\emm386.exe 2048

[lisa]
files=40
device=c:\net\network.sys

[common]
```

This CONFIG.SYS file configures the computer for either Steve or Lisa. For both configurations, MS-DOS carries out the three commands in the first [**common**] block: **dos=high**, **buffers=15**, and **device=c:\dos\himem.sys**. In this case, the [**common**] block appears first because it contains the device command for HIMEM.SYS, which must be loaded before other commands. Steve uses a desktop publishing program that requires expanded memory, so his configuration includes a command for EMM386. He does not use the network. Lisa uses the network but not desktop publishing. Her configuration starts the network driver. The [**common**] block at the end is for commands that might be added when you install new applications.

## Example: Using the Include Command

You can include the contents of one configuration block in another by using the **include** command, which specifies the name of the block you want to include. The **include** command can be used only within a configuration block.

The following CONFIG.SYS file defines several configuration blocks and uses the **include** command to include the [windows] and [network] blocks in the [winnet] block:

```
[menu]
menuitem=Windows, Configure for Windows
menuitem=Network, Start the network
menuitem=WinNet, Configure for Windows and start the network

[common]
files=40
buffers=20
device=c:\dos\himem.sys
dos=high

[windows]
set path=c:\windows;c:\dos
set temp=c:\windows\temp

[network]
device=c:\net\network.sys
set path=c:\dos;c:\network
lastdrive=z

[winnet]
include=windows
include=network
set path=c:\windows;c:\network;c:\dos

[common]
```

This CONFIG.SYS file includes three configurations: Windows, Network, and WinNet. The [winnet] configuration block includes the commands in the [windows] and [network] configuration blocks, in addition to its own **path** command. The first [**common**] block in this CONFIG.SYS file includes commands common to all configurations. The last [**common**] block, which is currently empty, is for commands that might be added to your CONFIG.SYS file when you install new applications.

# Modifying Your AUTOEXEC.BAT File for Multiple Configurations

When you use multiple configurations, you might want to have MS-DOS carry out different AUTOEXEC.BAT commands for each one. You can create branches in your AUTOEXEC.BAT file by using batch commands such as **if** and **goto**. (For more information about batch commands, type **help batch** at the command prompt.)

When a configuration is selected from the startup menu, MS-DOS defines an environment variable named CONFIG and sets it to the name of the selected configuration block. In your AUTOEXEC.BAT file, you can use the **goto** command to have MS-DOS carry out different sets of commands for different CONFIG values.

▶  **To define multiple configurations in your AUTOEXEC.BAT file**

1. Insert the following command in your AUTOEXEC.BAT file:

   **goto %config%**

   The command should appear *after* any commands you want MS-DOS to carry out for all configurations.

2. Add labels to your AUTOEXEC.BAT file that match the names of the corresponding configuration blocks in your CONFIG.SYS file. The labels should appear before the group of commands for each configuration. For example, you would insert the following label before the group of commands for the [steve] configuration:

   **:steve**

3. Insert the following label at the end of your AUTOEXEC.BAT file:

   **:end**

4. After the group of commands for each configuration, add the following command:

   **goto end**

   This command directs MS-DOS to the line marked by the **:end** label. Any commands that appear after that line are carried out for both configurations.

---

**Note**  You can also use the **if** command to test the value of the CONFIG variable. If you do, you must enclose the CONFIG variable both in percent marks (%) and double quotation marks ("), as in the following example: "%CONFIG%". For information about the **if** command, type **help if** at the command prompt.

---

## Example: Using the Goto Command with the CONFIG Variable

The following AUTOEXEC.BAT file uses the **goto** command with the CONFIG variable to carry out different sets of commands. This AUTOEXEC.BAT file is designed to work with the "Steve and Lisa" sample CONFIG.SYS file in "Defining Configuration Blocks" earlier in this chapter.

```
c:\dos\smartdrv.exe
set temp=c:\temp
c:\dos\msav

rem Go to the section that matches the current
rem value of the CONFIG variable
goto %config%

:Steve
path c:\dos;c:\deskpub;c:\typeset
c:\mouse\mouse.com
deskpub
rem now skip Lisa's section and go to end
goto end

:Lisa
path=c:\dos;c:\network;c:\utility
doskey
net logon lisa /y
goto end

:end
```

When MS-DOS runs this AUTOEXEC.BAT file, it starts SMARTDrive, sets the TEMP environment variable, and starts the Microsoft Anti-Virus program. MS-DOS then goes to the section that matches the value of the CONFIG variable.

If the name of the selected configuration is "Steve," MS-DOS goes to the Steve section. It then sets the search path for Steve, loads the MOUSE.COM program from the C:\MOUSE directory, and runs the desktop publishing program. The **goto end** command instructs MS-DOS to skip to the line marked by the **:end** label, bypassing the commands in the Lisa section.

If the current configuration is "Lisa," the PATH variable is set differently, MS-DOS runs the Doskey program, and a **net logon** command reestablishes Lisa's persistent network connections.

CHAPTER 5

# Freeing Disk Space

Floppy disks and hard disks are the most common types of storage media for computers. They provide both long-term and temporary storage for program and data files. Files are stored on a disk magnetically, much as sound is stored on a cassette tape. When you store files on a disk, they use up some of the available space on that disk.

Your hard disk should always contain some free disk space. You need free disk space to save documents and other data files. In addition, many programs create temporary files and store them on your hard disk while they're running. These programs might not run properly if you do not have enough free disk space.

Keep track of how much disk space is available on your computer. You can use the **chkdsk** and **dir** commands to do this. For information about these commands, type **help chkdsk** or **help dir** at the command prompt.

You can make more disk space available in two ways. You can:

- Free disk space by deleting unnecessary files. For more information about deleting files, including a list of MS-DOS files you might want to delete, see the following section.

- Create 50 to 100 percent more disk space by compressing the data on your hard disk. For more information, see the section "Increasing Disk Space by Using DoubleSpace" later in this chapter.

The rest of this chapter explains both methods.

# Deleting Unnecessary Files

Disk space is a valuable system resource. If you need more disk space, one solution is to delete unnecessary files. You might want to delete files in one or more of the following categories:

- Program and data files that you no longer use.

- Temporary files that were left on your hard disk when a program stopped running unexpectedly.

- Files that were installed with MS-DOS that you don't plan to use. The tables at the end of this section list the MS-DOS files you might want to delete.

- Lost file allocation units, which can take up space on your hard disk. For more information about finding lost file allocation units, converting them to files, and deleting those files, see the following section, "Using Chkdsk to Free Disk Space."

In general, keep as much disk space free as possible. To delete unnecessary files, use the **del** command. For information about the **del** command, type **help del** at the command prompt.

Use the following guidelines to decide which files to delete:

- Delete any temporary files created by your programs.

  Many programs create temporary files while they are running. Some programs store those files in a directory specified by the TEMP environment variable. To determine whether your computer has a directory designated for temporary files, type **set** at the command prompt, and then check the value that MS-DOS displays for the TEMP variable. For more information about environment variables, type **help set** at the command prompt.

  Periodically delete any files in the directory specified by the TEMP environment variable. (This is not necessary if the directory is on a RAM disk.) To avoid deleting a temporary file that is currently in use, quit all programs (including Windows and MS-DOS Shell) before deleting files in the directory specified by the TEMP variable.

- If you haven't used a file in a long time, consider copying it to a floppy disk and then deleting it from your hard disk. You can use Microsoft Backup to archive files. For more information about using Backup, see the chapter "Managing Your System."

- If you are sure you will not need to restore your previous version of DOS, you can delete the OLD_DOS.x directory and the files it contains. To do this, type **deloldos** at the command prompt, and then follow the instructions on your screen.

- As a last resort, delete some MS-DOS files that you do not plan to use.

---

**Caution**  Do not delete any MS-DOS files other than the ones listed in the following tables. Never delete the files COMMAND.COM, IO.SYS, MSDOS.SYS, or any file that has a name beginning with "DBLSPACE," such as DBLSPACE.000 or DBLSPACE.BIN. (Most of these files have Hidden or System attributes.) If you delete any of these files, you might lose data or your system might not start.

Also, be sure you quit all programs (including Windows and MS-DOS Shell) before deleting any temporary files.

---

Use the following tables to determine which MS-DOS files you can delete.

| Filename(s) | Description | When to delete |
|---|---|---|
| APPEND.EXE | Enables programs to open data files as if they were in the current directory, even when they are not | If you do not plan to use the **append** command |
| NLSFUNC.EXE, KEYB.COM, *.CPI, COUNTRY.SYS, DISPLAY.SYS, KEYBOARD.SYS | Provide international and character-set support | If you do not need international (foreign language) support |
| RAMDRIVE.SYS | RAMDrive memory-disk program; speeds up your system | If you do not need a RAM disk, or if your computer has only conventional memory |
| DOSSHELL.*, *.VID | The MS-DOS Shell program. | If you do not plan to use MS-DOS Shell |
| POWER.EXE | Conserves battery power on a laptop computer | If your computer is not a laptop |
| INTERLNK.*, INTERSVR.* | Connect two computers via parallel or serial ports so that the two computers can share disks and printer ports | If you do not plan to use the Interlnk program |
| EMM386.EXE, MEMMAKER.*, SIZER.EXE, CHKSTATE.SYS | Manage and optimize memory on an 80386 or higher computer | If your computer is not an 80386 or higher, or if it has no extended memory |
| SMARTDRV.EXE | SMARTDrive disk-caching program; speeds up your system | If your computer does not have a hard disk, or if it has no extended memory |

The directory that contains your MS-DOS 6 files might still include files from your previous version of DOS. The following table lists files from previous versions of DOS that you might want to delete.

| Filename(s) | Description | When to delete |
|---|---|---|
| 4201.CPI, 4208.CPI, 5202.CPI, LCD.CPI, PRINTER.SYS | Provide international and character-set support for certain printers. | If you do not plan to download different character sets to an IBM Proprinter ® model 4201, 4202, 4207, or to an IBM Quietwriter ® model 5202. |
| GRAFTABL.COM | Provides international support for CGA monitors. | If you do not need international support for a CGA monitor. |
| ASSIGN.COM | Redirects requests for disk operations on one drive to a different drive. | You can safely delete this file; use the **subst** command instead. |
| CV.COM, EXE2BIN.EXE, LINK.EXE, GWBASIC.*, BASICA.*, *.BAS | Programming tools and sample files. | If you do not plan to do any programming. |
| EDLIN.EXE | A line-oriented text editor. | If you do not use Edlin. You can safely delete this file; use the **edit** command, which starts MS-DOS Editor, instead. |
| HDBKUP.EXE, HDRSTORE.EXE | Used during MS-DOS 5 Setup to back up and restore files. | You can safely delete these files; they are not necessary with MS-DOS 6. |
| JOIN.EXE | Joins a disk drive with a directory on another drive. | If you do not plan to use the **join** command. |
| MSHERC.COM | Provides support for a Hercules monitor running with MS-DOS Editor or QBasic. | If you do not have a Hercules monitor. |
| PRINTFIX.COM | Disables verification of a printer's status. | If you are not currently using the Printfix program and you can successfully use your printer. |
| SMARTDRV.SYS | The version of the SMARTDrive program that came with MS-DOS 5. | You can safely delete this file; the file for the MS-DOS 6 SMARTDrive program is named SMARTDRV.EXE. |

# Using Chkdsk to Free Disk Space

You can use the **chkdsk /f** command to recover lost *allocation units* that are taking up space on your hard disk. An allocation unit is the smallest part of a hard disk that can be allocated to a file. Allocation units can get lost when a program unexpectedly stops running without saving or deleting temporary files properly. Over time, lost allocation units can accumulate and take up disk space.

When you use the **/f** switch with the **chkdsk** command, **chkdsk** converts lost allocation units to files that have a .CHK extension. You can then examine and delete these .CHK files.

---

**Caution**   Before using **chkdsk /f**, quit all running applications, including Windows and MS-DOS Shell. You might also need to disable the commands that load memory-resident programs in your CONFIG.SYS and AUTOEXEC.BAT files and restart your computer. (You do not need to disable any memory-resident programs that came with MS-DOS 6.) If you use the **chkdsk /f** command while programs are running, you might lose data.

---

You can use the **chkdsk /f** command to do the following:

- Make sure there are no lost allocation units on a disk.
- Check a disk before running the Defragmenter or DoubleSpace.
- Check a disk after a program stops running unexpectedly.

▶ **To recover lost allocation units**

1. Quit all running programs.
2. Change to the hard disk you want to check (for example, if you want to recover lost allocation units on drive C, type **c:** at the command prompt).
3. Type the following at the command prompt:

   **chkdsk /f**

   The Chkdsk program finds and recovers any lost allocation units and displays information about the disk. (It also finds and reports any cross links or directory errors.) If **chkdsk** detects lost allocation units, a prompt similar to the following appears:

   ```
   10 lost allocation units found in 3 chains.
   Convert lost chains to files?
   ```

   To save the information in the lost allocation units, press Y.

4. The Chkdsk program converts any lost file allocation units to files with filenames such as FILE0000.CHK. It stores these files in your root directory.

   Sometimes a .CHK file contains information you want to keep. For example, if a word-processing application stops unexpectedly before you save your edits, you might find your lost edits in a recovered .CHK file.

5. To examine the contents of .CHK files, use the **more** command.

   For example, to examine the contents of the FILE0000.CHK file, you would type the following at the command prompt: **more < file0000.chk**

   If the file contains more than one screen of information, press any key to see the next screen.

6. Delete any .CHK files you don't want by using the **del** command. For example, to delete the FILE0000.CHK file, type the following at the command prompt:

   **del file0000.chk**

For more information about the **chkdsk**, **more**, or **del** command, type **help chkdsk**, **help more**, or **help del** at the command prompt.

# Increasing Disk Space by Using DoubleSpace

DoubleSpace frees space on hard and floppy disks by compressing the data that is on them. DoubleSpace is easy to set up and use. For instructions on setting up DoubleSpace, see "Setting Up DoubleSpace" later in this chapter. After you set up DoubleSpace, your disk will have 50 to 100 percent more free space.

After you set up DoubleSpace, you can maintain your compressed drives by using the full-screen DoubleSpace maintenance program or by typing commands at the MS-DOS command prompt. For example, you can pack compressed data even more tightly, change the size of a compressed drive, or check the validity of a compressed drive. For information about using the DoubleSpace program to manage compressed drives, see "Using DoubleSpace to Manage Compressed Drives" later in this chapter. For more information about managing compressed drives from the MS-DOS command prompt, type **help dblspace** at the command prompt.

You can also use DoubleSpace to compress floppy disks, removable-media drives, or additional hard disk drives. For more information, see "Compressing Additional Drives" later in this chapter.

The rest of this chapter explains how to set up and use DoubleSpace.

# Getting Help

DoubleSpace includes extensive online help for commands, dialog boxes, and procedures.

▶ **To get help while running DoubleSpace**

- Press F1 when a DoubleSpace screen, dialog box, or error message appears.

▶ **To get help about the dblspace command**

- Type **help dblspace** at the command prompt.

# Setting Up DoubleSpace

When you run DoubleSpace for the first time, the DoubleSpace Setup program starts. DoubleSpace Setup compresses the data on the drive you select. After DoubleSpace Setup is complete, your disk will have 50 to 100 percent more free space than it did before.

**Note** After you run DoubleSpace Setup, you cannot use the Uninstall program to restore your previous version of DOS. Do not set up DoubleSpace if you want to be able to use the Uninstall program.

During DoubleSpace Setup, you can select either Express Setup or Custom Setup. To compress the existing files on drive C and have DoubleSpace determine the compression settings for you, choose Express Setup. To compress a hard disk drive other than drive C, or to use the empty space on an existing drive to create a new compressed drive, choose Custom Setup. When you use Custom Setup, you can determine compression settings yourself. For more information about running Custom Setup, see "Using Custom Setup" later in this chapter.

The following sections explain each setup method.

## Using Express Setup

Express Setup is the easiest way to install DoubleSpace. It compresses the existing files on drive C. (To compress the files on a drive other than C, use Custom Setup. For more information, see the following section.)

**Note** Before you run Express Setup, you might want to back up the files on drive C. For information about using Microsoft Backup, see the chapter "Managing Your System."

▶ **To install DoubleSpace by using Express Setup**

1. Quit all running programs (including Windows or MS-DOS Shell).

   If you use a network, start the network software and connect to any drives you usually use.

2. Type the following at the command prompt:

   **dblspace**

   The Welcome screen appears.

3. To continue DoubleSpace, press ENTER.

   DoubleSpace displays a screen that prompts you to choose between Express and Custom Setup.

4. Choose Express Setup by pressing ENTER.

   DoubleSpace displays a confirmation screen that estimates the amount of time it will take to compress drive C.

5. To compress drive C, press C.

   DoubleSpace defragments and compresses drive C. This process can take from several minutes to several hours, depending on the speed of your hard disk and processor and the amount of data your hard disk contains. Because DoubleSpace checks and rechecks the validity of the data as it compresses your files, the process is very safe. In fact, if the compression process is accidentally interrupted (for example, by a power outage), DoubleSpace will recover and continue without losing any data.

   During the compression process, DoubleSpace Setup restarts your computer twice.

   When DoubleSpace Setup is complete, it displays a screen that shows how long the compression process took and how much free space your new drive contains.

6. To quit DoubleSpace after it has compressed drive C, press ENTER.

After you set up DoubleSpace, your computer's drives will be configured differently:

- Drive C will be compressed and will contain more free space than it did before. You will use drive C just as you did before you set up DoubleSpace.

- Your computer will have a new drive that is not compressed. This drive is used to store files that must remain uncompressed. For example, the Windows permanent swap file does not work properly when it is compressed; if your Windows permanent swap file was previously located on drive C, DoubleSpace moves it to the new uncompressed drive.

DoubleSpace also uses the new uncompressed drive to store important system files such as IO.SYS, MSDOS.SYS, DBLSPACE.BIN, DBLSPACE.INI, and DBLSPACE.000. If you try to list the files on this drive, it will probably appear empty. This is because most of the files it contains have the Hidden attribute; many also have the Read-Only attribute. To view the files, type **dir /a** at the command prompt.

---

**Caution**  Do not tamper with the hidden files on the new drive. If you change or delete these files, you might lose all the files on drive C.

---

For information about adjusting the configuration of your compressed drive, see "Using DoubleSpace to Manage Compressed Drives" later in this chapter. For information about compressing additional drives, see "Compressing Additional Drives" later in this chapter. For information about compressing floppy disks, see "Using DoubleSpace with Floppy Disks" later in this chapter.

## Using Custom Setup

Custom Setup gives you more control over the compression process than Express Setup does. You should use Custom Setup:

- To compress the data on a hard disk other than drive C.
- If you don't want to compress existing data.

    Compressing existing data can take a long time. If you don't want to compress your existing data, you can have DoubleSpace use some of the free space on an existing drive to create a new compressed drive. This method does not compress existing data and is much faster.

- To determine compression settings yourself.

    Depending on whether you are compressing an existing drive or creating a new one, you can specify the drive letter for the new drive, the estimated compression ratio, and the amount of space to leave uncompressed.

---

**Note**  Before you use Custom Setup to compress an existing drive, you might want to back up the files on that drive. For information about using Microsoft Backup, see the chapter "Managing Your System."

---

▶ **To install DoubleSpace by using Custom Setup**

1. Quit all running programs (including Windows or MS-DOS Shell).

    If you use a network, start the network software and connect to any drives you usually use.

2. Type the following at the command prompt:

   **dblspace**

   The Welcome screen appears.

3. To continue DoubleSpace, press ENTER.

   DoubleSpace displays a screen that prompts you to choose between Express and Custom Setup.

4. Select Custom Setup by pressing the DOWN ARROW key, and then press ENTER.

   DoubleSpace displays a screen in which you can choose between compressing an existing drive and creating a new compressed drive. For information about choosing a compression method, press F1.

5. Select the compression method you want by pressing the UP ARROW or DOWN ARROW key, and then press ENTER.

   If your computer has more than one hard disk drive, DoubleSpace displays a list of drives. If you chose to compress an existing drive, select the drive you want to compress, and then press ENTER. If you are creating a new compressed drive, select the drive that contains the free space DoubleSpace should use to create the new drive, and then press ENTER.

   DoubleSpace displays a screen that shows the default compression settings.

6. If necessary, change the compression settings to suit your needs. To change a setting, press the UP ARROW or DOWN ARROW key until the setting is highlighted, and then press ENTER to display alternatives. For information about compression settings, press F1.

7. When all the settings are correct, press ENTER to continue DoubleSpace.

   DoubleSpace displays a confirmation screen that estimates the amount of time it will take to compress the drive or free space you selected.

8. To begin the compression process, press C.

   DoubleSpace carries out the compression process with the settings you specified. This process can take from several minutes to several hours, depending on the speed of your hard disk and processor, the amount of data your hard disk contains, and whether you chose to compress existing data or create a new compressed drive. Because DoubleSpace checks and rechecks the validity of the data as it compresses existing files, the process is very safe. In fact, if the compression process is accidentally interrupted (for example, by a power outage), DoubleSpace will recover and continue without losing any data.

   During the compression process, DoubleSpace Setup restarts your computer twice.

   When DoubleSpace Setup is complete, it displays a screen that shows how long the compression process took and how much space your new drive contains.

9. To quit DoubleSpace after it has compressed the drive or free space you selected, press ENTER.

After you set up DoubleSpace, your computer's drives will be configured differently. The results differ, depending on whether you chose to compress an existing drive or create a new compressed drive.

## If you chose to compress an existing drive

If you chose "Compress an existing drive" during Custom Setup:

- The drive you selected will be compressed and will contain more free space than it did before. You will use the compressed drive just as you did before you set up DoubleSpace.

- Your computer will have a new drive that is not compressed. This drive is used to store files that must remain uncompressed. For example, the Windows permanent swap file does not work properly when it is compressed; if your Windows permanent swap file was previously located on drive C, DoubleSpace moves it to the new uncompressed drive.

  If you compressed drive C, DoubleSpace also uses the new uncompressed drive to store important system files such as IO.SYS, MSDOS.SYS, DBLSPACE.BIN, DBLSPACE.INI, and DBLSPACE.000. If you try to list the files on this drive, it will probably appear empty. This is because most of the files it contains have the Hidden attribute; many also have the Read-Only attribute. To view the files, type **dir /a** at the command prompt.

---

**Caution**  Do not tamper with the hidden files on the new drive. If you change or delete these files, you might lose the files on your compressed drive.

---

## If you chose to create a new compressed drive

If you chose "Create a new compressed drive" during Custom Setup:

- Your computer will have a new compressed drive that is currently empty. Although the new drive does use some disk space, it makes up for it by providing more free space than it uses.

- The drive that contained the free space you used to create the new compressed drive will contain less free space than it did before. This space is now being used by your new compressed drive.

For information about adjusting the configuration of your compressed drive, see "Using DoubleSpace to Manage Compressed Drives" later in this chapter. For information about compressing additional drives, see "Compressing Additional Drives" later in this chapter. For information about compressing floppy disks, see "Using DoubleSpace with Floppy Disks" later in this chapter.

# Understanding Disk Compression

You don't need to know anything about disk compression to run DoubleSpace Setup: just type **dblspace** at the command prompt, follow the instructions on your screen, and DoubleSpace takes care of the rest.

However, if you want to adjust or modify your DoubleSpace configuration, you need to understand some disk-compression concepts and terms. This section explains the terms you will encounter when you use DoubleSpace to manage or modify your compressed drives.

## Compressed Volume Files and Host Drives

A compressed drive is not a real disk drive, although it appears that way to most programs. Instead, a compressed drive exists on your hard disk as a *compressed volume file* (CVF).

A CVF is a file with Read-Only, Hidden, and System attributes that contains a compressed drive. Each CVF is located on an uncompressed drive, which is referred to as the CVF's *host drive*. A CVF is stored in the root directory of its host drive and has a filename such as DBLSPACE.000.

Most CVFs can store more data than the space they use on their host drives; for example, a typical CVF might use 10 MB of space on its host drive but contain 20 MB of compressed data. DoubleSpace assigns a drive letter to the CVF so that you can use it as a disk drive, and can access the files it contains.

---

**Caution**  Do not tamper with a CVF. If you do, you might lose all the files on your compressed drive.

---

The following diagram illustrates the relationship between a compressed drive, a CVF, and a host drive:

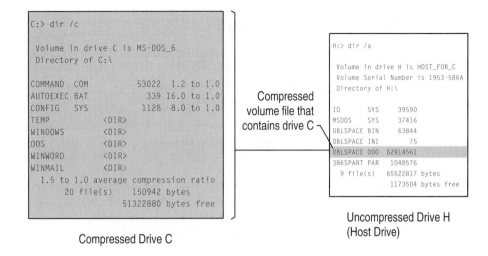

```
C:> dir /c

Volume in drive C is MS-DOS_6
Directory of C:\

COMMAND  COM           53022  1.2 to 1.0
AUTOEXEC BAT             339 16.0 to 1.0
CONFIG   SYS            1128  8.0 to 1.0
TEMP          <DIR>
WINDOWS       <DIR>
DOS           <DIR>
WINWORD       <DIR>
WINMAIL       <DIR>
   1.5 to 1.0 average compression ratio
        20 file(s)     150942 bytes
                     51322880 bytes free
```

Compressed
volume file that
contains drive C

```
H:> dir /a

Volume in drive H is HOST_FOR_C
Volume Serial Number is 1953-5B6A
Directory of H:\

IO       SYS        39590
MSDOS    SYS        37416
DBLSPACE BIN        63844
DBLSPACE INI           75
DBLSPACE 000     62914561
386SPART PAR      1048576
   9 file(s)     65522817 bytes
                  1173504 bytes free
```

Uncompressed Drive H
(Host Drive)

Compressed Drive C

This illustration shows two drives: drive C, which is compressed, and drive H, which is uncompressed. The **dir /c** command has been carried out on compressed drive C. This command lists the files in the current directory and displays the compression ratio of each file. Drive C contains several directories and the COMMAND.COM, AUTOEXEC.BAT, and CONFIG.SYS files.

The **dir /a** command has been carried out on drive H. This command lists the files in the current directory, including any files that have the Hidden attribute. Drive H contains several files, including the compressed volume file for drive C, DBLSPACE.000.

Compressed drive C is contained in the compressed volume file DBLSPACE.000, which is located on uncompressed drive H. Drive C's compressed volume file uses a substantial amount of space on drive H. However, drive C provides far more storage capacity than the space it uses on drive H.

## How DoubleSpace Calculates Free Space on a Compressed Drive

On an uncompressed drive, free space indicates how much additional data you can store on that drive. For example, if a drive has 2 megabytes (MB) of free space, you can expect to fit 2 MB of data on it. However, the free space on a compressed drive is only an estimate of how much data you can fit on that drive.

When you store a file on a compressed drive, DoubleSpace compresses the file so that it takes up as little space as possible. Some files can be compressed more tightly than others; for example, a bitmap file can be compressed much more than a program file. DoubleSpace cannot detect the compressibility of files you haven't stored yet, so it can only estimate a compressed drive's free space.

DoubleSpace estimates a drive's free space by using the *estimated compression ratio*, which you can set to specify the compressibility of the files you plan to store. For example, if the estimated compression ratio is set to 3 to 1, DoubleSpace calculates the drive's free space based on the assumption that the files you will store will be compressible at a 3-to-1 ratio—that is, that each file can be compressed to one-third its original size.

From time to time, you might want to reset the estimated compression ratio of each drive to match the actual compression ratio of the files stored on the drive. To do this for all your compressed drives, type **dblspace /ratio /all** at the command prompt.

You might want to change the estimated compression ratio if it differs greatly from the actual compressibility of the files you plan to store. For example, if you plan to store extremely compressible files, such as bitmap files, you might want to specify a higher estimated compression ratio. Or, if you plan to store files that will not compress much further, you might specify a lower ratio.

---

**Note**  Changing a drive's estimated compression ratio does not affect how much DoubleSpace actually compresses the files on that drive; it changes only the way DoubleSpace estimates the free space on the compressed drive.

---

# Using DoubleSpace to Manage Compressed Drives

Generally, you work with a compressed drive just as you would with an uncompressed drive. For example, saving, copying, and deleting files works the same way on both a compressed and an uncompressed drive. However, there are some tasks that you carry out only on compressed drives; for example, you can change the size of a compressed drive, but not that of an uncompressed drive.

To maintain or modify compressed drives or to create additional compressed drives, use the DoubleSpace maintenance program, which provides a full-screen interface with easy-to-use menu commands.

You can also manage compressed drives from the MS-DOS command prompt by using switches with the **dblspace** command. For more information, type **help dblspace** at the command prompt.

▶   **To start the DoubleSpace program**

 • Type **dblspace** at the command prompt.

DoubleSpace starts and displays a screen similar to the following:

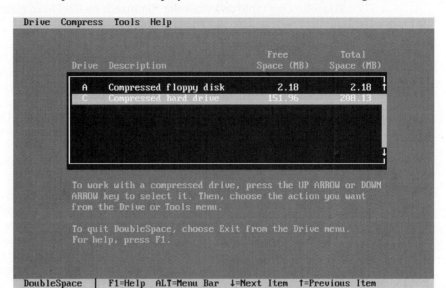

The main DoubleSpace screen lists your existing compressed drives. You can work with these drives, compress additional drives, or create new compressed drives. From this screen, you can carry out the following tasks:

- Work with a compressed drive. To do this, select the drive by clicking it with your mouse or by pressing the UP ARROW or DOWN ARROW key until the drive you want is selected. Then, choose the command you want from the Drive or Tools menu. (For a description of the commands on these menus, see the tables later in this section.)

- Compress an existing drive. To do this, choose the Existing Drive command from the Compress menu. Use this command to compress files on a hard disk drive or floppy disk. For more information, see "Compressing Additional Drives" later in this chapter.

- Add a new compressed drive. You can create a new compressed drive by using free space on an existing drive; to do this, choose the Create New Drive command from the Compress menu. For more information, see "Compressing Additional Drives" later in this chapter. (You can also add a compressed drive by mounting an unmounted compressed volume file. For more information, see "Creating a New Compressed Drive" later in this chapter.)

The Drive menu includes commands you can use to work with the selected drive. The following table describes the commands on the Drive menu.

| Command | Purpose |
|---------|---------|
| Info | Displays information about the selected drive. When you choose this command, the Compressed Drive Information dialog box appears and displays information about the drive's free and used space, the name of its CVF, and its actual and estimated compression ratios. You can also display the Compressed Drive Information dialog box by double-clicking the name of the drive or by pressing ENTER when the drive is selected. For more information, press F1 when the Compressed Drive Information dialog box is on your screen. |
| Change Size | Enlarges or reduces the size of the selected drive. Unlike an uncompressed drive, you can change the size of a compressed drive. You might want to enlarge a compressed drive if its host drive contains a lot of free space. You might want to reduce the size of a compressed drive if you need more free space on the host drive. For more information, choose the Change Size command, and then press F1. |
| Change Ratio | Changes the estimated compression ratio of the selected drive. DoubleSpace uses this ratio to estimate how much free space the compressed drive contains. You might want to change the estimated compression ratio if you plan to store new files with a compression ratio that differs greatly from the current ratio. For more information, choose the Change Ratio command and then press F1. |
| Mount | Establishes a connection between a compressed volume file and a drive letter, so you can use the files the CVF contains. DoubleSpace usually mounts CVFs automatically. You need to mount a CVF only if you previously unmounted it or if the CVF is located on a floppy disk. For more information, choose the Mount command, and then press F1. For more information about using DoubleSpace with floppy disks, see "Using DoubleSpace with Floppy Disks" later in this chapter. |
| Unmount | Breaks the connection between the selected drive's CVF and its drive letter. Unmounting a drive makes it temporarily inaccessible. For more information, choose Index from the Help menu, and then select the topic "Unmounting a Compressed Drive." |
| Format | Formats the selected compressed drive. Like formatting an uncompressed drive, formatting a compressed drive deletes all the files it contains. For more information, choose the Index command from the Help menu, and then select the topic "Formatting." For more information about using compressed floppy disks, see "Using DoubleSpace with Floppy Disks" later in this chapter. |

| Command | Purpose |
| --- | --- |
| Delete | Deletes the selected compressed drive and the associated CVF. Deleting a compressed drive erases it and all the files it contains. For more information, choose the Index command from the Help menu, and then select the topic "Deleting a Compressed Drive." |
| Exit | Quits the DoubleSpace program. (MS-DOS continues to provide access to your compressed drives after you quit DoubleSpace.) |

The Compress menu contains commands you can use to create additional compressed drives or to compress floppy disks. For information about compressing additional drives, see the following section, "Compressing Additional Drives." For information about compressing and working with floppy disks, see "Using DoubleSpace with Floppy Disks" later in this chapter.

The Tools menu includes commands you can use to maintain compressed drives. The following table describes the commands on the Tools menu.

| Command | Purpose |
| --- | --- |
| Defragment | Defragments the selected compressed drive. Defragmenting a compressed drive consolidates the free space on it. If you are planning to reduce the size of a compressed drive, you should first use the Defragment command to consolidate the drive's free space. For more information, choose the Defragment command, and then press F1. |
| Chkdsk | Checks the structural validity of the selected compressed drive. DoubleSpace Chkdsk searches for errors such as lost clusters or cross-linked files and informs you of any errors it finds. If you choose the Fix button, DoubleSpace Chkdsk also corrects any errors it can. (DoubleSpace Chkdsk checks the internal structure of the CVF; to check the compressed drive's MS-DOS directory structure and file allocation tables, type **chkdsk** at the command prompt.) For more information, choose the Chkdsk command, and then press F1. |
| Options | Displays the DoubleSpace Options dialog box, in which you can specify the last drive letter you want DoubleSpace to use. You can also specify the number of additional drives you want to be able to mount after you start your computer. For more information, choose the Options command, and then press F1 when the DoubleSpace Options dialog box is on your screen. |

# Compressing Additional Drives

DoubleSpace provides two ways to add compressed drives. You can:

- Compress an existing hard disk drive or floppy disk.
- Create a new, empty compressed drive by using free space on an existing drive.

The rest of this section explains each method.

## Compressing an Existing Drive

You can use DoubleSpace to compress the files on existing hard disk drives, floppy disks, or other removable media. Compressing an existing drive makes more space available on that drive.

---

**Note**  Before you compress an existing drive, you might want to back up the files on that drive. For information about using Microsoft Backup, see the chapter "Managing Your System."

---

▶ **To compress an existing drive**

1. In the main DoubleSpace screen, choose the Existing Drive command from the Compress menu. (If you are compressing a floppy disk or other removable media, make sure it is formatted and is in the drive before you choose the Existing Drive command.)

   DoubleSpace scans your computer and then displays a list of drives that can be compressed. (The list does not include drives that are too full to be compressed, compressed drives, RAM drives, network drives, CD-ROM drives, Interlnk drives, or paths that have been associated with a drive letter by using the **subst** command. For more information, press F1 when this list is displayed.)

2. Select the drive you want to compress by pressing the UP ARROW or DOWN ARROW key, and then press ENTER.

A screen appears, giving you the opportunity to change the settings DoubleSpace will use to compress the drive.

3. Change the settings as needed. For more information about changing settings, press F1.

4. When you have finished changing settings, press ENTER.

   DoubleSpace displays a confirmation screen stating that it is ready to compress the drive.

5. To compress the drive, press C.

   DoubleSpace defragments and compresses the selected drive, and then restarts your computer so your new drive configuration can take effect.

## Creating a New Compressed Drive

If your hard disk drive contains a lot of uncompressed space, you might want to convert that unused space into a new compressed drive. The new drive will provide more storage capacity than the amount of space it uses.

▶ **To convert free space into a new compressed drive**

1. From the main DoubleSpace screen, choose the Create New Drive command from the Compress menu.

   DoubleSpace scans your computer and then displays a list of uncompressed drives that contain free space. (The list does not include uncompressed drives that are too full to be compressed, RAM drives, network drives, CD-ROM drives, Interlnk drives, or paths that have been associated with a drive letter by using the **subst** command.)

   The list shows the free space on each uncompressed drive and how large the new compressed drive will be.

2. Select the drive that contains the space you want to use, and then press ENTER.

   A screen appears, giving you the opportunity to change the settings DoubleSpace will use when it creates the new compressed drive.

3. Change the settings as needed. For more information about changing settings, press F1.

4. When you have finished changing settings, press ENTER.

   A confirmation screen appears.

5. To create the new compressed drive, press C.

   DoubleSpace creates the new compressed drive, and then updates the list of drives on the main DoubleSpace screen to include the new compressed drive.

# Using DoubleSpace with Floppy Disks

You can use DoubleSpace to increase the storage capacity of floppy disks. After compressing a floppy disk, you can use it to store data or to transfer data from one computer to another.

---

**Note**  To use a compressed floppy disk to transfer data from one computer to another, both computers must be using DoubleSpace.

---

## Compressing a Floppy Disk

Compressing a floppy disk is similar to compressing a hard disk drive. You can compress a floppy disk that is completely empty or one that contains files.

---

**Note**  Make sure the floppy disk is formatted and has at least .65 MB of free space. DoubleSpace cannot compress a 360K disk, an unformatted disk, or a disk that is completely full.

---

▶ **To compress a floppy disk**

1.  Insert a formatted disk in a floppy disk drive.

2.  In the main DoubleSpace screen, choose the Existing Drive command from the Compress menu.

    DoubleSpace scans your computer and then displays a list of drives that can be compressed. (If the list does not include the floppy disk you just inserted, make sure the disk is formatted and has at least .65 MB of free space.)

3.  Select the drive that contains the floppy disk you want to compress by pressing the UP ARROW or DOWN ARROW key, and then press ENTER.

    DoubleSpace displays a confirmation screen stating that it is ready to compress the drive you selected.

4.  To compress the floppy disk, press C.

    DoubleSpace defragments, compresses, and mounts the floppy disk, and then updates the list of drives on the main DoubleSpace screen to include the newly compressed disk.

After DoubleSpace finishes compressing the floppy disk:

- The floppy disk will contain more free space than it did before. You use the floppy disk just as you did before you compressed it, except that if you change floppy disks or restart your computer, you must remount the floppy disk. For more information about using a compressed floppy disk, see the following section.

- Your computer will have a new drive letter. This new drive letter represents the compressed floppy disk's host drive, which contains the floppy disk's CVF. Both the new drive letter and the original drive letter are associated with the same physical floppy disk drive. For more information, see "Understanding Disk Compression" earlier in this chapter.

## Using a Compressed Floppy Disk

In general, you use a compressed floppy disk just as you would a normal floppy disk. The main difference is that you must mount a compressed floppy disk before you can use it.

When you first compress a floppy disk, DoubleSpace mounts it for you. However, if you change floppy disks or restart your computer, you must remount the floppy disk before you can use it again.

---

**Note**  Before it is mounted, a compressed floppy disk appears nearly full. If you change to the floppy disk drive and carry out the **dir** command, MS-DOS usually lists one file: a text file named READTHIS.TXT, which briefly explains how to mount the floppy disk. The **dir** command usually reports that the floppy disk contains almost no free space, since most of the space is used by the CVF. The CVF is a file with Hidden, Read-Only, and System attributes named DBLSPACE.000.

---

To gain access to the contents of a compressed floppy disk, mount it from the main DoubleSpace screen or at the MS-DOS command prompt.

▶  **To mount a compressed floppy disk from the main DoubleSpace screen**

1. Insert the compressed floppy disk in a drive.

2. In the main DoubleSpace screen, choose the Mount command from the Drive menu.

   DoubleSpace searches your computer for unmounted CVFs and lists the ones it finds.

3. Select the CVF that is located on your compressed floppy disk by using the UP ARROW or DOWN ARROW key, and then press ENTER.

4. DoubleSpace mounts the CVF and then updates the list of compressed drives on the main DoubleSpace screen to include the newly mounted floppy disk.

The compressed floppy disk remains mounted, and the files on it remain available, until you change floppy disks or restart your computer.

▶ **To mount a compressed floppy disk at the MS-DOS command prompt**

1. Insert the compressed floppy disk in a drive.

2. At the command prompt, type **dblspace /mount** and the letter of the drive the floppy disk is in. For example, to mount the compressed floppy disk in drive A, you would type:

   **dblspace /mount a:**

   DoubleSpace displays the following messages:

   ```
   DoubleSpace is mounting drive A.
   DoubleSpace has mounted drive A.
   ```

   The compressed floppy disk remains mounted until you change floppy disks or restart your computer.

   If you want, you can include the **dblspace /mount** command in your AUTOEXEC.BAT file. For example, if you usually keep a compressed floppy disk in drive B and want to mount it each time you start your computer, you could add the command **dblspace /mount b:** to your AUTOEXEC.BAT file. For more information about your AUTOEXEC.BAT file, see the chapter "Configuring Your System."

# Getting Information About Compressed Drives

You can display information about your compressed drives in several ways:

- In DoubleSpace, choose the Info command from the Drive menu to display detailed information about a compressed drive. For more information, press F1 while the Compressed Drive Information dialog box is on your screen.

- At the MS-DOS command prompt, change to the compressed drive you want information about, and then type **dir /c**. MS-DOS lists the files in the current directory and displays the actual compression ratio for each file. It also shows the average compression ratio for the entire list of files. (If the compressed drive is empty, **dir /c** does not display compression information.) For more information, type **help dir** at the command prompt.

- At the MS-DOS command prompt, type **dblspace /list** to see a list of your computer's drives and their compression status. This command lists and briefly describes all your computer's drives (except network drives). Use this command to get a more complete picture of your computer's drive configuration.

- If you use Windows, choose DoubleSpace Info from the Tools menu in File Manager. For more information, press F1 while the DoubleSpace Info dialog box is on your screen.

# Understanding DoubleSpace and Memory

When you start your computer, MS-DOS loads DBLSPACE.BIN into memory. DBLSPACE.BIN is the part of MS-DOS that provides access to your compressed drives. MS-DOS loads DBLSPACE.BIN, along with other operating system functions, before carrying out the commands in your CONFIG.SYS and AUTOEXEC.BAT files. DBLSPACE.BIN always loads at the top of conventional memory.

When MS-DOS carries out the commands in your CONFIG.SYS file, it loads the DBLSPACE.SYS device driver, which moves DBLSPACE.BIN from the top of conventional memory to its final location in memory. (DoubleSpace Setup automatically adds a **device** command for the DBLSPACE.SYS device driver to your CONFIG.SYS file. This device driver does not provide access to compressed drives; it simply determines the final location in memory of DBLSPACE.BIN.)

There are two reasons you might want to move DBLSPACE.BIN from the top of conventional memory:

- To avoid conflicts with programs that require access to the top of conventional memory.

  A few programs require access to the top of conventional memory and do not work properly if DBLSPACE.BIN is located there. To avoid any possible conflicts with such programs, DoubleSpace Setup automatically configures the **device** command for DBLSPACE.SYS to move DBLSPACE.BIN from the top of conventional memory to the bottom.

- To free conventional memory.

  If you have an 80386 or higher computer with extended memory, you can free some conventional memory by moving DBLSPACE.BIN from conventional to upper memory. To move DBLSPACE.BIN to upper memory, if it is available, run the MemMaker program. (For instructions on how to run MemMaker, see the chapter "Making More Memory Available.") If there is enough upper memory to accommodate DBLSPACE.BIN, MemMaker changes the **device** command for DBLSPACE.BIN to a **devicehigh** command, which moves DBLSPACE.BIN to upper memory. If there is not enough upper memory for DBLSPACE.BIN, MemMaker leaves the **device** command for DBLSPACE.SYS unchanged.

# Troubleshooting DoubleSpace

If you encounter problems while running DoubleSpace, or if you encounter problems with your compressed drives, see the DoubleSpace section of the README.TXT file. The README.TXT file is located in the directory that contains your MS-DOS files. You can view this file by using any text editor. For example, to view the file by using MS-DOS Editor, change to the directory that contains your MS-DOS files, and then type **edit readme.txt** at the command prompt.

C H A P T E R   6

# Making More Memory Available

Memory (also called random-access memory, or RAM) provides temporary storage for programs and data. It resides on the main system board of your computer or on add-on memory boards.

All programs need memory to run. Some require more memory than others. How much memory is available affects which programs you can run, how fast they run, and how much data a program can work with at one time.

If you're having trouble running programs because your computer doesn't have enough memory, you can:

- Install additional physical memory. Typically, this involves plugging a memory board into a slot inside your computer or adding more memory to an existing memory board.

- Make the most of the memory your computer already has. One way to do this is to run the MemMaker memory-optimization program, which adjusts the way your device drivers and programs use memory.

This chapter explains how to make the most of the memory you have by adjusting your system's memory configuration.

## Identifying Your Computer's Memory Configuration

It's important to know how much and what type of memory your computer has. To display information about your computer's memory, type **mem** at the command prompt.

The **mem** command displays a summary of your computer's memory configuration. It shows how much of each kind of memory your computer has, how much is currently in use, and how much is currently free. For more information about the **mem** command, type **help mem** at the command prompt.

The following table describes the kinds of memory your computer might have.

| Type of memory | Description |
| --- | --- |
| Conventional memory | Up to the first 640 kilobytes (K) of memory on a computer. Because MS-DOS manages conventional memory, you don't need an additional memory manager to use conventional memory. All MS-DOS–based programs require conventional memory. |
| Upper memory area | The 384K of memory above your computer's 640K of conventional memory. The upper memory area is used by system hardware, such as your display adapter. Unused parts of the upper memory area are called *upper memory blocks* (UMBs). On an 80386 or 80486 computer, UMBs can be used for running device drivers and memory-resident programs. (If you are using an upper-memory-area manager other than EMM386, or if you use the **mem** command while Windows version 3.0 is running, the **mem** command will not report information about upper memory.) |
| Extended memory (XMS) | Memory beyond 1 megabyte (MB) on computers with 80286, 80386, or 80486 processors. Extended memory requires an extended-memory manager, such as HIMEM. Windows and Windows-based applications require extended memory. |
| High memory area (HMA) | The first 64K of extended memory. On a computer with extended memory, Setup installs MS-DOS to run in the high memory area. This leaves more conventional memory available for programs. |
| Expanded memory (EMS) | Memory in addition to conventional memory that some MS-DOS–based applications can use. Most personal computers can accommodate expanded memory. Expanded memory is installed on an expanded-memory board and comes with an expanded-memory manager. Programs use expanded memory 64K at a time by addressing a part of the upper memory area called an EMS page frame. Because an expanded-memory manager gives access to a limited amount of expanded memory at a time, using expanded memory is slower than using extended memory. EMM386 can simulate expanded memory for programs that require it. Although Windows and Windows-based applications do not use expanded memory, Windows can also simulate expanded memory for MS-DOS–based applications that need it. |

The following illustration shows the memory configuration of a typical computer:

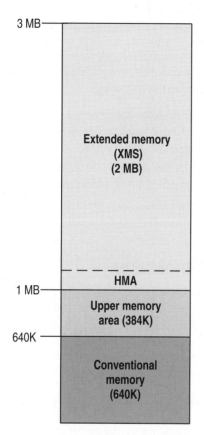
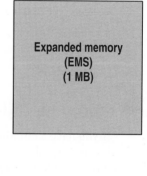

This illustration shows the memory configuration of a computer that has 640K of conventional memory and 2 MB of extended memory. The computer also has an expanded-memory board that contains 1 MB of expanded memory.

# Freeing Conventional Memory

Most programs require conventional memory to run. If a program fails to run because of insufficient memory, the problem is most often because there is insufficient conventional memory.

---

**Note**  If you receive an out-of-memory message while running Windows and Windows-based applications, it's more likely that the problem is insufficient extended memory. For more information, see "Freeing Extended Memory" later in this chapter.

---

You can make more conventional memory available for applications by minimizing how much conventional memory MS-DOS, installable device drivers, and other memory-resident programs use. (Memory-resident programs are sometimes called terminate-and-stay-resident programs, or TSRs.) On many computers, device drivers and memory-resident programs take up so much conventional memory that there is not enough left over for other programs. You can free conventional memory in several ways:

- If you have an 80386 or 80486 computer with extended memory, you can run the MemMaker program. MemMaker moves device drivers and other memory-resident programs from conventional memory to the upper memory area.

- You can streamline your CONFIG.SYS and AUTOEXEC.BAT files so that they don't start unnecessary memory-resident programs.

- If your computer has extended memory, you can run MS-DOS in the high memory area instead of in conventional memory.

## Optimizing Memory by Using MemMaker

If you have a computer with an 80386 or 80486 processor and extended memory, you may be able to free conventional memory by running the MemMaker program. MemMaker modifies your CONFIG.SYS and AUTOEXEC.BAT files so that your device drivers and other memory-resident programs use less conventional memory. MemMaker frees conventional memory by loading some of those device drivers and programs into the upper memory area.

The *upper memory area* is the range of memory addresses that is normally set aside for use by hardware expansion cards. However, on most computers, hardware expansion cards do not use up the entire upper memory area. The unused areas of upper memory are called *upper memory blocks* (UMBs). You can use UMBs for running installable device drivers and other memory-resident programs. Moving these programs out of conventional memory makes more conventional memory available for other programs.

---

**Note**  The EMM386 memory manager makes UMBs available by mapping extended memory to unused addresses in the upper memory area. Because of this, running programs in upper memory uses up some extended memory. Therefore, you might not need to run MemMaker if you use only Windows and Windows-based applications. Windows and Windows-based applications need as much free extended memory as possible. Running MemMaker frees conventional memory, but can result in less free extended memory. For more information about freeing extended memory, see "Freeing Extended Memory" later in this chapter. (If you run MS-DOS–based applications with Windows, run MemMaker. MS-DOS–based applications need free conventional memory even when running with Windows.)

---

## Before You Run MemMaker

To prepare your computer to run MemMaker, do the following:

- Make sure your system's hardware and memory work properly, and that your CONFIG.SYS and AUTOEXEC.BAT files do not start any unnecessary programs. (For more information, see "Streamlining Your CONFIG.SYS and AUTOEXEC.BAT Files" later in this chapter.)

- Quit any programs that are running.

- Start any hardware or memory-resident programs that you usually use. For example, if you use a network, start the network.

---

**Important**  If your CONFIG.SYS file contains multiple configurations, see "Using MemMaker with Multiple Configurations," later in this chapter, before you run MemMaker.

---

## Running MemMaker Using Express Setup

When you run MemMaker, you will be prompted to choose between Express and Custom Setup. In general, you can successfully optimize your system's memory by choosing Express Setup. However, sometimes MemMaker can free more conventional memory if you choose Custom Setup and then change some settings. For more information about using Custom Setup, see "Running MemMaker Using Custom Setup" later in this chapter.

The following procedure explains how to run MemMaker using Express Setup.

▶ **To run MemMaker using Express Setup**

1. Type the following at the command prompt:

   **memmaker**

   MemMaker displays the Welcome screen.

2. Choose the Continue option by pressing ENTER.

   MemMaker displays a screen that prompts you to choose between Express and Custom Setup.

3. Choose Express Setup by pressing ENTER.

   MemMaker displays a screen that prompts you to specify whether you use any programs that require expanded memory.

4. If none of your programs require expanded memory, or if you are not sure whether your programs require expanded memory, choose No by pressing ENTER.

   If you use programs that require expanded memory, select Yes by pressing the SPACEBAR, and then press ENTER. For more information about this screen, press F1.

   If you use Windows, MemMaker might prompt you to provide more information. If it does, follow the instructions on your screen. (For information about a screen, press F1.)

   MemMaker displays a screen stating that it is ready to restart your computer.

5. To restart your computer, press ENTER.

   As each device driver and memory-resident program starts, MemMaker determines the program's memory requirements by monitoring how it allocates memory. (If your computer doesn't start properly, don't worry: just press CTRL+ALT+DEL or turn your computer off and on again. MemMaker will recover. For more information, see "Troubleshooting While Using MemMaker" later in this chapter.)

   After your computer has restarted, MemMaker uses the information it gathered to determine the optimum memory configuration for your computer. MemMaker fits your device drivers and memory-resident programs into the available UMBs as efficiently as possible. To do this, MemMaker may consider thousands of possible memory configurations before selecting the most efficient one. Even so, this process usually takes only a few seconds.

   When its calculations are complete, MemMaker makes the necessary changes to your CONFIG.SYS and AUTOEXEC.BAT files, and then displays a screen stating that it is ready to restart your computer using the new configuration.

6. To restart your computer with its new configuration, press ENTER.

   Your computer starts with its new memory configuration. Watch carefully as device drivers and programs display their startup messages, and note any unusual messages.

   After your computer has restarted, MemMaker displays a screen that prompts you to specify whether your system appears to be working properly.

7. If you did not see any error messages during startup and your system appears to work properly, choose Yes by pressing ENTER. (If your system later turns out not to work properly, you can undo MemMaker's changes. For more information, see "Undoing the Changes MemMaker Made" later in this chapter.)

If you suspect that your system is not working properly, press the SPACEBAR to select No, and then press ENTER. Then follow the instructions on your screen. For more information, press F1, or see "Troubleshooting While Using MemMaker" later in this chapter.

If you indicated that your computer is working properly, MemMaker displays a final screen that shows the amount of each type of memory available before and after you ran MemMaker.

8.  To quit MemMaker, press ENTER.

---

**Note**  When MemMaker changes your CONFIG.SYS and AUTOEXEC.BAT files, it might add some new commands or edit existing commands. For example, MemMaker might add or change some switches on your EMM386.EXE command line. MemMaker also changes certain **device** commands to **devicehigh** commands and adds switches to those **devicehigh** commands. In your AUTOEXEC.BAT file, MemMaker adds the **loadhigh** (**lh**) command to the beginning of certain commands, and also adds switches to those **loadhigh** commands.

---

## Running MemMaker Using Custom Setup

Express Setup works well for most computers. However, in some situations you can free more conventional memory by using Custom Setup. The following list describes the situations in which you should use Custom Setup.

- If you have an EGA or VGA monitor (but not a Super VGA monitor), choose Custom Setup, and then answer Yes to the advanced option "Use monochrome region (B000-B7FF) for running programs?"

- If you do not run MS-DOS–based applications with Windows, choose Custom Setup, and then answer No to the advanced option "Optimize upper memory for use with Windows?"

- If a device driver or program has been causing problems when you run MemMaker (for example, if it causes your computer to stop responding), choose Custom Setup, and then answer Yes to the advanced option "Specify which drivers and TSRs to include in optimization?" (You can permanently exclude a driver or program from the optimization process by adding its name to the MEMMAKER.INF file. This file is located in the same directory as the MEMMAKER.EXE file. For more information, open the MEMMAKER.INF file and read the comments it contains.)

▶ **To run MemMaker using Custom Setup**

1. Type the following at the command prompt:

   **memmaker**

   MemMaker displays the Welcome screen.

2. Choose the Continue option by pressing ENTER.

   MemMaker displays a screen that prompts you to choose between Express and Custom Setup.

3. Select Custom Setup by pressing the SPACEBAR, and then press ENTER.

   MemMaker displays a screen that prompts you to specify whether you use any programs that require expanded memory.

4. If none of your programs require expanded memory, or if you are not sure whether your programs require expanded memory, choose No by pressing ENTER.

   If you use programs that require expanded memory, select Yes by pressing the SPACEBAR, and then press ENTER. For more information about this screen, press F1.

   The Advanced Options screen appears. The settings on this screen determine how MemMaker configures your computer's memory during optimization.

5. Change the settings on the Advanced Options screen as necessary.

   To change an option, press the UP ARROW or DOWN ARROW key until the Yes or No beside that option is highlighted. Then press the SPACEBAR to change the setting. For information about each setting, press F1.

   Be sure to check the setting for each option. Accepting the default settings might change your current configuration.

6. When you have finished changing settings, press ENTER to continue.

   If you use Windows, MemMaker might prompt you to provide more information. If it does, follow the instructions on your screen. (For information about a screen, press F1.)

   MemMaker displays a screen stating that it is ready to restart your computer.

7. To restart your computer, press ENTER.

   As each device driver and memory-resident program starts, MemMaker determines the program's memory requirements by monitoring how it allocates memory. (If your computer doesn't start properly, don't worry: just press CTRL+ALT+DEL or turn your computer off and on again. MemMaker will recover. For more information, see "Troubleshooting While Using MemMaker" later in this chapter.)

After your computer has restarted, MemMaker uses the information it has gathered to determine the optimum memory configuration for your computer. MemMaker fits your device drivers and memory-resident programs into the available UMBs as efficiently as possible. To do this, MemMaker may consider thousands of possible memory configurations before selecting the most efficient one. Even so, this process usually takes only a few seconds.

When its calculations are complete, MemMaker makes the necessary changes to your CONFIG.SYS and AUTOEXEC.BAT files, and then displays a screen stating that it is ready to restart your computer using the new configuration.

8. Restart your computer with its new configuration by pressing ENTER.

   Your computer starts with its new memory configuration. Watch carefully as device drivers and programs display their startup messages and note any unusual messages.

   After your computer has restarted, MemMaker displays a screen that prompts you to specify whether your system appears to be working properly.

9. If you did not see any error messages during startup and your system appears to work properly, choose Yes by pressing ENTER. (If your system later turns out not to work properly, you can undo MemMaker's changes. For more information, see the following section.)

   If you suspect that your system is not working properly, press the SPACEBAR to select No, and then press ENTER. Then follow the instructions on your screen. For more information, press F1, or see "Troubleshooting While Using MemMaker" later in this chapter.

   If you indicated that your computer is working properly, MemMaker displays a final screen that shows the amount of each type of memory available before and after you ran MemMaker.

10. To quit MemMaker, press ENTER.

---

**Note**  When MemMaker changes your CONFIG.SYS and AUTOEXEC.BAT files, it might add some new commands or edit existing commands. For example, MemMaker might add or change some switches on your EMM386.EXE command line. MemMaker also changes certain **device** commands to **devicehigh** commands and adds switches to those **devicehigh** commands. In your AUTOEXEC.BAT file, MemMaker adds the **loadhigh** (**lh**) command to the beginning of certain commands, and also adds switches to those **loadhigh** commands.

---

## Undoing the Changes MemMaker Made

MemMaker changes your system's memory configuration by editing the commands in your CONFIG.SYS and AUTOEXEC.BAT files (and sometimes your Windows SYSTEM.INI file). Before changing these files, MemMaker makes a backup copy of each one.

If you encounter problems during the optimization process, you can have MemMaker undo the changes it made by restoring the previous versions of your CONFIG.SYS, AUTOEXEC.BAT, and SYSTEM.INI files.

You can undo MemMaker's changes even after quitting MemMaker. You might want to do this if, after completing MemMaker, you discover that your system does not work properly with its new memory configuration. After undoing the changes, you can rerun MemMaker using Custom Setup and specify different settings to avoid the problem.

▶ **To undo MemMaker's changes**

1. Quit any running programs.
2. Start MemMaker by typing the following at the command prompt:

   **memmaker /undo**

   A screen appears, prompting you to choose between restoring your original system files and quitting MemMaker.

3. To restore your original files, press ENTER. MemMaker displays a confirmation screen.

4. If the screen shows that MemMaker has finished restoring your startup files, press ENTER to restart your computer with its original configuration.

   If you have edited your CONFIG.SYS, AUTOEXEC.BAT, or SYSTEM.INI files since you last ran MemMaker, MemMaker displays a screen stating that your changes to those files will be lost when MemMaker replaces them with backup files. To restore the previous versions of the files, press Y, and then press ENTER to restart your computer with its original configuration.

## Fine-Tuning Your Memory Configuration

After you run MemMaker, you might want to fine-tune your memory configuration to free additional memory. You can use the following techniques:

- Run MemMaker again and change some memory-configuration options. For more information, see the following section.
- Change the order of device drivers and programs in your CONFIG.SYS and AUTOEXEC.BAT files. For more information, see "Freeing Additional Memory by Changing the Order of Commands in Your Startup Files" later in this section.

- Remove unnecessary device drivers and memory-resident programs from your CONFIG.SYS and AUTOEXEC.BAT files. For more information, see "Streamlining Your CONFIG.SYS and AUTOEXEC.BAT Files" later in this chapter.

## Freeing Additional Memory by Changing MemMaker Options

To try to free additional memory, you can run MemMaker again and change some memory-configuration options. The rest of this section explains some situations in which changing MemMaker options can free additional memory.

### If you do not use programs that require expanded memory

If none of your programs require expanded memory, run MemMaker again (you can choose either Custom or Express Setup). When MemMaker displays a screen that prompts you to indicate whether you use any programs that require expanded memory, choose No.

Choosing No disables expanded memory and frees an additional 64K of upper memory. If you choose No and then have problems running programs (for example, a program won't start, or it displays a message such as "EMS Page Frame Not Found" or "Expanded Memory Unavailable"), run MemMaker again and answer Yes to the same question.

### If your computer has an EGA or VGA monitor

If your computer has an EGA or VGA monitor (but not a Super VGA monitor), run MemMaker again and choose Custom Setup. When MemMaker displays the Advanced Options screen, answer Yes to the question "Use monochrome region (B000-B7FF) for running programs?"

Answering Yes to this question frees additional upper memory. If you answer Yes, then later have problems with your monitor (for example, a program doesn't display correctly), or if your computer stops responding when you start Windows, run MemMaker again and answer No to the same question.

### If you do not run MS-DOS–based applications with Windows

If you do not run MS-DOS–based applications with Windows, run MemMaker again and choose Custom Setup. When MemMaker displays the Advanced Options screen, answer No to the question "Optimize upper memory for use with Windows?"

Answering No to this question can free additional conventional memory when you are not running Windows. However, while you are running Windows, less conventional memory will be available for MS-DOS–based (non-Windows) applications. If you answer No, then encounter memory problems when you run MS-DOS–based applications with Windows, run MemMaker again and answer Yes to the same question.

For more information about using Custom Setup, see "Running MemMaker Using Custom Setup" earlier in this chapter.

## Freeing Additional Memory by Changing the Order of Commands in Your Startup Files

When memory-resident programs are loaded into upper memory, it is most efficient to load programs that require more memory before programs that require less memory. Although MemMaker fits your device drivers and memory-resident programs into memory as efficiently as possible, it does not change the order in which those drivers and programs load.

You can fine-tune your memory configuration by changing the order of the commands in your CONFIG.SYS and AUTOEXEC.BAT files. When you run MemMaker, it measures the memory requirements of each driver or memory-resident program and stores this information in the MEMMAKER.STS file. You can use the information in this file to determine the optimum order for your CONFIG.SYS and AUTOEXEC.BAT commands.

When you change the order of commands in your CONFIG.SYS and AUTOEXEC.BAT files:

- Follow the guidelines for determining the order of CONFIG.SYS commands described in the chapter "Configuring Your System."

- Make sure the HIMEM.SYS and EMM386.EXE command lines appear before any commands that start device drivers or programs you want to run in upper memory.

- If your startup files contain commands that start network drivers or memory-resident programs, do not change the relative order of the network commands.

▶ **To optimize the order of device drivers and memory-resident programs**

1. Create a startup disk by inserting an unformatted floppy disk in drive A and then typing the following at the command prompt:

   **format a: /s**

2. Copy your CONFIG.SYS and AUTOEXEC.BAT files to the startup disk you just created by typing the following at the command prompt:

**copy c:\config.sys a:\**
**copy c:\autoexec.bat a:\**

3. Open the MEMMAKER.STS file by using a text editor such as MS-DOS Editor. The MEMMAKER.STS file is located in the same directory as the MEMMAKER.EXE file.

For example, to open the MEMMAKER.STS file in the C:\DOS directory by using MS-DOS Editor, type the following at the command prompt:

**edit c:\dos\memmaker.sts**

4. Find the [SizeData] section in the MEMMAKER.STS file. This section lists the memory requirements of each driver or memory-resident program started by your CONFIG.SYS and AUTOEXEC.BAT files. For example, the MEMMAKER.STS file might contain the following information about the SETVER.EXE program:

```
Command=C:\DOS\SETVER.EXE
Line=9
FinalSize=672
MaxSize=12048
FinalUpperSizes=0
MaxUpperSizes=0
ProgramType=DEVICE
```

5. For each driver or memory-resident program, examine the MaxSize line, which specifies the amount of memory the driver or program requires to start and run. The driver or memory-resident program requires a block of memory at least this large to load properly.

6. Print the MEMMAKER.STS file or write down the name of each driver or program and its MaxSize value.

7. Quit the text editor you used to open the MEMMAKER.STS file. (Do not save any changes to the file.) If you are using MS-DOS Editor, quit by pressing ALT, F, X.

8. Open your CONFIG.SYS file and move commands that load device drivers or programs with larger MaxSize values before those with smaller MaxSize values. (However, make sure the HIMEM.SYS and EMM386.EXE command lines appear before commands that start other drivers or programs. For guidelines in determining the order of commands in your CONFIG.SYS file, see "Configuring Your System by Using CONFIG.SYS Commands" in the chapter "Configuring Your System.")

---

**Note**  When you run MS-DOS Setup, it adds a command that starts the SETVER program to the beginning of your CONFIG.SYS file. If you use only the HIMEM and EMM386 memory managers, you can move the SETVER command line after the EMM386.EXE command line (but before any commands that start programs that require SETVER.) Moving the SETVER.EXE command line after the EMM386.EXE command line makes it possible to run SETVER in the upper memory area.

---

9. Save the changes to your CONFIG.SYS file, and then open your AUTOEXEC.BAT file.

10. In your AUTOEXEC.BAT file, move commands that start programs with larger MaxSize values before those with smaller MaxSize values.

11. Save the changes to your AUTOEXEC.BAT file, and then quit the text editor.

12. Remove any disks from your floppy disk drives, and then restart your computer by pressing CTRL+ALT+DEL.

13. If your system starts properly, run MemMaker to optimize your revised CONFIG.SYS and AUTOEXEC.BAT files. To do this, follow the instructions in "Running MemMaker Using Express Setup" or "Running MemMaker Using Custom Setup" earlier in this chapter. (You might be able to free additional memory by changing some MemMaker options. For more information, see the previous section, "Freeing Additional Memory by Changing MemMaker Options.")

If your computer, hardware devices, or programs do not work properly with your revised CONFIG.SYS and AUTOEXEC.BAT files, you might need to restore the backup copies of those files. For example, if the backup copies are on a floppy disk in drive A, you would type the following at the command prompt:

**copy a:\config.sys c:\config.sys**
**copy a:\autoexec.bat c:\autoexec.bat**

# Using MemMaker with Multiple Configurations

If your CONFIG.SYS file defines multiple startup configurations, run MemMaker by carrying out the procedures in this section. If you run MemMaker without following these procedures, your computer might not start properly after MemMaker revises your CONFIG.SYS and AUTOEXEC.BAT files.

▶ **To optimize your computer's memory for multiple configurations**

1. Create a separate set of CONFIG.SYS and AUTOEXEC.BAT files for each configuration on your startup menu. Each set should contain only the commands for that configuration. For instructions on creating these files, see the following section, "Creating CONFIG.SYS and AUTOEXEC.BAT Files for Each Configuration."

2. Run MemMaker separately for each configuration. For instructions on how to do this, see "Running MemMaker for Each Configuration" later in this chapter.

3. Combine the optimized CONFIG.SYS files into a single multiple-configuration CONFIG.SYS file; combine the AUTOEXEC.BAT files into a single AUTOEXEC.BAT file. For instructions on combining the files, see "Combining the Optimized Files into New CONFIG.SYS and AUTOEXEC.BAT Files" later in this chapter.

For instructions on creating multiple startup configurations, see the chapter "Configuring Your System" earlier in this guide.

## Creating CONFIG.SYS and AUTOEXEC.BAT Files for Each Configuration

First, create a set of CONFIG.SYS and AUTOEXEC.BAT files for each configuration. Each set will contain only the commands for that configuration.

▶ **To create separate startup files for each configuration**

1. In the root directory of your startup drive (usually drive C), make one copy of your CONFIG.SYS file for each item on your startup menu, and give each copy a name that matches the corresponding item number. To do this, use the **copy** command. For example, if your startup menu contains three items, you could type the following at the command prompt:

   **copy config.sys config.1**
   **copy config.sys config.2**
   **copy config.sys config.3**

2. Make one copy of your AUTOEXEC.BAT file for each item on your Startup menu. For example, if your startup menu contains three items, you could type the following at the command prompt:

   **copy autoexec.bat autoexec.1**
   **copy autoexec.bat autoexec.2**
   **copy autoexec.bat autoexec.3**

3. Open each copy of your CONFIG.SYS file by using a text editor such as MS-DOS Editor. Edit the file so that it can be used as a single-configuration CONFIG.SYS file. Delete the menu-definition commands (the commands in the **[menu]** section) and any commands that do not apply to the configuration that corresponds to the file's extension. For example, leave in the CONFIG.1 file only those commands that are necessary to start your computer with the configuration for startup menu item 1. Save the file when you have finished.

   Repeat this step for each copy of your CONFIG.SYS file. In each file, keep only the commands that are necessary to start the computer with that configuration.

4. Open each copy of your AUTOEXEC.BAT file. Delete the **goto config** command and any commands that do not apply to the configuration that corresponds to the file's extension. For example, leave in the AUTOEXEC.1 file only those commands that are necessary to start your computer with the configuration for startup menu item 1. Save the file when you have finished.

   Repeat this step for each copy of your AUTOEXEC.BAT file. In each file, keep only the commands that are necessary to start the computer with that configuration.

5. Quit the text editor.

When you have carried out this procedure, the root directory of your startup drive should contain your original CONFIG.SYS and AUTOEXEC.BAT files, as well as one set of CONFIG.x and AUTOEXEC.x files for each startup menu item.

## Running MemMaker for Each Configuration

To optimize your system's memory, you will need to run MemMaker for each configuration.

▶ **To optimize memory for each configuration**

1. Rename your original CONFIG.SYS and AUTOEXEC.BAT files by typing the following at the command prompt:

   **ren config.sys config.bak**
   **ren autoexec.bat autoexec.bak**

2. Rename one set of the CONFIG.*x* and AUTOEXEC.*x* files to CONFIG.SYS and AUTOEXEC.BAT. For example, to rename the set of files you created for startup menu item 1, you would type the following at the command prompt:

   **ren config.1 config.sys**
   **ren autoexec.1 autoexec.bat**

3. Restart your computer by pressing CTRL+ALT+DEL.

4. To optimize the current CONFIG.SYS and AUTOEXEC.BAT files, run MemMaker by typing **memmaker** at the command prompt, and then follow the instructions on your screen. For more information, see "Running MemMaker Using Express Setup" or "Running MemMaker Using Custom Setup" earlier in this chapter.

5. When MemMaker is complete, rename the current CONFIG.SYS and AUTOEXEC.BAT files to their original filenames. For example, to rename the set of files you created for startup menu item 1, you would type the following:

   **ren config.sys config.1**
   **ren autoexec.bat autoexec.1**

6. Repeat steps 2 through 5 for each additional set of CONFIG.*x* and AUTOEXEC.*x* files you created.

## Combining the Optimized Files into New CONFIG.SYS and AUTOEXEC.BAT Files

Once you have optimized each configuration separately, you need to combine the separate files into a single set of CONFIG.SYS and AUTOEXEC.BAT files. The exact procedure for this will depend on the contents of your files. The rest of this section gives some tips on how to merge your files.

The following tips can help you construct a new CONFIG.SYS file:

- Start with a blank CONFIG.SYS file rather than trying to edit your original file.

- Copy the menu-definition commands from the CONFIG.BAK file and paste them into your new CONFIG.SYS file.

- Create a separate configuration block for each item on the menu, and paste the commands from each CONFIG.*x* file into the corresponding configuration block.

- Avoid using [common] blocks or **include** commands. Instead, each configuration block should contain a complete set of commands for that configuration.

The following tips can help you construct a new AUTOEXEC.BAT file:

- Start with a blank AUTOEXEC.BAT file rather than trying to edit your original file.

- Add a **goto %config%** command to the beginning of your new AUTOEXEC.BAT file.

- For each item on your startup menu, add a label to your AUTOEXEC.BAT file with the same name as the corresponding configuration block in your CONFIG.SYS file. For example, if your CONFIG.SYS file contains a configuration block named [Steve], you would add the label **:Steve** to your AUTOEXEC.BAT file. (For a sample AUTOEXEC.BAT file that uses labels to define multiple configurations, see the chapter "Configuring Your System.")

  Paste the commands from each AUTOEXEC.*x* file into your new AUTOEXEC.BAT file after the label that corresponds to that configuration. For example, if the [Steve] configuration is startup menu item 1, you would paste the contents of the AUTOEXEC.1 file immediately after the **:Steve** label in your AUTOEXEC.BAT file.

- Add a **goto end** command to the end of each section in your AUTOEXEC.BAT file that starts with a label.

- Add an **:end** label to the end of your AUTOEXEC.BAT file.

- For the best results, each section of your AUTOEXEC.BAT file should contain a complete set of AUTOEXEC.BAT commands for that configuration.

## Troubleshooting While Using MemMaker

The following topics explain how to solve common problems you might encounter while using MemMaker. If you don't find the help you need in these topics, view the README.TXT file on Setup Disk 1 by using any text editor.

### Your computer stops responding while you are using MemMaker.

By default, MemMaker uses aggressive settings when it configures your computer's use of memory. If your computer stops responding while you are running MemMaker, first try using more conservative settings.

#### Using Conservative Settings

While it configures your computer's memory, MemMaker restarts your computer twice. If your computer stopped responding when MemMaker restarted it the first time, carry out Procedure 1. If your computer stopped responding after MemMaker restarted it the second time, carry out Procedure 2.

▶ **Procedure 1   To use more conservative settings**

1. When your computer stops responding, restart it by pressing CTRL+ALT+DEL. MemMaker automatically restarts.

2. Choose the "Try again with conservative settings" option by pressing ENTER.

   Your computer restarts, and then processes your CONFIG.SYS and AUTOEXEC.BAT files.

3. If your computer runs successfully, follow the instructions on your screen.

   If your computer stops responding again, carry out the procedure in the following section, "Your computer stops responding again after the 'MemMaker will now restart your computer' message appears."

▶ **Procedure 2   To use more conservative settings by using Custom Setup**

1. When your computer stops responding, restart it by pressing CTRL+ALT+DEL. MemMaker automatically restarts.

2. Select the "Exit and undo changes" option by pressing the SPACEBAR, and then press ENTER.

   Your computer restarts with its original memory configuration.

3. Restart the MemMaker program by typing **memmaker** at the command prompt.

   When the "Welcome to MemMaker" screen appears, press ENTER.

4. When the second MemMaker screen appears, press the SPACEBAR to select "Custom Setup," and then press ENTER.

5. Continue with the MemMaker program until the Advanced Options screen appears. Then press the DOWN ARROW key until the "Yes" beside "Scan the upper memory aggressively?" is selected.

6. Press the SPACEBAR to select "No," and then press ENTER.

   Follow the instructions on your screen.

   If your computer stops responding again, carry out the procedure in "Your computer stops responding again after the 'MemMaker will now restart your computer to test the new memory configuration' screen appears" later in this chapter.

**Your computer stops responding again after the "MemMaker will now restart your computer" message appears.**

The first step in solving this problem is to determine whether your computer stops responding while MemMaker is loading EMM386.

▶ **To determine whether your computer stops responding while MemMaker is loading EMM386**

1. When your computer stops responding, restart it by pressing CTRL+ALT+DEL.

   MemMaker automatically restarts.

2. Display the "Cancel and undo all changes" option by pressing the SPACEBAR twice, and then press ENTER.

   Your computer restarts with its original memory configuration.

3. Restart MemMaker by typing **memmaker** at the command prompt.

4. Follow the instructions on your screen. After MemMaker restarts your computer, MS-DOS displays the following text:

   ```
   Starting MS-DOS...
   ```

5. While the text is on your screen, press and release the F8 key. The following text appears:

   ```
   MS-DOS will prompt you to confirm each CONFIG.SYS command.
   ```

   As MS-DOS processes the commands in your CONFIG.SYS file, it displays each command, followed by a prompt. For example, when MS-DOS reaches the **dos=high** command, it displays the following prompt:

   ```
   DOS=HIGH [Y,N]?
   ```

6. Carry out all the commands in your CONFIG.SYS file by pressing Y each time you are prompted.

   If your computer stops responding when it is trying to load EMM386, carry out the procedure in "You have tried the troubleshooting procedures, and your computer still stops responding when you run MemMaker" later in this chapter.

   If your computer stops responding when it tries to load a device driver other than EMM386, skip the rest of this procedure and carry out the procedure in the following section, "Your computer stops responding while MemMaker is loading a program or device driver other than EMM386."

   If your computer runs successfully, continue to step 7.

7. When MS-DOS finishes processing the commands in your CONFIG.SYS file, it displays the following prompt:

   ```
   Process AUTOEXEC.BAT [Y,N]?
   ```

   Press Y to process the AUTOEXEC.BAT file.

   When your computer stops responding, note which program it is trying to load. Then carry out the procedure in the following section.

**Your computer stops responding while MemMaker is loading a program or device driver other than EMM386.**

If your computer stops responding when loading a device driver or program other than EMM386, the program or device driver probably does not function correctly with MemMaker or in your computer's upper memory area.

▶ **To load your program or device driver properly**

1. When your computer stops responding, restart it by pressing CTRL+ALT+DEL.

   MemMaker automatically restarts.

2. Display the "Cancel and undo all changes" option by pressing the SPACEBAR twice, and then press ENTER.

   Your computer restarts with its original memory configuration.

3. Restart the MemMaker program by typing **memmaker** at the command prompt.

   When the Welcome screen appears, press ENTER.

4. When the second MemMaker screen appears, press the SPACEBAR to select "Custom Setup," and then press ENTER.

5. Continue with the MemMaker program until the Advanced Options screen appears. Press the SPACEBAR to change the "No" beside "Specify which drivers and TSRs to include during optimization?" to "Yes."

6. Press ENTER. If you use Windows, MemMaker might prompt you to provide more information. If it does, follow the instructions on your screen.

7. One by one, MemMaker prompts you to include device drivers and programs in the optimization process. Press ENTER each time you are prompted, *except* when you are prompted to include the device driver or program that caused your computer to stop responding. When you are prompted to include this device driver or program, press the SPACEBAR to select "No," and then press ENTER.

   Follow the instructions on your screen.

8. MemMaker will restart your computer. If your computer stops responding when MemMaker tries to load a different program or device driver, repeat steps 1 through 7.

   If your computer still stops responding when you run MemMaker, carry out the procedure in "You have tried the troubleshooting procedures, and your computer still stops responding when you run MemMaker" later in this chapter.

**Your computer stops responding again after the "MemMaker will now restart your computer to test the new memory configuration" screen appears.**

When your computer stops responding, note which program or device driver it is trying to load. This program or device driver probably does not run correctly in the upper memory area. You should run this program or device driver in conventional memory.

▶ **To load properly the program or device driver that causes your computer to stop responding**

1. Restart your computer by pressing CTRL+ALT+DEL.

   MemMaker automatically restarts.

2. Choose the "Exit and undo changes" option by pressing the SPACEBAR, and then press ENTER.

   Your computer restarts with its original memory configuration.

3. Restart the MemMaker program by typing **memmaker** at the command prompt.

4. When the Welcome screen appears, press ENTER.

5. When the second MemMaker screen appears, press the SPACEBAR to select "Custom Setup," and then press ENTER.

6. Continue with the MemMaker program until the Advanced Options screen appears. Press the SPACEBAR to change the "No" beside "Specify which drivers and TSRs to include during optimization?" to "Yes."

7. Press ENTER. If you use Windows, MemMaker might prompt you to provide more information. If it does, follow the instructions on your screen.

8. One by one, MemMaker prompts you to include device drivers and programs in the optimization process. Press ENTER each time you are prompted, *except* when when you are prompted to include the device driver or program that caused your computer to stop responding. When you are prompted to include this device driver or program, press the SPACEBAR to select "No," and then press ENTER.

   Follow the instructions on your screen.

9. MemMaker will restart your computer. If your computer stops responding when MemMaker tries to load a different program or device driver, repeat steps 1 through 8.

   If your computer still stops responding when you use MemMaker, carry out the procedure in the following section.

**You have tried the troubleshooting procedures, and your computer still stops responding when you run MemMaker.**

If you have tried the appropriate troubleshooting procedures described earlier in this chapter, but your computer still stops responding when you run MemMaker, carry out the following procedure.

▶ **To try additional troubleshooting techniques**

1. When your computer stops responding, restart it by pressing CTRL+ALT+DEL.

   MemMaker automatically restarts.

2. Select the "Cancel and undo all changes" option or the "Exit and undo changes" option, and then press ENTER.

3. When the MS-DOS command prompt appears, open your CONFIG.SYS file by typing the following:

   **edit c:\config.sys**

   Make sure your CONFIG.SYS file contains the command that loads EMM386.EXE. The command should look similar to the following:

   ```
   DEVICE=C:\DOS\EMM386.EXE
   ```

   If your CONFIG.SYS file does not contain the command that loads EMM386.EXE, insert it on a new line below the **device** command that loads HIMEM.SYS.

4. Press ALT, F, X to quit MS-DOS Editor. When a dialog box appears prompting you to save your changes, press Y.

5. Turn to the following sections in the chapter "Diagnosing and Solving Problems":

   ■ "MS-DOS won't start after you run Setup"

   Carry out the procedure titled "To determine whether the problem is in your CONFIG.SYS file."

   ■ "You installed a hardware device, and your computer stopped working correctly"

   Carry out the procedure titled "To make sure EMM386 and another device driver or program don't conflict."

### There is not enough memory to continue MemMaker.

If you receive the "MemMaker cannot continue because there is not enough free conventional memory" message, carry out the following procedure.

▶ **To free enough conventional memory to run MemMaker**

1. When MemMaker displays the "MemMaker cannot continue because there is not enough free conventional memory" message, press ENTER to restart your computer.

2. After MemMaker restarts your computer, MS-DOS displays the following text:

   ```
   Starting MS-DOS...
   ```

3. While the text is on your screen, press and release the F8 key. The following text appears:

   ```
   MS-DOS will prompt you to confirm each CONFIG.SYS command.
   ```

   As it processes the commands in your CONFIG.SYS file, MS-DOS displays each command, followed by a prompt. For example, when MS-DOS reaches the **dos=high** command, it displays the following prompt:

   ```
   DOS=HIGH [Y,N]?
   ```

4. Bypass all the commands in your CONFIG.SYS file by pressing N each time you are prompted, *except* when you are prompted for the following commands:

   HIMEM.SYS
   EMM386.EXE
   SHELL

   The prompts will appear similar to the following:

   ```
   DEVICE=C:\DOS\HIMEM.SYS [Y,N]?
   DEVICE=C:\DOS\EMM386.SYS [Y,N]?
   SHELL=C:\DOS\COMMAND.COM C:\DOS\ /P [Y,N]?
   ```

   When prompts similar to these appear, press Y.

   ---

   **Note** If MS-DOS prompts you for a command that loads a third-party device driver that starts a disk-compression program or provides access to your hard disk, press Y.

   ---

5. When MS-DOS finishes processing the commands in your CONFIG.SYS file, it displays the following prompt:

   ```
   Process AUTOEXEC.BAT [Y,N]?
   ```

   Press N to bypass the AUTOEXEC.BAT file.

6. When the MS-DOS command prompt appears, type the following:

**find /i "memmaker" autoexec.bat**

The **find** command should display a line similar to the following:

```
C:\DOS\MEMMAKER.EXE /SESSION:13396
```

7. At the command prompt, type the entire line exactly as **find** displays it.

   MemMaker should continue normally.

8. Follow the instructions on your screen.

## After running MemMaker, a program or device driver that was loaded into the upper memory area does not work.

If a program that MemMaker loaded into the upper memory area does not work after you run MemMaker, run the program or device driver in conventional memory instead.

▶ **To load properly the program or device driver that does not work correctly**

1. Restore your computer to the memory configuration it had before you ran MemMaker by typing the following at the command prompt:

   **memmaker /undo**

2. When MemMaker starts, choose the "Restore files now" option by pressing ENTER.

   MemMaker displays a screen confirming that it restored your original CONFIG.SYS and AUTOEXEC.BAT files.

3. Restart your computer by pressing ENTER.

4. Restart MemMaker by typing the following at the command prompt:

   **memmaker**

   When the Welcome screen appears, press ENTER.

5. When the second MemMaker screen appears, press the SPACEBAR to select Custom Setup, and then press ENTER.

6. Continue with the MemMaker program until the Advanced Options screen appears. Press the SPACEBAR to change the "No" beside "Specify which drivers and TSRs to include during optimization?" to "Yes."

7. Press ENTER. If you use Windows, MemMaker might prompt you to provide more information. If it does, follow the instructions on your screen.

8. Press ENTER. One by one, MemMaker prompts you to include device drivers and programs in the optimization process. Press ENTER each time you are prompted, *except* when you are prompted to include the device driver or program that does not work correctly. When you are prompted to include this device driver or program, press the SPACEBAR to select "No," and then press ENTER.

Follow the instructions on your screen.

# Streamlining Your CONFIG.SYS and AUTOEXEC.BAT Files

When you start your computer, it carries out the commands in your CONFIG.SYS and AUTOEXEC.BAT files. Many of the commands in these files start device drivers and other memory-resident programs that use conventional memory. You can make more conventional memory available by disabling or removing unnecessary commands from these files. (To disable an unnecessary command, add a **rem** command to the beginning of that command. For more information, type **help rem** at the command prompt.)

---

**Note** Streamlining your startup files is especially important if you want MemMaker to provide you with an optimum memory configuration. Removing unnecessary memory-resident programs means you'll have more conventional memory to start with. You can also optimize your MemMaker configuration by fine-tuning the order of commands in your startup files. For more information, see "Freeing Additional Memory by Changing the Order of Commands in Your Startup Files" earlier in this chapter.

---

To effectively streamline your CONFIG.SYS and AUTOEXEC.BAT files, you should know the purpose of each of the commands in those files. For more information about the commands in these files, see the chapter "Configuring Your System" earlier in this guide.

---

Caution  Be careful when changing your CONFIG.SYS and AUTOEXEC.BAT files. Your system may not function properly if you incorrectly change some values or disable some commands. If your computer fails to start after you change these files, follow the instructions in "Bypassing CONFIG.SYS and AUTOEXEC.BAT Commands" in the chapter "Configuring Your System."

---

The following basic recommendations can help you conserve conventional memory by streamlining your CONFIG.SYS and AUTOEXEC.BAT files:

- Whenever possible, load programs that require extra memory during startup before those that do not. Some programs or device drivers require more memory when they start than they do afterward. For more information, see "Fine-Tuning Your Memory Configuration" earlier in this chapter.

- If your computer has expanded memory, your CONFIG.SYS file should include a **device** command for the expanded-memory manager that came with your memory board. For more information, see the documentation that came with your expanded-memory board.

- If your computer has extended memory, your CONFIG.SYS file should include the **dos=high** command as well as a **device** command for the HIMEM.SYS extended-memory manager. The **dos=high** command saves conventional memory by running MS-DOS in the high memory area. For more information about the **dos** command, type **help dos** at the command prompt. For more information about HIMEM.SYS, type **help himem.sys** at the command prompt.

- If your computer has extended memory, disable any commands in your CONFIG.SYS or AUTOEXEC.BAT files that start the Fastopen program. (To speed up a computer that has extended memory, use SMARTDrive instead of Fastopen.) If your computer has only expanded memory and you find that Fastopen noticeably improves your computer's speed, load Fastopen in expanded memory by using the **/x** switch. For more information about Fastopen, type **help fastopen** at the command prompt.

- Disable any **append /e** or **append c:\dos** commands in your AUTOEXEC.BAT file. These commands are not necessary with MS-DOS 6.

- If your CONFIG.SYS file contains a command that loads the double-buffering feature of SMARTDrive, you might be able to disable this command. To find out whether you need to use double buffering, type **help smartdrv** at the command prompt and choose <double-buffering> in the second paragraph. Then, follow the procedure in the section "Determining whether you need to use double buffering."

---

**Note**  If you ran MemMaker before streamlining your CONFIG.SYS and AUTOEXEC.BAT files, run it again after changing the files so that MemMaker can optimize your system's memory for the new configuration. For more information about MemMaker, see "Optimizing Memory with MemMaker" earlier in this chapter.

---

For more information about your CONFIG.SYS and AUTOEXEC.BAT files, see the chapter "Configuring Your System."

# Running MS-DOS in the High Memory Area

By default, MS-DOS runs in conventional memory, which makes less conventional memory available to other programs. However, if your computer has extended memory, portions of MS-DOS can run in the high memory area (HMA).

Because few programs use the HMA, it makes sense to run MS-DOS there. To run MS-DOS in the HMA, you need a computer with an 80286, 80386, or 80486 processor and extended memory.

---

**Note**  If your computer has extended memory, the MS-DOS Setup program adds the required commands to your CONFIG.SYS file so that MS-DOS runs in the HMA.

---

To determine whether MS-DOS is running in the HMA, type **mem** at the command prompt. If MS-DOS displays the line "MS-DOS is resident in the high memory area," it is running in the HMA.

If MS-DOS is not running in the HMA, you can add commands to your CONFIG.SYS file that load the HIMEM.SYS extended memory-manager and load MS-DOS into the HMA. The commands you add should appear similar to the following:

```
device=c:\dos\himem.sys
dos=high
```

The **device=c:\dos\himem.sys** command in this example loads the HIMEM.SYS extended-memory manager from the C:\DOS directory; the **dos=high** command loads most of MS-DOS into extended memory. For more information about editing your CONFIG.SYS file, see "Editing Your CONFIG.SYS File" in the chapter "Configuring Your System."

# Freeing Extended Memory

Some programs require extended memory to run. If you are having trouble running such a program, use the **mem** command to determine how much extended memory is available and how much is currently being used.

If **mem** reports that the total amount of extended memory is 0, make sure your system is set up to provide extended memory. To use extended memory, your computer must have as much physical extended memory as the program needs, and your CONFIG.SYS file must contain a **device** command for the HIMEM.SYS extended-memory manager or another memory manager that conforms to the Lotus/Intel/Microsoft/AST eXtended Memory Specification (XMS). Most programs need an extended-memory manager in order to use extended memory. For more information about HIMEM.SYS, type **help himem.sys** at the command prompt.

If you have extended memory but it is all being used, try the following:

- If your CONFIG.SYS or AUTOEXEC.BAT file starts programs that use extended memory, reduce the amount of extended memory you allocate for each program. For information about how to do this, see the documentation that accompanied each program.

- If your CONFIG.SYS file contains an EMM386.EXE command line that does not include the **noems** switch, add the **min=0** switch to the command line.

  When EMM386 starts without the **noems** switch, it normally reserves some extended memory for use as simulated expanded memory. The **min=0** switch directs EMM386 not to set aside any extended memory, but still allows EMM386 to provide expanded memory to applications that request it. For more information, type **help emm386.exe** at the command prompt.

- If you are using RAMDrive and creating a RAM disk in extended memory, use SMARTDrive instead. On most computers, SMARTDrive improves speed more effectively than RAMDrive. To disable RAMDrive, add a **rem** command to the beginning of the RAMDrive command line in your CONFIG.SYS file. To add SMARTDrive, add the **smartdrv** command to the end of your AUTOEXEC.BAT file. For more information about SMARTDrive, type **help smartdrv** at the command prompt.

- If you are conserving conventional memory by running programs in upper memory, try running them in conventional memory instead. Although running programs in upper memory conserves conventional memory, it uses some extended memory. (EMM386 creates UMBs using extended memory.)

  The simplest way to stop running programs in upper memory is to add a **rem** command to the beginning of the EMM386.EXE command line in your CONFIG.SYS file.

- If Windows won't start because not enough extended memory is available, try disabling the EMM386.EXE command line and the **dos=high** command in your CONFIG.SYS file. Although these commands enable you to conserve conventional memory, they use some extended memory.

# Freeing Expanded Memory

Some programs require additional expanded memory to run. If you are having trouble running such a program, do the following:

- Make sure your system contains as much physical expanded memory as the program needs, and that your CONFIG.SYS file contains a **device** command for the expanded-memory manager that came with your memory board.

  If you have an 80386 computer with extended memory, you can use EMM386 to provide expanded memory for programs. For information about EMM386, see the section "Using the EMM386 Memory Manager" later in this chapter.

- If you are using EMM386 with the **noems** switch, expanded memory will be unavailable. On the EMM386.EXE command line in your CONFIG.SYS file, change the **noems** switch to the **ram** switch. For information about EMM386.EXE, type **help emm386.exe** at the command prompt.

- If your CONFIG.SYS or AUTOEXEC.BAT file starts programs that use expanded memory, reduce the amount of expanded memory you allocate for each program. For information about how to do this, see the documentation that accompanied each program.

# Using MS-DOS Memory Managers

To use your computer's extended memory, expanded memory, or upper memory area, your CONFIG.SYS file must contain a command that loads a *memory manager*. A memory manager is a device driver that provides access to a particular type of memory. (You do not need a memory manager to use conventional memory, because MS-DOS has a built-in conventional-memory manager.)

MS-DOS includes the following memory managers:

- HIMEM, which provides access to extended memory. MS-DOS Setup installs HIMEM automatically if you have an 80286, 80386, or 80486 computer with extended memory. For more information about HIMEM, type **help himem.sys** at the command prompt.

- EMM386, which provides access to the upper memory area. EMM386 can also use extended memory to simulate expanded memory. For more information, see the following section.

MS-DOS does not include an expanded-memory manager for physical expanded memory, since each expanded-memory board requires its own memory manager. To use physical expanded memory, you must install the memory manager that came with your expanded-memory board.

---

**Note**  MS-DOS also includes the SMARTDrive and RAMDrive programs. These are not memory managers; they are optimization programs that use some memory to speed up your system. For information about SMARTDrive or RAMDrive, type **help smartdrv** or **help ramdrive.sys** at the command prompt.

---

# Using the EMM386 Memory Manager

EMM386, which comes with MS-DOS, is a dual-purpose memory manager for 80386 and 80486 computers that have extended memory. EMM386 performs two functions:

- It provides access to the upper memory area. This enables you to free conventional memory by running device drivers and memory-resident programs in upper memory.

- It uses extended memory to simulate expanded memory. Programs can then use that simulated expanded memory as if it were physical expanded memory.

EMM386 can perform either or both of these functions. In general, if you have an 80386 or 80486 computer with extended memory, you should be using EMM386 to provide access to upper memory. If you have programs that need expanded memory, you should also use EMM386 to emulate expanded memory.

The easiest way to install EMM386 is to run the MemMaker program, which installs and configures EMM386.

▶ **To install EMM386**

1. Run the MemMaker program by typing **memmaker** at the command prompt.

   MemMaker displays the Welcome screen.

2. Choose the Continue option by pressing ENTER.

   MemMaker displays a screen prompting you to choose between Express and Custom Setup.

3. Choose Express Setup by pressing ENTER.

   MemMaker displays a screen that prompts you to specify whether you use any programs that require expanded memory.

4. If none of your programs require expanded memory, or if you are not sure whether your programs require expanded memory, choose No by pressing ENTER.

   If you use programs that require expanded memory, select Yes by pressing the SPACEBAR, and then press ENTER. For more information about this screen, press F1.

5. Complete the MemMaker program by following the instructions on your screen. For more information about MemMaker, see the section "Optimizing Memory by Using MemMaker" earlier in this chapter.

For more information, type **help emm386.exe** at the command prompt.

CHAPTER 7

# Features for Your Laptop Computer

With the Interlnk program and a cable that connects two computers, you can use one computer to access data and run programs on another computer. You no longer have to use floppy disks to copy files from one computer to another.

For example, suppose you regularly visit your field sales force and record information you gather on a laptop computer. When you return to your home office, you transfer the information to your desktop computer, which is connected to a printer. Using Interlnk, you can add the information you've gathered to a database on your desktop computer and print out the new information.

After you connect your computers and start Interlnk, you use the laptop computer to type commands that control both it and your desktop computer. The desktop computer displays the status of the connection; you use its keyboard only to break the connection between the two computers.

## Using Interlnk to Connect Two Computers

The computer you use to type commands is called the *client*. Generally, this is your laptop computer. The computer connected to the client is the *server*. Generally, this is your desktop computer. The client uses the server's drives and printers, and the server displays the status of the connection between the computers.

For example, suppose you have connected a laptop and a desktop computer. The laptop computer has three drives: a floppy disk drive (A) and two hard disk drives (C and D). The desktop computer also has three drives: two floppy disk drives

(A and B) and a hard disk drive (C). The following table lists the drives on each computer.

| Laptop drives | Desktop drives |
| --- | --- |
| A | A |
| C | B |
| D | C |

When the computers are connected using Interlnk, the drives on the desktop computer (the server) appear as additional drives on the laptop computer (the client). In addition to drives A, C, and D, the laptop computer now includes drives E, F, and G.

The following illustration shows how the drives of each computer are redirected.

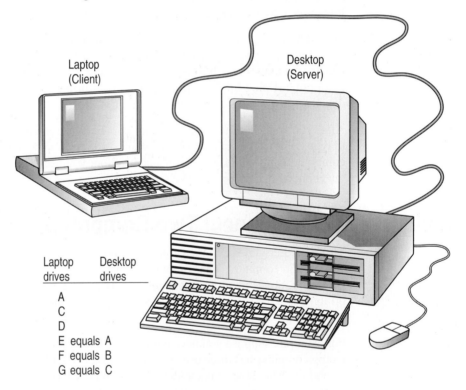

Drive E of the laptop computer (client) represents drive A of the desktop computer (server). If you make drive E current on the laptop computer, the commands you type affect drive A of the desktop computer. For example, if you type the following command on the laptop computer, MS-DOS displays a list of the files in the root directory of the desktop computer's hard drive:

**dir g:\**

The drives on your laptop and desktop computers will probably be redirected differently than the ones in this example. When you connect your computers and get Interlnk running, the server will display the way your drives are redirected.

# What You Need to Use Interlnk

Before you use Interlnk, make sure you have the following hardware, software, and available memory:

- A free serial port on both computers or a free parallel port on both computers
- A 3-wire serial cable, 7-wire null-modem serial cable, or bidirectional parallel cable
- MS-DOS version 6.0 on one computer and MS-DOS version 3.0 or later on the other
- 16 kilobytes (K) of free memory on the client and 130K of free memory on the server

## Setting Up the Client

▶   **To set up INTERLNK.EXE on the computer(s) you plan to use as a client**

1. Make sure the INTERLNK.EXE file is located on the computer's hard disk.

   If the client's hard disk does not contain the INTERLNK.EXE file, see "Using the Remote Copy Procedure" later in this chapter for instructions on copying Interlnk files from one computer to another.

2. Open your CONFIG.SYS file by using a text editor such as MS-DOS Editor. (Your CONFIG.SYS file is located in the root directory of your startup disk.)

   To open your CONFIG.SYS file using MS-DOS Editor, type the following at the command prompt:

   **edit c:\config.sys**

3. Add a **device** command that specifies the location of the INTERLNK.EXE file. You can also specify options for redirecting drives and printers. For more information about the options you can specify, type **help interlnk.exe** at the command prompt.

   The following example specifies that the INTERLNK.EXE file is located in the DOS directory on drive C. The command also specifies that INTERLNK.EXE should redirect five drives instead of the default three drives:

   **device=c:\dos\interlnk.exe /drives:5**

4. Save the changes to your CONFIG.SYS file, and then quit the text editor.

5. Restart your computer by pressing CTRL+ALT+DEL.

After you add the **device** command for INTERLNK.EXE to your CONFIG.SYS file, Interlnk displays the status of redirected drives and ports each time you start the client computer. You can also view the status of redirected drives and ports by typing **interlnk** at the command prompt.

For example, the following is a status report for a computer that has five redirected drives and two redirected printer ports:

```
Microsoft Interlnk version 1.00


Port=LPT1
Drive letters redirected: 5 (D: through H:)
Printer ports redirected: 2 (LPT1: through LPT2:)


This Computer    Other Computer
  (Client)         (Server)
- - - - - - - - -  - - - - - - - -
     D:    equals    A:
     E:    equals    B:
     F:    equals    C:(85Mb) MS-DOS_6
     G:    equals    D:
     H:    equals    E:
     LPT1: equals    LPT2:
     LPT2: equals    LPT3:
```

The Port line indicates which port Interlnk is using to connect to the other computer. Interlnk displays the sizes and volume labels of hard disk drives on the server. For example, drive C on the server is 85 megabytes (MB) and is labeled "MS-DOS_6."

For more information about the INTERLNK.EXE device driver, type **help interlnk.exe** at the command prompt.

## Starting the Server

You do not need to make any changes to your CONFIG.SYS file to start the Interlnk server. To start the server, type **intersvr** at the command prompt of the computer you are using as the server. Interlnk displays information about redirected drives and printer ports on the server's screen.

The column labeled "This Computer" lists all drives and printer ports on the server. The column labeled "Other Computer" lists the drives and printer ports on the client, in addition to the drives and ports on the server that are now available on the client.

A status bar at the bottom of the screen displays the status of the Interlnk connection. The Transfer field indicates whether the client is reading from or writing to the server. When the client reads from or writes to the server, Interlnk displays an asterisk (*) next to the drive letter that indicates which server drive is being affected. The Port field shows which server port Interlnk is using to connect to the client. The Speed field shows the baud rate at which Interlnk is transferring information.

---

**Note**  You cannot switch between tasks in Microsoft Windows or MS-DOS Shell while Interlnk is running.

---

For more information about the Interlnk server, type **help intersvr** at the command prompt.

# Establishing a Connection Between Computers

Interlnk establishes connections between all redirected drives and ports when you do one of the following:

- Restart the client computer when the server is running.
- Type **interlnk** at the command prompt of the client computer.
- Make one of the redirected drives on the client computer the active drive.

# Breaking the Connection Between Computers

To break the Interlnk connection between computers, stop the server by pressing ALT+F4 on the server's keyboard. To restart the server, type **intersvr** at the server's command prompt.

# Using the Remote Copy Procedure

If only one of the two computers you want to connect has the Interlnk files on it, you can use the Interlnk copy procedure instead of a floppy disk to copy the files to the other computer.

---

**Note**  To carry out the remote copy procedure, you must connect the serial ports of the two computers with a 7-wire null-modem serial cable. You must also have access to the **mode** command on the computer that you are copying Interlnk files to. If you do not have a 7-wire null-modem cable, use a floppy disk to transfer files.

---

▶   **To copy Interlnk files from one computer to another**

1.  Make the directory to which you want to copy files the current directory.

2.  If you are using a port other than COM1 on the computer you are copying files to, make sure that you are not running the Share program on that computer. If you are, disable the **share** command in your AUTOEXEC.BAT or CONFIG.SYS file, and then restart your computer by pressing CTRL+ALT+DEL.

3.  At the command prompt of the computer that has the Interlnk files on it, type the following:

    **intersvr /rcopy**

    The remote installation screen appears.

    Follow the instructions that appear on your screen.

As Interlnk copies the files, it displays the status at the bottom of each computer's screen.

# Conserving Power on Your Laptop Computer

The Power program conserves battery power on your laptop computer when applications and hardware devices are idle. If your hardware conforms to the Advanced Power Management (APM) specification, your power savings can be up to 25 percent, depending on your hardware. If your hardware does not conform to the APM specification, your power savings will be about 5 percent.

▶   **To use the Power program**

1.  Open your CONFIG.SYS file by using a text editor such as MS-DOS Editor. (Your CONFIG.SYS file is usually located in the root directory of your startup disk.)

    To open your CONFIG.SYS file using MS-DOS Editor, type the following at the command prompt:

    **edit c:\config.sys**

2.  At the end of your CONFIG.SYS file, add a **device** command that specifies the location of the POWER.EXE file.

    The following example specifies that the POWER.EXE file is located in the DOS directory on drive C, and that the default setting should be used:

    **device=c:\dos\power.exe**

3.  Save the changes to your CONFIG.SYS file, and then quit the text editor.

4.  Restart your computer by pressing CTRL+ALT+DEL.

To display the current power setting, type the following at the command prompt:

**power**

For more information about the POWER.EXE device driver, type **help power.exe** at the command prompt. For more information about the **power** command, type **help power** at the command prompt.

CHAPTER 8

# Diagnosing and Solving Problems

This chapter is divided into three sections: "Troubleshooting During Setup," "Using Fdisk to Configure Your Hard Disk," and "Troubleshooting While Running MS-DOS."

"Troubleshooting During Setup" explains how to finish installing MS-DOS 6 if you encounter a problem during Setup. "Using Fdisk to Configure Your Hard Disk" explains how to repartition your hard disk. "Troubleshooting While Running MS-DOS" explains how to solve the most common problems you might encounter while using MS-DOS.

If you encounter a problem with one of the programs included with MS-DOS 6, consult the following table to find the troubleshooting help you need.

| For problems with | See this source | In this location |
|---|---|---|
| Anti-Virus | The chapter "Managing Your System" | In this guide |
| Backup | The chapter "Managing Your System" | In this guide |
| MemMaker | The chapter "Making More Memory Available" | In this guide |
| Undelete | The chapter "Managing Your System" | In this guide |
| DoubleSpace | The README.TXT file | The directory that contains your MS-DOS files |

If you do not find the troubleshooting information you need in this guide, view the README.TXT file on Setup Disk 1 by using any text editor.

# Troubleshooting During Setup

This section explains how to solve the most common problems you might encounter while setting up MS-DOS 6. Before you carry out any of the procedures in this section, make a startup disk. For instructions, see the following section.

## Making a Startup Disk

A startup disk is a floppy disk you can use to start your computer while you are troubleshooting or reconfiguring your computer.

---

**Note**  By carrying out the following procedure, you will create a startup disk that contains the files needed to start your computer, in addition to commands and programs that you might need. However, in an emergency, you can also use Setup Disk 1 or your Uninstall disk to start your computer.

---

Before you carry out this procedure, prepare a formatted or unformatted floppy disk that is compatible with drive A by labeling it "Startup."

▶  **To make a startup disk**

1. Quit Setup if you have not already done so.
2. Insert Setup Disk 1 in drive A or B.

    If your Setup disks are compatible with drive B, place Setup Disk 1 in drive B. This will speed up the process of creating a startup disk.

3. Type the following at the command prompt:

    **a:setup /f**

    or

    **b:setup /f**

4. Follow the instructions on your screen.

## Using the Uninstall Disk

The primary purpose of the Uninstall disk is to safeguard the files on your computer while you are installing MS-DOS 6. The Uninstall disk protects the files on your computer if Setup cannot finish installing MS-DOS or if you encounter problems with MS-DOS 6 after Setup is complete. By using the Uninstall disk, you can restore your previous version of DOS if you need to.

The first time you set up MS-DOS 6, the Setup program creates a directory named OLD_DOS.1 on your hard disk. Setup copies your previous DOS files to this directory. Setup then copies information about your previous version of DOS, your AUTOEXEC.BAT file, and your CONFIG.SYS file to the Uninstall disk. Setup gives the copies of your AUTOEXEC.BAT and CONFIG.SYS files the extension .DAT.

If you decide to restore your previous version of DOS, use the Uninstall program. This program copies the files in the OLD_DOS.1 directory back to their original location.

If you run Setup again, it creates an OLD_DOS directory with a new numeric extension. For example, the second time you run Setup, it creates the OLD_DOS.2 directory.

You cannot use the Uninstall disk to restore your previous version of DOS if you do any of the following after installing MS-DOS 6:

- Repartition or reformat your hard disk
- Delete or move either of the two hidden MS-DOS system files (IO.SYS and MSDOS.SYS)
- Delete the OLD_DOS.*x* directory
- Install DoubleSpace or a third-party disk-compression program

---

**Note**  If your startup drive uses a third-party disk-compression program, you might not be able to create an Uninstall disk during Setup or restore your previous version of DOS during or after Setup. To protect your data files, back them up before you run Setup. You should also create a startup disk that includes the system files of your previous version of DOS and then copy the **fdisk**, **format**, and **sys** commands to the disk. For more information about creating a startup disk, see the documentation that came with your previous version of DOS.

---

▶ **To restore your previous version of DOS**

1. Insert the Uninstall disk in drive A.
2. Restart your computer by pressing CTRL+ALT+DEL.
3. Follow the instructions on your screen.

You can also use the Uninstall disk to start MS-DOS 6 without restoring your previous version of DOS.

▶ **To start your computer by using the Uninstall disk**

1. Insert the Uninstall disk in drive A.
2. Restart your computer by pressing CTRL+ALT+DEL.
3. When Uninstall information appears on your screen, press F3 twice to quit the Uninstall program.

The MS-DOS command prompt appears. Drive A will be your current drive, and your computer will start with a basic configuration instead of your usual configuration. For more information, see the chapter "Configuring Your System."

# Setup stops before MS-DOS 6 has been completely installed.

This section explains what to do if Setup stops or is interrupted before it finishes installing MS-DOS 6.

To determine which procedure to use, try to restart your computer by removing disks from all floppy disk drives, and then pressing CTRL+ALT+DEL. If MS-DOS does not prompt you for an Uninstall disk, carry out Procedure 1. If MS-DOS prompts you for an Uninstall disk, carry out Procedure 2.

▶  **Procedure 1    To complete setup if MS-DOS did not prompt you for an Uninstall disk**

1. Remove disks from all floppy disk drives, and then restart your computer by pressing CTRL+ALT+DEL.

2. To make sure you can access your hard disk, type the following at the command prompt:

   **dir c:\\**

   You should see a list of files and directories.

3. Type the following at the command prompt:

   **dir c:\\***directory*

   For *directory*, type the name of any directory on drive C. You should see a list of the files and subdirectories in the directory you specified.

   If you see lists of files and directories when you carry out steps 2 and 3, proceed to step 4.

   If you do not see a list of files and directories, you probably cannot access your hard disk. Contact Microsoft Product Support Services. For information about how to reach Microsoft Product Support Services, see the "Welcome" section at the beginning of this guide.

4. Create a startup disk by inserting a floppy disk in drive A, and then typing the following at the command prompt:

   **format a: /s**

   The **format** command formats the floppy disk and transfers system files to it.

5. Leave the disk you made in step 4 in drive A, and then restart your computer by pressing CTRL+ALT+DEL.

6. To make sure you can access your hard disk, type the following at the command prompt:

**dir c:\**

You should see a list of files and directories.

7. Type the following at the command prompt:

   **dir c:\**_directory_

   For _directory_, type the name of any directory on drive C. You should see a list of the files and subdirectories in the directory you specified.

   If you see lists of files and directories when you carry out steps 6 and 7, proceed to step 8.

   If you do not see a list of files and directories, you probably cannot access your hard disk. Contact Microsoft Product Support Services. For information about how to reach Microsoft Product Support Services, see the "Welcome" section at the beginning of this guide.

8. Insert Setup Disk 1 in drive A or B, and then type the following at the command prompt:

   **a:setup**

   or

   **b:setup**

   If Setup stops again, insert the startup disk you made in drive A, and then restart your computer by pressing CTRL+ALT+DEL. Proceed to step 9.

   If you receive a message about an incompatible partition, contact Microsoft Product Support Services. Do not use the **setup /u** command. For information about how to reach Microsoft Product Support Services, see the "Welcome" section at the beginning of this guide.

9. Insert Setup Disk 1 in drive A or B, and then restart Setup by typing the following at the command prompt:

   **a:setup /i**

   or

   **b:setup /i**

   The **/i** switch causes Setup to skip hardware detection. When Setup prompts you to provide information about your computer system, choose settings that match the hardware you are using.

If MS-DOS prompts you for an Uninstall disk after you restart your computer, carry out the following procedure.

▶  **Procedure 2   To complete installation if MS-DOS prompted you for an Uninstall disk**

1. Insert the Uninstall disk in drive A, and then press ENTER.

2. Follow the instructions on your screen.

If Setup stops again, call Microsoft Product Support Services. For information about how to reach Microsoft Product Support Services, see the "Welcome" section at the beginning of this guide.

# Setup screens are unreadable.

This section explains what to do if your monitor cannot display Setup screens properly. If your computer's operating system is DOS, carry out the following procedure.

If your computer's only operating system is OS/2, contact your hardware vendor for information about setting up MS-DOS 6.

▶ **To set up MS-DOS 6 if your computer's operating system is DOS**

1. Quit Setup if you have not already done so.

   To quit Setup, press F3 twice.

2. Insert Setup Disk 1 in drive A or B, and then type the following at the command prompt:

   **a:setup /i**

   or

   **b:setup /i**

   The **/i** switch causes Setup to skip automatic hardware detection. When Setup prompts you for the type of monitor you are using, make sure you specify the correct type.

# Setup displays the "There is not enough free space on drive C to install MS-DOS" screen.

If you receive a message during Setup stating that you don't have enough space to install MS-DOS, you can make room on your hard disk by carrying out one of the procedures in this section.

If you have a version of DOS on your computer, carry out Procedure 1. If you have only OS/2 on your computer, carry out Procedure 2.

▶ **Procedure 1    To determine how much disk space you need to free if you have DOS on your computer**

1. Setup indicates which drive needs more free space. Note how much disk space you need to free.

2. Quit Setup by pressing F3 twice.

3.  Type the following at the command prompt:

    **chkdsk c:**

    The first line shown by **chkdsk** should look similar to the following:

    ```
    61739008 bytes total disk space
    ```

    This number represents the total capacity of the drive. If the capacity of drive C is smaller than the number indicated on the Setup screen, repartition your hard disk. For instructions, see "Using Fdisk to Configure Your Hard Disk" later in this chapter.

4.  The **chkdsk** command should also show a line similar to the following:

    ```
    32672128 bytes available on disk
    ```

    This number represents the free space available on the drive. If drive C is large enough but you don't have enough free disk space to set up MS-DOS, delete unnecessary files or move them to another disk drive until you have enough free disk space. You might want to back up any files you plan to delete.

    If your drive doesn't have enough disk space to set up MS-DOS because you chose to keep OS/2, see "Removing OS/2 and Saving the Data on Your Computer" in "If You Have OS/2 Dual Boot with DOS or OS/2 Boot Manager with DOS" in the chapter "Getting Started."

5.  Run Setup again.

---

**Note**  If your computer uses a third-party disk-compression program or DoubleSpace, the **chkdsk** command might not accurately estimate the amount of free disk space on your computer. However, regardless of what **chkdsk** reports, Setup correctly detects the amount of free disk space it needs. If Setup again indicates that you don't have enough free disk space to set up MS-DOS, quit Setup, free more disk space, and then run Setup again.

---

▶ **Procedure 2    To determine how much disk space you need to free if you have only OS/2 on your computer**

1.  Before quitting Setup, note how much disk space needs to be free on drive C. Then quit Setup by pressing F3 twice.

2.  Type the following at the command prompt:

    **dir c:\ /s**

This command lists all the files and directories on drive C. At the bottom of the list, you should see lines similar to the following:

```
64 file(s)  53608448 bytes
            2488383 bytes free
```

Delete unnecessary files or move them to another disk drive until you have enough free disk space. You might want to back up any files you plan to delete.

If you don't have enough disk space because you chose to keep OS/2, see "Upgrading from OS/2 to MS-DOS 6" in the chapter "Getting Started."

3. Run Setup again.

# Setup displays the "Your computer uses a disk-compression program" screen.

If your startup drive uses a third-party disk-compression program, you will not be able to create an Uninstall disk during Setup or restore your previous version of DOS during or after Setup. For that reason, you might want to protect your data files by backing them up before you run Setup. In addition, you might want to create a startup disk that includes the system files of your previous version of DOS, and then copy the **fdisk**, **sys**, and **format** commands to the disk. For more information about the Uninstall feature, see "Using the Uninstall Disk" earlier in this chapter. For information about creating a startup disk, see the documentation that came with your previous version of DOS.

For information about converting your disk-compression program to Microsoft DoubleSpace, view the README.TXT file on Setup Disk 1 by using any text editor.

# Setup displays the "Your computer uses a disk-compression program and does not have enough free disk space to set up MS-DOS" screen.

When Setup displays this screen, it indicates which drive does not have enough disk space. The drive Setup indicates is your uncompressed drive.

▶ **To free enough disk space to set up MS-DOS 6**

1. Note how much disk space you need to free.

2. Quit Setup by pressing F3 twice.

3. Type the following at the command prompt:

   **chkdsk** *drive***:**

   For *drive*, type the drive letter of your uncompressed drive.

   A screen of information appears. It should include a line similar to the following:

   ```
   500128 bytes available on disk
   ```

   Delete unnecessary files or move them to another drive until you have enough free disk space. You might want to back up any files you plan to delete.

   ---

   **Important**  Do not delete your COMMAND.COM, AUTOEXEC.BAT, or CONFIG.SYS files, or any files used by your disk-compression program. If you cannot delete enough unnecessary files, see your disk-compression documentation for instructions on how to enlarge the capacity of your uncompressed drive, or contact the vendor of your disk-compression software.

   ---

4. When you have freed enough disk space, run Setup again.

# Setup displays the "Your computer uses SuperStor disk compression" screen.

If Setup displays this screen, you need to run the ADD2SWP program to make your computer's uncompressed drive accessible to Setup. If your SuperStor ™ installation disks contain the ADD2SWP.EXE file, carry out the following procedure. If your disks do not contain the file, contact AddStor, Inc. for information about how to obtain it.

▶ **To make your computer's uncompressed drive accessible to Setup**

1. Insert the SuperStor disk with the ADD2SWP.EXE file in drive A or B.

2. Type the following at the command prompt:

   **a:add2swp** *drive***:**

   or

   **b:add2swp** *drive***:**

   For *drive*, type the letter of your hard disk's startup drive. Typically, this is drive C.

3. Follow the instructions on your screen.

4. After you restart your computer, run Setup again.

# Setup displays the "Your computer uses a disk-compression program and has run out of disk space" screen.

If Setup displays this message, carry out the following procedure. If Setup displays this message and also indicates that you will not be able to restart your computer, contact Microsoft Product Support Services. For information about how to contact Microsoft Product Support Services, see the "Welcome" section at the beginning of this guide.

▶ **To free enough disk space to set up MS-DOS 6**

1. Setup indicates which drive needs more free disk space. Note how much disk space you need to free.

2. Quit Setup by pressing F3 twice.

3. Insert Setup Disk 1 in drive A or B, and then type the following at the command prompt:

   **a:\chkdsk** *drive***:**

   or

   **b:\chkdsk** *drive***:**

   For *drive*, type the letter of the drive on which Setup indicated that you need to free disk space.

   A screen of information appears. It should include a line similar to the following:

   ```
   500128 bytes available on disk
   ```

4. Delete unnecessary files or move them to another drive until you have enough free disk space. You might want to back up any files you plan to delete.

5. When you have freed enough disk space, run Setup again.

---

**Note** Because your computer uses a third-party disk-compression program or DoubleSpace, the **chkdsk** command might not accurately estimate the amount of free disk space on your computer. However, regardless of what the **chkdsk** command reports, Setup correctly detects the amount of free disk space it needs. If Setup again indicates that you don't have enough free disk space to set up MS-DOS, quit Setup, free more disk space, and then run Setup again.

---

# Setup displays the "Your computer uses password protection" screen.

If your computer is using a password protection program, you must quit Setup and disable the password program before you can install MS-DOS 6. When you have disabled the password program, restart your computer by pressing CTRL+ALT+DEL, and then run Setup again. For more information, see the documentation that came with your password protection program.

# Setup displays the "Your computer is using an incompatible delete-protection program" screen.

If Setup displays this screen and your computer is using the DELWATCH program, carry out the following procedure.

---

**Note**  To determine if your computer has been using DELWATCH and has been creating pending delete files, use the **chkdsk** command. For information about the **chkdsk** command, see the documentation that came with your previous version of DOS.

Even if you run DELWATCH from a floppy disk, you need to run the program DELPURGE as described in step 4 below.

---

▶ **To disable the DELWATCH program**

1. Open your AUTOEXEC.BAT file by using a text editor.

2. Remove the command that loads DELWATCH, and then save the file.

   For information about which command loads DELWATCH, see the documentation that came with your previous version of DOS.

3. Remove disks from all floppy disk drives, and then restart your computer by pressing CTRL+ALT+DEL.

4. Remove disks from all floppy disk drives, and then run the DELPURGE program to purge your hard disk of pending delete files.

   For information about the DELPURGE program, see the documentation that came with your previous version of DOS.

5. Run Setup again.

# Setup displays the "Cannot find a hard disk on your computer" screen.

Setup displays this screen when your computer:

- Has a hard disk that is incompatible with Setup or is supported by a device driver.

- Has a hard disk that isn't functioning properly.

For information about how to set up MS-DOS 6 on your computer, contact Microsoft Product Support Services. For information about how to reach Microsoft Product Support Services, see the "Welcome" section at the beginning of this guide.

# Setup displays the "Too Many Primary Partitions" or "Incompatible Primary DOS Partition" screen.

If Setup displays one of these messages, you probably need to repartition your hard disk before you can install MS-DOS 6. For information about repartitioning your hard disk, see "Using Fdisk to Configure Your Hard Disk" later in this chapter.

# Setup displays the "Incompatible hard disk or device driver" screen.

This section explains how to set up MS-DOS 6 if your computer has one of the following:

- Priam ® or Everex ™ partition
- Syquest ® removable hard disk
- Vfeature ™ Deluxe partition
- Novell ® partition
- UNIX ® or XENIX ® partition
- Bernoulli ™ drive
- Disk Manager ® partition

If Setup displays the "Incompatible hard disk or device driver" screen and your computer does not include a component from the preceding list, you might have an incompatible partition that you need to delete from your hard disk. To delete the partition, follow the instructions in "Using Fdisk to Configure Your Hard Disk" later in this chapter.

## Priam or Everex Partitions

If you used Priam or Everex disk-partitioning software to partition your hard disk, you cannot use the Setup program to install MS-DOS 6. For information about installing MS-DOS manually (without using the Setup program), see "You need to install MS-DOS manually" later in this chapter.

## Syquest Removable Hard Disk

If your computer contains a Syquest removable hard disk, disable the **device=syq55.sys** command line in your CONFIG.SYS file by using the **rem** command. Then run Setup again. After MS-DOS 6 is set up, re-enable the command line by removing the **rem** command.

## Novell Partitions

If your hard disk includes Novell partitions, quit Setup, and then restart Setup by typing **a:setup /u** (or **b:setup /u**) at the command prompt. The **/u** switch enables Setup to install MS-DOS 6 even if Setup detects partitions that might be incompatible.

## Vfeature Deluxe Partitions

Contact Golden Bow Systems for information about Vfeature upgrades. Or delete Vfeature partitions by repartitioning your hard disk using the Fdisk program. To repartition your hard disk, follow the instructions in "Using Fdisk to Configure Your Hard Disk" later in this chapter.

## UNIX or XENIX Partitions

If your hard disk has UNIX or XENIX partitions in addition to standard DOS partitions and you receive a message stating that a partition is incompatible with MS-DOS 6, quit Setup, and then type **a:setup /u** (or **b:setup /u**) at the command prompt. The **/u** switch enables Setup to install MS-DOS 6 even if Setup detects partitions that might be incompatible.

---

**Important**  If your computer's operating systems include UNIX or XENIX and a screen from which you choose an operating system appears when you start your computer, do not run Setup; you need to install MS-DOS manually (without using the Setup program). For information about manually installing MS-DOS, see "You need to install MS-DOS manually" later in this chapter.

---

## Disk Caching with a Bernoulli Drive

If your computer uses disk caching with an Iomega Bernoulli drive, use the **rem** command to disable the command lines that install the caching software for your Bernoulli drive. Then run Setup again. After MS-DOS 6 is set up, re-enable the command lines by removing the **rem** commands.

## Disk Manager Partitions and Drivers

If you are using MS-DOS version 3.*x* on a computer that has a Disk Manager partition larger than 512 MB, contact Ontrack Computer Systems to get an updated version of Disk Manager and instructions for making the partition compatible with MS-DOS 6.

If you have MS-DOS version 4.*x* or later on your computer, Setup could not find the command line in your CONFIG.SYS file for the device driver that supports your Disk Manager partition. Add the **device** command line to your CONFIG.SYS file, restart your computer by pressing CTRL+ALT+DEL, and then run Setup again. For more information about adding the command line to your CONFIG.SYS file, see your Disk Manager documentation.

# Setup displays the "Incompatible partition" screen.

If you have a SpeedStor Bootall partition, you cannot use the Setup program to install MS-DOS 6. For information about installing MS-DOS manually (without using the Setup program), see "You need to install MS-DOS manually" later in this chapter.

# Setup repeatedly prompts you for the Uninstall disk.

If Setup displays the following message when you insert the Uninstall disk in drive A, make sure you are using an unformatted disk:

```
ERROR
This is not the correct disk.
Press ENTER to continue.
```

If using an unformatted disk does not work, carry out the following procedure.

▶ **To prevent Setup from repeatedly prompting you for the Uninstall disk**

1. Quit Setup if you have not already done so. To quit Setup, press F3 twice.

2. Create a startup disk.

   To do this, insert a floppy disk in drive A, and type the following at the command prompt:

   **format a: /s**

The **format /s** command formats the floppy disk and transfers your system files to it.

3. Type the following command lines, substituting a value for *x* that is listed in the table following this procedure. At the end of each line, press ENTER.

   **copy con a:config.sys**
   **drivparm /d:0 /f:***x*

   These commands create a CONFIG.SYS file on the disk in drive A. The file will contain the **drivparm** command, which modifies the parameters of drive A.

4. To save the CONFIG.SYS file you just created, press F6, and then press ENTER.

5. Leave the disk in drive A, and then restart your computer by pressing CTRL+ALT+DEL.

6. To make sure you can access your hard disk, type the following at the command prompt:

   **dir c:\**

   You should see a list of files and directories.

7. Type the following at the command prompt:

   **dir c:\***directory*

   For *directory*, type the name of any directory on drive C. You should see a list of files and subdirectories in the directory you specified.

   If you see lists of files and directories when you carry out steps 6 and 7, proceed to step 8.

   If you do not see a list of files and directories, you probably cannot access your hard disk. Call Microsoft Product Support Services. For information about how to reach Microsoft Product Support Services, see the "Welcome" section at the beginning of this guide.

8. Insert Setup Disk 1 in drive A or B.

9. Type the following at the command prompt:

   **a:setup**

   or

   **b:setup**

   Follow the instructions on your screen.

The value you specify for *x* in step 3 depends on the size and capacity of drive A. The following table describes valid values for *x*.

| Disk size | Disk capacity | Value to use |
|-----------|---------------|--------------|
| 5.25 inches | 160K, 180K, 320K, 360K | 0 |
| 5.25 inches | 1.2 MB | 1 |
| 3.5 inches | 720K | 2 |
| 3.5 inches | 1.44 MB | 7 |
| 3.5 inches | 2.88 MB | 9 |

# Setup displays the "Root directory of your hard disk contains some of your original DOS files" screen.

If Setup displays this message, you must remove the DOS files from your root directory before setting up MS-DOS 6.

**Note**  If your startup drive is a drive other than C, substitute the appropriate drive letter in the following procedure.

▶ **To remove DOS files from your root directory**

1.  Create a startup disk.

    To do this, insert a floppy disk in drive A, and then type the following at the command prompt:

    **format a: /s**

    The **format /s** command formats the floppy disk and transfers your system files to it.

2.  Type the following at the command prompt:

    **dir c:\ > root.txt**

    This command creates a file named ROOT.TXT, which contains a list of the files in your root directory.

3.  Print the ROOT.TXT file.

4.  Open the PACKING.LST file on Setup Disk 1 by using any text editor. The PACKING.LST file contains the names of the files located on each of the MS-DOS 6 Setup disks. Compare the files in the right column of the PACKING.LST file with the list of files on your ROOT.TXT printout. On your printout, mark the name of every file that appears on the Setup disks.

    **Note**  In some cases, the extensions of files may vary. For example, you might have a file named PRINT.COM in your root directory, and there might be a file named PRINT.EXE on a Setup disk. In these cases, you can mark the similarly named files on your list.

5. If you do not already have a directory named DOS, create one by typing the following at the command prompt:

   **md c:\dos**

6. Use the **copy** command to copy the files you marked from your root directory to the DOS directory.

   For example, if the file FORMAT.COM is in your root directory, type the following at the command prompt:

   **copy c:\format.com c:\dos**

7. If there is a file named BASIC or GWBASIC (with any filename extension) in your root directory, copy the file to the DOS directory.

8. After you copy all the marked files to the DOS directory, delete them from the root directory, *except* the following three files:

   CONFIG.SYS
   AUTOEXEC.BAT
   COMMAND.COM

   These three files must remain in the root directory.

   To delete a file such as FORMAT.COM from your root directory, type the following at the command prompt:

   **del c:\format.com**

9. Use the **del** command to delete any files named BASIC or GWBASIC (with any filename extension) from your root directory.

10. After you have deleted the DOS files from your root directory (except the CONFIG.SYS, AUTOEXEC.BAT, and COMMAND.COM files), run Setup again.

# Setup reports that your computer does not have enough available space to install the selected programs.

If Setup displays a screen or message reporting that you do not have enough available disk space, note the amount of space Setup requires for MS-DOS and the optional programs you want to install. The amount of required disk space is displayed on the screen from which you choose the programs.

There are two ways to install Anti-Virus, Backup, and Undelete:

- You can choose to install only those programs that will fit on drive C. After you complete Setup, you can install Microsoft DoubleSpace to create more space on drive C. Then rerun Setup to install the programs you want.

For more information about DoubleSpace, see the chapter "Freeing Disk Space." For more information about installing the optional programs, see "Installing Anti-Virus, Backup, and Undelete After Setup" in the chapter "Getting Started."

■ You can also quit Setup and free enough disk space to install the programs you want. To do this, carry out the following procedure.

▶ **To free enough disk space to install the programs you want**

1. Note how much disk space you need to free to install the programs you want.

2. Quit Setup by pressing F3 twice.

3. Type the following at the command prompt:

   **chkdsk c:**

   The first line shown by **chkdsk** should appear similar to the following:

   ```
   61739008 bytes total disk space
   ```

   This number represents the total capacity of the drive. If the capacity of drive C is smaller than the number indicated on the Setup screen, repartition your hard disk. For instructions, see "Using Fdisk to Configure Your Hard Disk" later in this chapter.

4. The **chkdsk** command should also show a line similar to this:

   ```
   4267212 bytes available on disk
   ```

   This number represents the free space available on the drive. If drive C is large enough, but you don't have enough free disk space to set up MS-DOS and the programs you want, delete unnecessary files or move them to another drive until you have enough free space. You might want to back up any files you plan to delete.

5. Run Setup again.

---

**Note** If your computer uses a third-party disk-compression program or DoubleSpace, the **chkdsk** command might not accurately estimate the amount of free disk space on your computer. However, regardless of what **chkdsk** reports, Setup correctly detects the amount of free disk space it needs. If Setup again indicates that you don't have enough free disk space to set up the programs you want, quit Setup, free more disk space, and then run Setup again.

---

# You need to copy Setup files directly to your computer.

The files on the Setup disks are compressed and are not usable until they are decompressed. Usually, Setup decompresses the compressed files as they are copied to your hard disk. In some cases, you may need to copy files directly from a Setup disk without using Setup.

An underscore (_) at the end of a filename extension identifies a compressed file —for example, EMM386.EX_. When you decompress a compressed file, you must specify the full extension for the decompressed file. For example, to decompress the compressed file EMM386.EX_ and copy it from the disk in drive A to the C:\DOS directory, you would type the following at the command prompt:

**expand a:\emm386.ex_ c:\dos\emm386.exe**

For information about what extension to give decompressed files, view the PACKING.LST file on Setup Disk 1 by using any text editor. The PACKING.LST file contains a list of the files located on each of the MS-DOS 6 Setup disks.

▶ **To decompress and copy files to your computer**

1. Make sure the EXPAND.EXE file is on your hard disk.

   Usually, the EXPAND.EXE file is in the directory that contains your MS-DOS files. If you don't find it there, copy it from Setup Disk 1 to that directory.

2. Insert in drive A (or another floppy disk drive) the disk containing the file you want to decompress.

   If you don't know which disk the file you want to decompress is on, open the PACKING.LST file on Setup Disk 1 by using any text editor.

3. Type the following at the command prompt:

   **expand** *x:\filename1* **y:\***directory\filename2*

   For *x*, type the letter of the floppy disk drive you are copying the file from. For *filename1*, type the name of the compressed file you want to decompress. For *y*, type the drive letter of the hard disk you are copying the file to. For *directory*, type the name of the directory that will contain the decompressed file. For *filename2*, type the name the file will have after it has been decompressed.

   The compressed file is decompressed as it is copied to your hard disk.

# You need to install MS-DOS manually.

Setup cannot install MS-DOS on computers with certain types of partitions or disk-partitioning software. In these cases, you might need to install MS-DOS manually.

If you cannot install MS-DOS 6 by using the Setup program, carry out the following procedure.

▶ **To install MS-DOS 6 manually**

1. If your Setup disks are compatible with drive A, insert Setup Disk 1 in drive A, and then restart your computer by pressing CTRL+ALT+DEL. After Setup displays the first screen, quit Setup by pressing F3 twice.

   If your Setup disks are not compatible with drive A, you must create a startup disk. To do this, carry out the procedure in "Making a Startup Disk" earlier in this chapter. After you create the startup disk, leave it in drive A, and then restart your computer by pressing CTRL+ALT+DEL.

2. Transfer system files to your hard disk by typing the following at the command prompt:

   **sys a: c:**

3. Insert Setup Disk 1 in drive A or B if you haven't already done so. Then type the following at the command prompt:

   **a:setup /u /q**

   or

   **b:setup /u /q**

   The **/u** switch causes Setup to skip hard-disk detection. The **/q** switch causes Setup to copy MS-DOS 6 files directly to your hard disk.

4. Follow the instructions on your screen.

5. After Setup is complete, insert Setup Disk 1 or your startup disk in drive A, and then press ENTER.

6. Edit your CONFIG.SYS and AUTOEXEC.BAT files to ensure that the commands listed in these files specify the correct location of each of the device drivers and programs you use. In your AUTOEXEC.BAT file, make sure the **path** command line includes the name of the directory your MS-DOS 6 files are in.

---

**Note**   You can start MS-DOS Editor from the disk in drive A by typing **a:edit**.

---

7. Save the files, remove disks from all floppy disks drives, and then restart your computer by pressing CTRL+ALT+DEL.

   For instructions on installing the optional programs that come with MS-DOS 6, see "Installing Anti-Virus, Backup, and Undelete After Setup" in the chapter "Getting Started."

# MS-DOS won't start after you run Setup.

This section explains what to do if you cannot start MS-DOS after you run Setup.

If your computer is an IBM PS/1 ®, carry out the procedure in the following section, "Your computer is an IBM PS/1, and you cannot start MS-DOS."

## You cannot start MS-DOS.

If your computer is not an IBM PS/1, MS-DOS might not be working properly because:

- There is a problem involving the EMM386 memory manager or the upper memory area.

- A memory-resident program or device driver conflicts with MS-DOS.

The following procedures describe how to determine which commands in your CONFIG.SYS and AUTOEXEC.BAT files are causing problems, and how to remedy those problems. Carry out the procedures in order.

▶ **To determine if the problem involves EMM386.EXE or the upper memory area**

1. Restart your computer by pressing CTRL+ALT+DEL. After your computer starts, MS-DOS displays the following text:

   ```
   Starting MS-DOS...
   ```

2. While the text is on your screen, press and release the F8 key.

   MS-DOS displays the following text:

   ```
   MS-DOS will prompt you to confirm each CONFIG.SYS command.
   ```

   One at a time, MS-DOS displays each command in your CONFIG.SYS file followed by a prompt. For example, when MS-DOS reaches the **dos=high** command, it displays the following prompt:

   ```
   DOS=HIGH [Y,N]?
   ```

3. Carry out all the commands in your CONFIG.SYS file by pressing Y each time you are prompted *except* when you are prompted for the device command that loads EMM386.EXE. When a prompt such as the following appears, press N to bypass it:

```
DEVICE=C:\DOS\EMM386.EXE
```

4. When MS-DOS finishes processing the CONFIG.SYS file, it displays the following prompt:

```
Process AUTOEXEC.BAT [Y,N]?
```

Press Y to process the AUTOEXEC.BAT file.

5. If your computer doesn't start, a memory-resident program or device driver might be conflicting with MS-DOS. Carry out the following procedure.

   If your computer does start, you might have a problem involving the EMM386 memory manager. To reconfigure the EMM386 memory manager and your system's use of upper memory, start the MemMaker program by typing **memmaker** at the command prompt. For information about using MemMaker, see "Optimizing Memory by Using MemMaker" in the chapter "Making More Memory Available."

▶ **To determine if there is a conflicting memory-resident program or device driver in your CONFIG.SYS or AUTOEXEC.BAT file**

1. Restart your computer by pressing CTRL+ALT+DEL. After your computer starts, MS-DOS displays the following text:

```
Starting MS-DOS...
```

2. While the text is on your screen, press and release the F5 key.

   MS-DOS displays the following text:

```
MS-DOS is bypassing your CONFIG.SYS and AUTOEXEC.BAT files.
```

   If your computer starts, a command in your CONFIG.SYS or AUTOEXEC.BAT file is probably causing the problem. Carry out the following procedures.

   If your computer doesn't start, contact Microsoft Product Support Services. For information about how to reach Microsoft Product Support Services, see the "Welcome" section at the beginning of this guide.

▶ **To determine whether the problem is in your CONFIG.SYS file**

1. Restart your computer by pressing CTRL+ALT+DEL. After your computer starts, MS-DOS displays the following text:

   Starting MS-DOS...

2. While the text is on your screen, press and release the F8 key.

   MS-DOS displays the following text:

   MS-DOS will prompt you to confirm each CONFIG.SYS command.

   One at a time, MS-DOS displays each command in your CONFIG.SYS file, followed by a prompt. For example, when MS-DOS reaches the **dos=high** command, it displays the following prompt:

   DOS=HIGH [Y,N]?

3. Carry out all the commands in your CONFIG.SYS file by pressing Y each time you are prompted.

4. When MS-DOS finishes processing your CONFIG.SYS file, it displays the following prompt:

   Process AUTOEXEC.BAT [Y,N]?

   Press N to bypass the AUTOEXEC.BAT file.

   If your computer doesn't start, your CONFIG.SYS file is causing problems; proceed to step 5.

   If your computer starts, there is probably a problem with your AUTOEXEC.BAT file. Skip the following steps and carry out the next procedure.

5. Restart your computer by pressing CTRL+ALT+DEL. After your computer starts, MS-DOS displays the following text:

   Starting MS-DOS...

6. While the text is on your screen, press and release the F8 key.

   MS-DOS displays the following text:

   MS-DOS will prompt you to confirm each CONFIG.SYS command.

7. When MS-DOS prompts you to verify whether it should carry out each command in your CONFIG.SYS file, press Y to carry out only the following commands:

   - The command that loads HIMEM.SYS. The prompt will appear similar to the following:

     DEVICE=C:\DOS\HIMEM.SYS [Y,N]?

- The command that loads EMM386.EXE. The prompt will appear similar to the following:

```
DEVICE=C:\DOS\EMM386.EXE [Y,N]?
```

- Any commands that begin with DOS=
- Any commands that begin with SHELL=

Press N to bypass all other commands.

---

**Note**  Do not bypass any commands that load a third-party device driver which starts a disk-compression program or provides access to your hard disk. For more information, see your disk-compression or hardware documentation.

---

8. When MS-DOS finishes processing your CONFIG.SYS file, it displays the following prompt:

```
Process AUTOEXEC.BAT [Y,N]?
```

Press N to bypass your AUTOEXEC.BAT file.

If your computer starts successfully, proceed to step 9.

If your computer stops running, there may be a problem with EMM386.EXE, HIMEM.SYS, or your hardware. Do not continue with this procedure. Instead, determine if the following apply to your computer:

- If your computer uses an Adaptec ® controller card, you may not be able to use EMM386 unless you have the ADAPTEC.SYS device driver. To obtain the device driver, contact Adaptec or your user-group bulletin board (BBS) on the Association of PC User Groups (APCUG) network.

- If your computer uses an SCSI (small computer system interface) hard disk or other device, or an ESDI (enhanced system device interface), or an MCA (Micro Channel Architecture) device, you might need to use double-buffering with EMM386.EXE. For more information about adding double-buffering, restart your computer without EMM386.EXE (as described earlier in the procedure "To determine if the problem involves EMM386.EXE or the upper memory area"), and then type **help double-buffering** at the MS-DOS command prompt.

- If your computer does not have an Adaptec controller card and does not need to use double-buffering, contact Microsoft Product Support Services. For information about how to reach Microsoft Product Support Services, see the "Welcome" section at the beginning of this guide.

9. Restart your computer by pressing CTRL+ALT+DEL. Test the commands in your CONFIG.SYS file one at a time by bypassing each of them *except* the command you're testing and the following:

HIMEM.SYS
EMM386.EXE
DOS=HIGH,UMB
DOS=UMB
SHELL=

For example, to test the DEVICEHIGH=C:\DOS\EGA.SYS line in your
CONFIG.SYS file, you would press N after every prompt *except* the following:

```
DEVICE=C:\DOS\HIMEM.SYS [Y,N]?
DEVICE=C:\DOS\EMM386.EXE [Y,N]?
DOS=HIGH,UMB [Y,N]?
DOS=UMB [Y,N]?
SHELL=C:\DOS\COMMAND.COM C:\DOS\ /P [Y,N]?
DEVICEHIGH=C:\DOS\EGA.SYS [Y,N]?
```

When prompts such as these appear, you would press Y.

---

**Note**   Do not bypass any commands that load a third-party device driver which
starts a disk-compression program or provides access to your hard disk. For
more information, see your disk-compression or hardware documentation.

---

10. When MS-DOS finishes processing your CONFIG.SYS file, it displays the
    following prompt:

    ```
    Process AUTOEXEC.BAT [Y,N]?
    ```

    Press N to bypass your AUTOEXEC.BAT file.

11. If your computer runs successfully when you test a command, restart your
    computer by pressing CTRL+ALT+DEL, and then test a different command.

    When your computer stops running, the command you tested is causing a
    problem. Continue testing commands until you've tested all the commands in
    your CONFIG.SYS file.

12. After you have identified all the commands in your CONFIG.SYS file that are
    causing problems, make a backup copy of the file.

13. Open your original CONFIG.SYS file by using any text editor, and insert the
    **rem** command followed by a space in front of every command that is causing
    a problem.

14. Save your CONFIG.SYS file, and quit the text editor. Then carry out the
    following procedure.

▶ **To determine whether the problem is in your AUTOEXEC.BAT file**

1. Restart your computer by pressing CTRL+ALT+DEL.

   If MS-DOS doesn't start, your AUTOEXEC.BAT file is causing a problem; proceed to step 2.

   If MS-DOS starts, there is probably no problem with your AUTOEXEC.BAT file.

2. Open your AUTOEXEC.BAT file by using any text editor.

3. Insert the **rem** command and a space in front of every command line in your AUTOEXEC.BAT file except the **@echo off**, **prompt**, and **path** commands.

   When you are finished, your AUTOEXEC.BAT file might look similar to the following:

   ```
   @ECHO off
   prompt $p$g
   path c:\dos
   rem temp=c:\temp
   rem tmp=c:\temp
   rem init=c:\init
   rem start workstation
   rem logon johnd
   rem netime time
   rem net use 1: \\john\doe
   rem net use lpt1: \\sally\public
   rem cd \qs
   rem quickshr - - - y \qs
   rem cd \
   ```

4. To determine which command is causing a problem, remove the first **rem** command, save your AUTOEXEC.BAT file, quit the text editor, and then restart your computer by pressing CTRL+ALT+DEL. Repeat this, one command at a time, until your computer doesn't start.

   When your computer doesn't start after you have removed a **rem** command, you have identified a command that is causing a problem. Restart your computer by pressing CTRL+ALT+DEL, and then press F5 when "Starting MS-DOS..." appears on your screen. Open your AUTOEXEC.BAT file (you might have to specify the full path to your text editor). Then reinsert the **rem** command that you removed before you restarted your computer.

   Repeat step 4 until you have tested the remaining commands in your AUTOEXEC.BAT file.

5. After you identify the commands that are causing problems, make a backup copy of your AUTOEXEC.BAT file.

6.  Make sure the **rem** command is in front of every command in your AUTOEXEC.BAT file that is causing a problem.

After you identify the drivers or programs in your CONFIG.SYS and AUTOEXEC.BAT files that are causing problems, you have two options:

- If the driver or program is not essential, leave it disabled by the **rem** command, as described earlier in this section.

- Contact the manufacturer of the driver or program for assistance.

## Your computer is an IBM PS/1, and you cannot start MS-DOS.

By default, the IBM PS/1 computer uses system files located on a read-only memory (ROM) chip. Setup installs MS-DOS files on either a hard disk or a floppy disk. Therefore, before you run MS-DOS, you have to change the default startup procedure so that your computer uses system files on a disk instead of on the ROM chip.

▶ **To install MS-DOS 6 on an IBM PS/1 computer**

1.  Press and hold down both mouse buttons, and then turn on your computer. When the floppy disk drive light comes on, release the mouse buttons.

    If your mouse is not working, press and hold down the ALT and PRINT SCREEN keys, and then turn on your computer. When the floppy disk drive light comes on, release the keys.

    The System menu appears on your screen.

2.  From the System menu, choose the Your Software icon.

    A group of folders appears.

3.  Choose the DOS folder.

    A list of the files in your DOS folder appears.

4.  Double-click the CUSTOMIZ file.

    The How System Starts screen appears.

5.  Select the Try Diskette First, Then Try Fixed Disk option by using the DOWN ARROW key.

6.  Press the SPACEBAR to choose the option.

7.  Use the DOWN ARROW key to select the Read CONFIG.SYS option.

8.  Use the RIGHT ARROW key to select the From Disk option.

9.  Press the SPACEBAR to choose the option.

10.  Use the DOWN ARROW key to select the Read AUTOEXEC.BAT option.

11.  Use the RIGHT ARROW key to select the From Disk option.

12. Press the SPACEBAR to choose the option.

13. Save the system startup changes by pressing ENTER.

14. Restart your computer by pressing CTRL+ALT+DEL.

15. Run Setup again.

If this procedure does not work, contact your PS/1 computer vendor for more information.

# Using Fdisk to Configure Your Hard Disk

The following topics describe how to use the Fdisk program to configure your hard disk. For example, if you want to combine several partitions into one large partition, you must use Fdisk; there is no method for automatically combining partitions.

You should install MS-DOS 6 before using the Fdisk program. During Setup, choose to install Microsoft Backup for MS-DOS. This program will make it easier to restore your files after you've reconfigured your hard disk. After you set up MS-DOS 6, make sure you can access all the drives on your computer. Then carry out the following procedures.

In some cases, you cannot install MS-DOS 6 unless you first repartition your hard disk. If Setup displays an error message about your hard disk and you are not sure whether you should repartition your hard disk by using Fdisk, contact Microsoft Product Support Services. For information about how to reach Microsoft Product Support Services, see the "Welcome" section at the beginning of this guide.

---

**Caution**  If you are using certain types of partitions, such as Disk Manager, SpeedStor, Priam, or Everex, which replace the BIOS in interactions between DOS and your hard-disk controller, do not repartition your hard disk by using the DOS Fdisk program. For example, you might be using SpeedStor on a computer that has more than 1024 cylinders. In such a case, do not carry out the following procedures. Instead, use the same disk-partitioning program you originally used to partition your disk.

To determine whether you have a partition that was created by using one of these disk-partitioning programs, search for the following files: DMDRVR.BIN (Disk Manager), SSTOR.SYS (SpeedStor), HARDRIVE.SYS (Priam), and EVDISK.SYS (Everex). Generally, you will find **device** commands that load these files in your CONFIG.SYS file. If you need help repartitioning your hard disk or are unsure whether the BIOS is being replaced, contact the manufacturer of your original disk-partitioning program.

---

# Configuring Your Hard Disk

To configure your hard disk, you must:

- Back up the files on your hard disk.
- Make a startup disk.
- Repartition your hard disk by using Fdisk.
- Format your hard disk.
- Restore your backed-up files.

To do this, carry out all of the following procedures in order.

## Backing Up Your Files

You can back up files in several ways, depending on the operating system that is currently installed on your computer:

- If you have installed MS-DOS 6, you can use the Backup for MS-DOS program. For information about how to use Backup for MS-DOS, see "Backing Up Your Files" in the chapter "Managing Your System."

- If you have a previous version of MS-DOS on your computer, you can back up your files by using the **backup** command. You can use the MS-DOS 6 **restore** command to restore files that were backed up by using any version of MS-DOS. After you restore your files, you can run MS-DOS 6 Setup. For instructions on using the **backup** command, see the documentation that came with your previous version of DOS.

  If you make a startup disk by carrying out the procedure in "Making a Startup Disk" earlier in this chapter, the **restore** command will automatically be copied to that disk.

---

**Important**   If you have a non–MS-DOS partition on your hard disk, copy the data files on the partition to floppy disks or a network drive. For more information, see the documentation that came with your non–MS-DOS operating system or your third-party disk-partitioning program.

---

## Making a Startup Disk

For instructions on making a startup disk, see "Making a Startup Disk" in the section "Troubleshooting During Setup" earlier in this chapter.

## Using Fdisk

If you want to repartition your hard disk into one large drive, you must first delete any non–MS-DOS partitions, any logical drives, the extended partition if your computer has one, and the primary partition, then create a new primary partition and make it active. You can also repartition your hard disk so that it has more than one drive. When you configure your hard disk by using Fdisk, you:

- Delete any non–MS-DOS partitions.
- Delete the logical drives in the extended MS-DOS partition, if there are any.
- Delete the extended MS-DOS partition, if there is one.
- Delete the primary MS-DOS partition.
- Create a new primary MS-DOS partition.
- Create an extended partition and logical drives, if you want any.

If you have already set up MS-DOS 6, you can run the Fdisk program from your hard disk. If you have not yet set up MS-DOS 6, you can run the Fdisk program from your startup disk.

**Caution**  If you use Fdisk to repartition a hard disk, all the files on your original partitions will be deleted. Be sure to back up all data files on a partition before you use Fdisk.

▶ **To start Fdisk**

1. If you are starting Fdisk from your hard disk, type the following at the command prompt:

   **fdisk**

   If you are starting Fdisk from your startup disk, make sure the disk is in drive A, and then restart your computer by pressing CTRL+ALT+DEL. Then type the following at the command prompt:

   **a:fdisk**

The Fdisk Options screen appears:

```
           MS-DOS Version 6
        Fixed Disk Setup Program
   (C)Copyright Microsoft Corp. 1983 - 1993


              FDISK Options
Current fixed disk drive: 1

Choose one of the following:

1. Create DOS partition or Logical DOS Drive
2. Set active partition
3. Delete partition or Logical DOS Drive
4. Display partition information

Enter choice: [1]

Press Esc to exit FDISK
```

Each Fdisk screen displays a "Current fixed disk drive" line, followed by a number. If you have only one hard (fixed) disk drive, the number is always 1. If you have more than one hard disk drive, the number shows which drive Fdisk is currently working with. The first hard disk drive on your computer is 1, the second is 2, and so on. The "Current fixed disk drive" line refers only to physical disk drives.

**Note**  If your computer has two or more hard disks, Fdisk displays a fifth option on the Fdisk Options screen, named "Change current fixed disk drive." You can switch to another disk drive by choosing this option. Changing the current hard disk drive when you are using Fdisk doesn't change the current drive when you return to the command prompt.

2. To determine what partitions you have on your computer, choose 4, and then press ENTER.

The Display Partition Information screen appears:

```
                 Display Partition Information

Current fixed disk drive: 1

Partition  Status  Type    Volume Label  Mbytes  System  Usage
  C: 1        A    PRI DOS  MS-DOS_6        30     FAT16   43%
     2             EXT DOS                  39             57%

Total disk space is 69 Mbytes (1 Mbyte = 1048576 bytes)

The extended DOS Partition contains Logical DOS Drives.
Do you want to display the logical drive information (Y/N)...?[Y]

Press Esc to return to FDISK Options
```

---

**Note**  If you installed DoubleSpace or a third-party disk-compression program, Fdisk displays the uncompressed, not the compressed, size of the drives. Also, Fdisk might not display information about all the drives DoubleSpace, your third-party disk-compression program, or your network are using. For more information about DoubleSpace, the disk-compression program, see the chapter "Freeing Disk Space."

---

3. If your computer has logical drives, press ENTER to see logical drive information.

   The Display Logical DOS Drive Information screen appears:

```
      Display Logical DOS Drive Information

Drv Volume Label  Mbytes  System  Usage
D:                  20     FAT16    51%
E:                  19     FAT16    49%

Total Extended DOS Partition size is 39 Mbytes
(1 Mbyte=1048576 bytes)

Press Esc to continue
```

## Deleting Non–MS-DOS Partitions

With Fdisk, you can delete one or more non–MS-DOS partitions.

▶ **To delete non–MS-DOS partitions**

1. From the Fdisk Options screen, choose 3, and then press ENTER. The Delete DOS Partition or Logical DOS Drive screen appears:

```
                 Delete DOS Partition or Logical DOS Drive

Current fixed disk drive: 1

Choose one of the following:

1. Delete Primary DOS Partition
2. Delete Extended DOS Partition
3. Delete Logical DOS Drive(s) in the Extended DOS Partition
4. Delete Non-DOS Partition

Enter choice: [ ]

Press Esc to return to FDISK Options
```

2. To delete a non–MS-DOS partition, choose 4, and then press ENTER.

   The Delete Non-DOS Partition screen appears:

```
                      Delete Non-DOS Partition

Current fixed disk drive: 1

Partition  Status  Type   Volume label  Mbytes System Usage
C: 1         A     PRI DOS                 23   FAT16  33%
   2               Non-DOS                 23          33%
   3               EXT DOS                 23          33%

Total disk space is 69 Mbytes (1 Mbyte=1048576 bytes)

WARNING! Data in the deleted non-DOS partition will be lost.
What non-DOS partition do you want to delete..? [1]

Press Esc to return to FDISK Options
```

3. Choose the number of the partition you want to delete, and then press ENTER.

   A confirmation screen appears.

4. To confirm the deletion, press Y, and then press ENTER.

---

**Note**  Fdisk cannot delete certain types of non–MS-DOS partitions. If Fdisk cannot delete your non–MS-DOS partition, quit Fdisk, delete the non–MS-DOS partition by using the software you used to create it, and then restart Fdisk.

---

5. To return to the Fdisk Options screen, press ESC.

6. Repeat steps 1 through 5 if you have any other partitions that weren't created by using MS-DOS.

## Deleting Logical Drives

With Fdisk, you can delete logical drives. If you don't have an extended partition, you don't have logical drives.

▶ **To delete logical drives**

1. From the Fdisk Options screen, choose 3, and then press ENTER.

   The Delete DOS Partition or Logical DOS Drive screen appears.

2. Choose 3 again, and then press ENTER.

   The Delete Logical DOS Drive(s) in the Extended DOS Partition screen appears:

   ```
   Delete Logical DOS Drive(s) in the Extended DOS Partition

   Drv  Volume  Label  Mbytes  System Usage
   D:                     15    FAT12   65%
   E:                      8    FAT12   35%

   Total extended DOS partition size is 23 Mbytes
   (1 Mbyte=1048576 bytes)

   WARNING! Data in a deleted logical DOS drive will be lost.
   What drive do you want to delete........................? [ ]

   Press Esc to return to FDISK Options
   ```

3. Choose the letter of the drive you want to delete, and then press ENTER.

4. Type the volume label for that drive if there is one, and then press ENTER.

   A confirmation screen appears.

5. To confirm the deletion, press Y, and then press ENTER.

6. If there are other logical drives you want to delete, repeat steps 3 through 5.

7. When all logical drives have been deleted, press ESC.

   A confirmation screen appears.

8. To return to the Fdisk Options screen, press ESC again.

## Deleting an Extended MS-DOS Partition

After you have deleted any logical drives from your hard disk, you can delete your extended MS-DOS partition.

▶ **To delete an extended MS-DOS partition**

1. From the Fdisk Options screen, choose 3, and then press ENTER. The Delete DOS Partition or Logical DOS Drive screen appears.

2. Choose 2, and then press ENTER. The Delete Extended DOS Partition screen appears:

```
                    Delete Extended DOS Partition


Current fixed disk drive: 1

Partition  Status    Type    Volume Label  Mbytes  System  Usage
C: 1         A     PRI DOS                   23     FAT16    33%
   2               EXT DOS                   23              33%


Total disk space is 69 Mbytes (1 Mbyte=1048576 bytes)

WARNING! Data in the deleted extended DOS partition will be lost.
Do you wish to continue (Y/N)........................? [N]


Press Esc to return to FDISK Options
```

3. To delete the extended MS-DOS partition, press Y, and then press ENTER.

4. To return to the Fdisk Options screen, press ESC.

## Deleting a Primary MS-DOS Partition

After you have deleted the extended partition on your hard disk, you can delete the primary MS-DOS partition.

▶ **To delete the primary MS-DOS partition**

1. From the Fdisk Options screen, choose 3, and then press ENTER. The Delete DOS Partition or Logical DOS Drive screen appears.

2. Choose 1, and then press ENTER. The Delete Primary DOS Partition screen appears:

```
                    Delete Primary DOS Partition


Current fixed disk drive: 1

Partition  Status    Type    Volume Label  Mbytes  System  Usage
C: 1         A     PRI DOS                   23     FAT16    33%


Total disk space is 69 Mbytes (1 Mbyte=1048576 bytes)

WARNING! Data in the deleted primary DOS partition will be lost.
What primary partition do you want to delete..? [1]


Press Esc to return to FDISK Options
```

3. To delete your primary partition, press ENTER. The following prompt appears on the Delete Primary DOS Partition screen:

```
Enter volume label..........................? [            ]
```

4. Type the volume label if there is one, and then press ENTER.

A confirmation screen appears.

5. To confirm the deletion, press Y, and then press ENTER.

6. To return to the Fdisk Options screen, press ESC.

## Creating a Primary MS-DOS Partition

After you have deleted your primary MS-DOS partition, you can create a new primary MS-DOS partition.

▶ **To create a primary MS-DOS partition**

1. In the Fdisk Options screen, press ENTER. The Create DOS Partition or Logical DOS Drive screen appears:

```
          Create DOS Partition or Logical DOS Drive

Current fixed disk drive: 1

Choose one of the following:

1. Create Primary DOS Partition
2. Create Extended DOS Partition
3. Create Logical DOS Drive(s) in the Extended DOS Partition

Enter choice: [1]

Press Esc to return to FDISK Options
```

2. Press ENTER. The Create Primary DOS Partition screen appears:

```
          Create Primary DOS Partition

Current fixed disk drive: 1

Do you wish to use the maximum available size
for a primary DOS partition and make the partition
active (Y/N)..........................?[Y]

Press Esc to return to FDISK Options
```

3. If you want the partition to be the maximum size, press ENTER. Then insert your startup disk in drive A, and press any key. Skip to "Formatting Your Hard Disk" later in this section.

If you don't want the partition to be the maximum size, press N, and then press ENTER. Another Create Primary DOS Partition screen appears:

```
               Create Primary DOS Partition
Current fixed disk drive: 1

Total disk space is 69 Mbytes (1Mbyte=1048576 bytes)
Maximum space available for partition is 69 Mbytes (100%)

Enter partition size in Mbytes or percent of disk space (%) to
create a Primary DOS Partition...............................:[69]

No partitions defined

Press Esc to return to FDISK Options
```

4. Type the partition size you want, and then press ENTER.

   You can specify the partition size as a percentage of disk space or in megabytes of disk space. If you specify a percentage of disk space, include a percent (%) sign after the number.

5. Press ESC to return to the Fdisk Options screen.

6. To make the primary MS-DOS partition active, choose 2, and then press ENTER. The Set Active Partition screen appears:

```
                 Set Active Partition
Current fixed disk drive: 1

Partition  Status   Type    Volume Label   Mbytes   System   Usage
  C: 1              PRI DOS                    59    UNKNOWN   85%

Total disk space is 69 Mbytes (1 Mbyte=1048576)

Enter the number of the partition you want to make
active..........:[ ]

Press Esc to return to FDISK Options
```

7. To specify the partition you want to make active, type its number, and then press ENTER.

8. Press ESC to return to the Fdisk Options screen.

9. If you want to create an extended partition, continue with the following procedure.

   If you don't want to create an extended partition, press ESC to quit Fdisk. Then insert your startup disk in drive A, and press any key.

# Creating an Extended MS-DOS Partition and Logical Drives

If you have not allocated all the space on your disk drive to the primary MS-DOS partition, you can create an extended MS-DOS partition and logical drives.

▶ **To create an extended MS-DOS partition and logical drives**

1. In the Fdisk Options screen, press ENTER.

2. Choose 2, and then press ENTER. The Create Extended DOS Partition screen appears:

```
                    Create Extended DOS Partition
Current fixed disk drive: 1

Partition    Status    Type    Volume Label    Mbytes    System    Usage
 C: 1          A      PRI DOS                     59      UNKNOWN    85%


Total disk space is 69 Mbytes (1 Mbyte=1048576 bytes)
Maximum space available for partition is 10 Mbytes (15%)

Enter partition size in Mbytes or percent of
disk space (%) to create an Extended DOS
Partition............................:[10]

Press Esc to return to FDISK Options
```

3. Type the partition size you want, and then press ENTER.

   You can specify the partition size as a percentage of disk space or in megabytes of disk space. If you specify a percentage of disk space, include a percent (%) sign after the number.

4. Press ESC. The Create Logical DOS Drive(s) in the Extended DOS Partition screen appears:

```
Create Logical DOS Drives(s) in the Extended DOS Partition

No logical drives defined

Total Extended DOS partition size is 9 Mbytes
(1 MBytes=1048576 bytes)
Maximum space available for logical drive
is 9 Mbytes (100%)

Enter logical drive size in Mbytes or percent
of disk space (%)...[9]

Press Esc to return to FDISK Options
```

5. Type the logical drive size you want, and then press ENTER.

You can specify the logical drive size as a percentage of disk space or in megabytes of disk space. If you specify a percentage of disk space, include a percent (%) sign after the number.

6. If you want to create another logical drive, repeat step 5.

7. When you finish creating logical drives, press ESC.

8. To quit Fdisk, press ESC.

9. Insert your startup disk in drive A, and then press any key.

## Formatting Your Hard Disk

You cannot use your hard disk until you format it.

▶   **To format the drive(s) on your hard disk**

1. Make sure your startup disk is in drive A.

2. At the command prompt, type the following:

   **format** *drive***:**

   For *drive*, type the letter of the drive you want to format.

   If you are formatting drive C, copy system files to your hard disk by typing the following at the command prompt:

   **format c: /s**

   A warning message appears.

3. To proceed with formatting, press Y, and then press ENTER.

4. When formatting is complete, type a volume label if you want one, and then press ENTER.

5. If you have any other drives to format, repeat steps 2 through 4.

6. Remove floppy disks from all floppy disk drives, and then restart your computer by pressing CTRL+ALT+DEL.

## Restoring Your Files

If you backed up your files by using Backup for MS-DOS, carry out Procedure 1. If you used the **backup** command from a previous version of DOS, carry out Procedure 2.

▶   **Procedure 1   To restore your files if you used Backup for MS-DOS**

1. Insert Setup Disk 1 in drive A or B, and then type the following at the command prompt:

   **a:setup**

   or

   **b:setup**

2. Make sure you choose to install Backup for MS-DOS.

   For example, if you backed up your files by using Backup for MS-DOS, choose this option during Setup.

3. When Setup is complete, start Backup for MS-DOS by typing **msbackup** at the command prompt.

4. Restore your files. For instructions on using Backup, see "Backing Up Your Files" in the chapter "Managing Your System."

5. Restart your computer by pressing CTRL+ALT+DEL.

▶ **Procedure 2    To restore your files if you used the backup command from a previous version of DOS**

1. Make sure the startup disk is in drive A or B.

2. To restore the files to drive C, type the following at the command prompt:

   **restore a: c:\*.* /s**

   or

   **restore b: c:\*.* /s**

   To restore files to a drive other than C, type the following at the command prompt:

   **restore a:** *drive***:\*.* /s**

   or

   **restore b:** *drive***:\*.* /s**

   For *drive*, type the letter of the drive to which you want to restore files.

3. Follow the instructions on your screen.

4. When you have finished restoring your files, insert Setup Disk 1 in drive A or B, and then start Setup by typing the following at the command prompt:

   **a:setup**

   or

   **b:setup**

5. Follow the instructions on your screen.

# Troubleshooting While Running MS-DOS

The following topics explain how to solve common problems you might encounter while running MS-DOS 6. If you encounter a problem during Setup, see "Troubleshooting During Setup" earlier in this chapter.

If your computer stops running and you cannot restart it without its stopping repeatedly, carry out the following procedure to start your computer. Carrying out this procedure causes your computer to bypass your CONFIG.SYS and AUTOEXEC.BAT files when it starts.

▶ **To restart your computer**

1. Press CTRL+ALT+DEL. If your computer does not respond, wait at least 10 seconds, turn the power off, wait at least 30 seconds, and then turn the power back on.

   After your computer starts, MS-DOS displays the following text:

   ```
   Starting MS-DOS...
   ```

2. While the text is on your screen, press and release the F5 key.

   MS-DOS displays the following text:

   ```
   MS-DOS is bypassing your CONFIG.SYS and AUTOEXEC.BAT files.
   ```

   Then a command prompt appears on your screen.

   If this procedure does not work, contact Microsoft Product Support Services. For infomation about how to reach Microsoft Product Support Services, see the "Welcome" section at the beginning of this guide.

Your computer will start with a basic configuration instead of your usual configuration. Therefore, some parts of your system might not work as they usually do. For more information, see the chapter "Configuring Your System."

# A message states that HIMEM.SYS is missing or not loaded.

The following symptoms indicate that the HIMEM.SYS memory manager did not load properly:

- MS-DOS displays a message that HIMEM.SYS is not loaded when you start your computer, or when MS-DOS tries to load SMARTDRV.EXE or EMM386.EXE.

- MS-DOS displays a message that HIMEM.SYS is missing when you try to start Windows.

To ensure that HIMEM.SYS loads properly, carry out the following procedure.

▶ **To load HIMEM.SYS properly**

1. To confirm that HIMEM.SYS did not load properly, start the Microsoft Diagnostics program by typing the following at the command prompt:

   **msd**

2. Choose the Memory option by pressing M. If Microsoft Diagnostics does not display an "XMS Information" section on the right side of your screen, HIMEM.SYS did not load properly.

3. Choose the OK button by pressing ENTER.

4. Quit Microsoft Diagnostics by pressing ALT, F, X.

   For more information about Microsoft Diagnostics, type **help msd** at the command prompt.

5. Open your CONFIG.SYS file by using any text editor.

6. Determine whether your CONFIG.SYS file contains a **device** command for HIMEM.SYS. The command should appear before any other device commands and should look similar to the following:

   ```
   device=c:\dos\himem.sys
   ```

   If your CONFIG.SYS file does not contain this command, add it. If your MS-DOS files are in a directory other than DOS, substitute its name for "DOS" in the **device** command line for HIMEM.SYS.

7. Add the **/cpuclock:on** and **/v** switches to the **device** command for HIMEM.SYS. The command should now appear similar to the following:

   ```
   device=c:\dos\himem.sys /cpuclock:on /v
   ```

8. Save your CONFIG.SYS file, and then quit the text editor.

9. Restart your computer by pressing CTRL+ALT+DEL.

   To determine whether HIMEM.SYS is now loaded properly, repeat steps 1 through 4. If Microsoft Diagnostics displays XMS information, HIMEM.SYS started successfully. If you still don't see this information, continue to step 10.

10. Open your CONFIG.SYS file again. Locate the **device** command for HIMEM.SYS, and add the **/machine** switch to it. The **/machine** switch specifies the type of computer you have. The switch should be followed by a colon (:) and your machine number. (To determine which machine number you should use, see the table following this procedure.) For example, the following **device** command specifies that your computer is a Toshiba 1600, 1200XE, or 5100 (machine number 7):

    ```
    device=c:\dos\himem.sys /cpuclock:on /v /machine:7
    ```

11. Save your CONFIG.SYS file, and then quit the text editor.

12. Restart your computer by pressing CTRL+ALT+DEL.

    To determine whether HIMEM.SYS is now loaded properly, repeat steps 1 through 4. If Microsoft Diagnostics displays XMS information, HIMEM.SYS started successfully. If you still don't see this information, repeat steps 10 through 12, specifying a different machine number.

    If your computer stops running when you are experimenting with machine numbers, carry out the following procedure:

▶ **To restart your computer and specify a different machine number**

1. Restart your computer by pressing CTRL+ALT+DEL.

   After your computer starts, MS-DOS displays the following text:

   `Starting MS-DOS...`

2. While the text is on your screen, press and release the F8 key.

   MS-DOS displays the following text:

   `MS-DOS will prompt you to confirm each CONFIG.SYS command...`

3. MS-DOS prompts you to confirm each line in your CONFIG.SYS file.

   Carry out each command by pressing Y after the prompt, *except* when you are prompted for the HIMEM.SYS command. When you are prompted for this command, press N.

4. When MS-DOS finishes processing your CONFIG.SYS file, it displays the following prompt:

   `Process AUTOEXEC.BAT [Y,N]?`

   Press Y to process your AUTOEXEC.BAT file.

5. Open your CONFIG.SYS file by using any text editor, and carry out step 10 of the previous procedure to specify a different machine number.

6. Save your CONFIG.SYS file, quit the text editor, and then restart your computer by pressing CTRL+ALT+DEL.

   You might need to try several machine numbers before you identify the one that works for your computer.

The following table lists machine types in alphabetic order and shows the corresponding number to specify with the **/machine** switch.

| Machine type | Number | Machine type | Number |
|---|---|---|---|
| Abacus 386 | 1 | IBM PS/2 | 2 |
| Acer 1100 | 6 | Intel 301z or 302 | 8 |
| AT&T ® 6300 Plus | 5 | JDR 386/33 | 1 |
| Bull Micral 60 | 16 | OPT 386–25 motherboard | 1 |
| Chaplet | 1 | Pak 386SX | 1 |
| CompuAdd ® 386 systems | 1 or 8 | PC Limited | 4 |
| CSS Labs | 12 | PC 380/33C, PC 350/33C, or PC 300/33C BIOS revision 1.14 | 2 |

| Machine type | Number | Machine type | Number |
|---|---|---|---|
| Datamedia 386/486 | 2 | Philips ® | 13 |
| Everex AT ® Plus 1800 | 1 | Phoenix Cascade BIOS | 3, 1, or 8 |
| Everex Notebook ELX | 1 | Toshiba 1600 and 1200XE | 7 |
| Excel Computer Systems | 13 | Toshiba 5100 | 7 |
| Hitachi ® HL500C | 8 | Tulip SX | 9 |
| HP ® Vectra ® | 14 | Unisys PowerPort | 2 |
| HP Vectra (A and A+) | 4 | WYSE 12.5 MHz 286 | 8 |
| IBM PC/AT | 1, 11, 12, or 13 | Zenith Data Systems ZBIOS | 10 |

If your computer is not on the list, you are not sure which number to use, or the machine number for your computer doesn't solve the problem, try these machine numbers in the following order: 1, 11, 12, 13, 8, 2 through 7, 9 through 10, 14 through 16.

# You installed a hardware device, and your computer stopped working correctly.

If you installed a new network card or a card for a device, the EMM386 memory manager may be using the same memory address as the new card. Symptoms of a conflict with EMM386 include the following:

- Your computer stops responding when you restart it.

- MS-DOS won't load EMM386.EXE. To determine whether EMM386.EXE is loaded, type **emm386** at the command prompt. If the "EMM386 driver not installed" message appears on your screen, EMM386.EXE didn't load.

  If "EMM386 Active" appears after you type **emm386** at the command prompt, the problem might be that the device is not configured correctly for use with your computer. For more information, contact the manufacturer of the device.

If your computer stops responding when you restart it or if EMM386.EXE doesn't load, use the MemMaker program to create the command line for EMM386.EXE. To do this, carry out the following procedure.

▶ **To make sure EMM386 and another device driver or program don't conflict**

1. If your computer stops responding when you restart it, press CTRL+ALT+DEL. If your computer runs when you restart it, skip to step 5.

   After your computer starts, MS-DOS displays the following text:

   `Starting MS-DOS...`

2. While the text is on your screen, press and release the F8 key.

   MS-DOS displays the following text:

   `MS-DOS will prompt you to confirm each CONFIG.SYS command.`

   One at a time, MS-DOS displays each command in your CONFIG.SYS file followed by a prompt. For example, when MS-DOS reaches the **dos=high** command, it displays the following prompt:

   `DOS=HIGH [Y,N]?`

3. Carry out all the commands in your CONFIG.SYS file by pressing Y each time you are prompted, *except* when you are prompted for the EMM386.EXE command. When a prompt such as the following appears, press N to bypass it:

   `DEVICE=C:\DOS\EMM386.EXE [Y,N]?`

4. When MS-DOS finishes processing your CONFIG.SYS file, it displays the following prompt:

   `Process AUTOEXEC.BAT [Y,N]?`

   Press Y to process your AUTOEXEC.BAT file.

5. Start MemMaker by typing the following at the command prompt:

   **memmaker**

   When the Welcome screen appears, press ENTER.

6. When the second MemMaker screen appears, press the SPACEBAR to select Custom Setup, and then press ENTER.

7. Continue with the MemMaker program until the Advanced Options screen appears. Then press the SPACEBAR to change the "No" beside "Specify which drivers and TSRs to include during optimization?" to "Yes."

8. Press the DOWN ARROW key until the "Yes" beside "Keep current EMM386 exclusions and inclusions?" is highlighted. Then press the SPACEBAR to select "No," and press ENTER.

9. If you use Windows, MemMaker might prompt you to provide more information. If it does, follow the instructions on your screen.

10. One by one, MemMaker prompts you to include device drivers and programs in the optimization process. Press ENTER each time you are prompted.

11. Follow the instructions on your screen.

For more information about using MemMaker, see the chapter "Making More Memory Available," or type **help memmaker** at the command prompt.

If EMM386 still doesn't work, contact Microsoft Product Support Services. For information about how to reach Microsoft Product Support Services, see the "Welcome" section at the beginning of this guide.

# MS-DOS Shell won't start or switch between programs.

MS-DOS Shell will not start or switch between programs if the wrong video files were copied to your computer during Setup, or if your current video or MS-DOS Shell files are corrupt.

If you have problems using MS-DOS Shell, reinstall it by carrying out the following procedure.

▶ **To reinstall MS-DOS Shell**

1. Make a backup copy of your DOSSHELL.INI file. For example, if the file is in your DOS directory, type the following at the command prompt:

   **copy c:\dos\dosshell.ini c:\dos\dosshell.bak**

2. Insert Setup Disk 1 in drive A or B, and then type the following at the command prompt:

   **a:setup /q**

   or

   **b:setup /q**

   The **/q** switch causes Setup to copy MS-DOS files directly to your hard disk and bypasses the standard Setup program.

3. Follow the instructions on your screen. After Setup is finished, rename the backup copy of your DOSSHELL.INI file to its original name. For example, type the following at the command prompt:

   **copy c:\dos\dosshell.bak c:\dos\dosshell.ini**

# You receive the "Check the Mouse Compatibility List" message when you start MS-DOS Shell.

This section explains what to do if you receive the following message the first time you start MS-DOS Shell:

```
Check the Mouse Compatibility List.

The mouse driver on your computer is
version <x.xx>.

See 'Diagnosing and Solving Problems' for a
list of mouse drivers that are compatible with
MS-DOS 6, and make sure your driver is compatible.

If your mouse driver is not on the list, and
you have problems using your mouse, contact
your mouse vendor for an updated driver.

    <Disable Mouse>     <Use Mouse Anyway>
```

▶ **To make your mouse driver compatible with MS-DOS Shell**

1. Note which version number is displayed in the message.

2. Consult the table following this procedure to determine whether your mouse driver is compatible with MS-DOS Shell.

3. If your mouse driver is compatible, choose the Use Mouse Anyway button at the bottom of your screen.

   If your mouse driver is incompatible with MS-DOS Shell (according to the following list), contact your vendor for an updated mouse driver.

| Type of mouse | Compatible versions |
| --- | --- |
| Microsoft | Your mouse driver is outdated. Install the updated MOUSE.COM file (version 8.20) included with MS-DOS 6 by carrying out the procedure following this table. |
| Logitech ™ | Your mouse driver is incompatible, no matter what number is displayed. The number in the message differs from the actual version number of your mouse driver. Check your mouse package or startup message to determine which version you have. If you have a version earlier than 5.01, contact Logitech for an updated driver. |
| Genius | If you have a Genius mouse, MS-DOS Shell displays "version unknown" or a random number. Version 9.06 or later is compatible. Check your mouse package or startup message to determine which version you have. |

| Type of mouse | Compatible versions |
| --- | --- |
| IBM PS/2 ® | Your mouse driver is outdated. Install the updated MOUSE.COM file (version 8.20) included with MS-DOS 6 by carrying out the procedure following this table. |
| Hewlett-Packard | Your mouse driver is incompatible. Version 7.04 or later is compatible. Contact your vendor for an updated driver. |
| Mouse Systems | If you have a Mouse Systems mouse, MS-DOS Shell displays "version unknown" or a random number. Version 7.01 or later is compatible. Check your mouse package or startup message to determine which version you have. |
| ATI | If you have an ATI mouse, MS-DOS Shell displays "version unknown" or a random number. Version 2.0 or later is compatible. Check your mouse package or startup message to determine which version you have. |

▶ **To update your Microsoft or Microsoft-compatible mouse**

1. Make sure the MOUSE.COM file is in the directory that contains your MS-DOS files. If the MOUSE.COM file is not in that directory, expand the file from one of the Setup disks. To determine which Setup disk the file is on, open the PACKING.LST file on Setup Disk 1 by using any text editor. The PACKING.LST file also contains instructions on using the **expand** command to expand the file.

2. Open your CONFIG.SYS file by using any text editor.

3. Insert the **rem** command and a space in front of any command line that loads the MOUSE.SYS device driver. The modified command line should look similar to the following.

   ```
   rem device=c:\dos\mouse.sys
   ```

4. Save the file, and then open your AUTOEXEC.BAT file by using any text editor.

5. Add the following command line:

   ```
   mouse.com
   ```

6. Save the file, and then quit the text editor.

7. Restart your computer by pressing CTRL+ALT+DEL.

# You need to restore files you backed up by using an earlier version of the backup command.

If you need to restore files you backed up by using the **backup** command from an earlier version of MS-DOS, you can restore them by using the MS-DOS 6 **restore** command.

▶ **To restore files you backed up by using an earlier version of the backup command**

1. Insert the floppy disk that contains the backed-up files in drive A or B.

2. To restore the files to drive C, type the following at the command prompt:

   **restore a: c:\\*.\* /s**

   or

   **restore b: c:\\*.\* /s**

   To restore files to a drive other than C, substitute the drive letter you want for the "C" in the preceding example.

3. Follow the instructions on your screen.

# An MS-DOS–based program displays an out-of-memory message.

If an MS-DOS–based program such as Anti-Virus, Backup, or Undelete displays an out-of-memory message, you can make more memory available by carrying out one of the following procedures.

If your computer is an 80386 or 80486, carry out Procedure 1. If your computer is an 80286, carry out Procedure 2.

▶ **Procedure 1   To prevent out-of-memory errors by using MemMaker**

- Optimize your computer's use of memory by running the MemMaker program. To start MemMaker, type the following at the command prompt:

  **memmaker**

  For more information about using MemMaker, see the chapter "Making More Memory Available," or type **help memmaker** at the command prompt.

  If out-of-memory messages continue to appear when you try to run MS-DOS programs, carry out Procedure 2.

▶ **Procedure 2   To prevent out-of-memory errors by not loading other programs**

1. Restart your computer by pressing CTRL+ALT+DEL. After your computer starts, MS-DOS displays the following text:

   Starting MS-DOS...

2. While the text is on your screen, press and release the F8 key.

   MS-DOS displays the following text:

   ```
   MS-DOS will prompt you to confirm each CONFIG.SYS command.
   ```

   One at a time, MS-DOS displays each command in your CONFIG.SYS file, followed by a prompt. For example, when MS-DOS reaches the **dos=high** command, it displays the following prompt:

   ```
   DOS=HIGH [Y,N]?
   ```

3. Bypass any program or device driver you don't need when running your MS-DOS–based application. To bypass a program or device driver, press N when you are prompted.

   For example, if your CONFIG.SYS file loads your mouse driver and you don't need a mouse with your program, press N when you are prompted to load the mouse device driver.

4. When MS-DOS finishes processing your CONFIG.SYS file, it displays the following prompt:

   ```
   Process AUTOEXEC.BAT [Y,N]?
   ```

   Press Y to process your AUTOEXEC.BAT file.

5. If out-of-memory messages continue to appear when you try to run MS-DOS programs, repeat steps 1 through 4 and bypass additional programs or device drivers. If you don't need the commands or programs specified in your AUTOEXEC.BAT file, press N when you are prompted to process the file.

   If this procedure works, you might want to create an alternate startup configuration to use when you run your MS-DOS–based program. For instructions on how to create multiple startup configurations, see the chapter "Configuring Your System."

C H A P T E R    9

# Customizing for International Use

You can use the language conventions, keyboard layouts, and character sets of 24 countries or regions by changing settings in MS-DOS. Using MS-DOS commands, you can change:

- The country-specific conventions for displaying dates, times, and currency; conventions that determine the order in which characters are sorted; and conventions that determine which characters can be used in filenames. You change these conventions by using the **country** command in your CONFIG.SYS file. For more information, see the following section, "Changing Country-Specific Conventions."

- The layout of characters on your keyboard to fit the standard keyboard layout for another language. You do this by using the **keyb** command, which starts the Keyb program. For more information about changing your keyboard layout, see "Changing the Keyboard Layout" later in this chapter.

- The character set (code page), so you can type and display the characters of other languages. For more information about changing the character set, see "Changing Character Sets" later in this chapter.

MS-DOS can use language conventions, keyboard arrangements, and character sets for the following languages (countries):

| | | |
|---|---|---|
| Belgian | German (Germany) | Portuguese (Brazil) |
| Canadian-French | German (Switzerland) | Portuguese (Portugal) |
| Croatian | Hungarian | Serbian/Yugoslavian |
| Czech | English (International) | Slovak |
| Danish | English (United Kingdom) | Slovenian |
| Dutch | English (United States) | Spanish (Latin America) |
| Finnish | Italian | Spanish (Spain) |
| French (France) | Norwegian | Swedish |
| French (Switzerland) | Polish | |

# Changing Country-Specific Conventions

When you change languages, you may need to change the country settings on your computer. The country settings specify the following:

- How the date and time are displayed
- Which symbol is used for currency
- The sort order used when alphabetizing files
- The characters that can be used in filenames and directory names

By default, MS-DOS uses the United States country setting. To change the country setting, include a **country** command in your CONFIG.SYS file. When you use the **country** command, you must include a three-digit country code to specify which conventions you want to use. (Usually, the country code is the country's international long-distance telephone code preceded by a zero (0).) For a list of country codes, see "Country, Keyboard, and Character Set Codes" later in this chapter. For information about changing your CONFIG.SYS file, see the chapter "Configuring Your System."

You can use the **country** command regardless of whether you have loaded any character sets. Information about country conventions is stored in the COUNTRY.SYS file, which is usually located in the directory that contains your MS-DOS files.

For example, the country code for Spain is 034. To use the conventions of Spain, you would add the following command to your CONFIG.SYS file:

**country=034,,c:\dos\country.sys**

Note that there are two commas separating the country code and the path to the COUNTRY.SYS file.

For more information about the **country** command, type **help country** at the command prompt.

# Changing the Keyboard Layout

If you are using the language of another country or region, you may need to change your keyboard layout. For example, if you change from United States English to Latin American Spanish, four characters are added to your keyboard (one letter and three symbols), and several characters change locations.

The **keyb** command enables your keyboard to emulate the keyboards that are used with other languages. You do not have to physically exchange your keyboard for a keyboard that is designed for the language you want to use. If you can touch-type in the language you want to switch your keyboard to, this solution is ideal.

However, if you are accustomed to looking at keys while you type, changing your keyboard layout can be confusing. After you change your keyboard layout, pressing a key may no longer cause the character that is printed on the key to appear on your screen. To orient yourself to a new keyboard layout, see the keyboard illustrations in the appendix "Keyboard Layouts and Character Sets."

You can specify the **keyb** command in your AUTOEXEC.BAT file or at the command prompt. You can use the **keyb** command regardless of whether you have changed any other country-specific settings.

---

**Note**  If you are changing both the keyboard layout and the character set, you must load the character set before you change the keyboard layout. If you load the character set after changing the keyboard layout, you will receive an error message. For more information about loading character sets, see the following section, "Changing Character Sets."

---

When you use the **keyb** command, you must include a keyboard code to specify which keyboard you want to use. For a list of keyboard codes, see "Country, Keyboard, and Character Set Codes" later in this chapter. Keyboard codes are stored in the KEYBOARD.SYS file, which is usually located in the directory that contains your MS-DOS files.

For example, suppose you have loaded the preferred character set for Italy and now you want to change to the Italian keyboard layout. Suppose your KEYBOARD.SYS file is located in your C:\DOS directory. You would type the following in your AUTOEXEC.BAT file or at the command prompt:

**keyb it,,c:\dos\keyboard.sys**

Note that two commas separate the keyboard code and the path to the KEYBOARD.SYS file.

If you change keyboard layouts, you can switch back to the United States keyboard layout by pressing CTRL+ALT+F1. To return to the keyboard layout you were using, press CTRL+ALT+F2.

For illustrations of available keyboard layouts, see the appendix "Keyboard Layouts and Character Sets" later in this guide. For more information about the **keyb** command, type **help keyb** at the command prompt.

# Changing Character Sets

MS-DOS can use up to 256 different characters when you are displaying, printing, and working with text. Different languages use different combinations of these characters. The exact set of characters used at one time is known as a *character set* or *code page*.

By default, MS-DOS uses the character set that comes with your computer. This character set is called a *hardware character set*. Your computer includes a hardware character set for your keyboard and your monitor. Generally, the hardware character set in the United States is 437.

If you use only the characters provided by your hardware character set, you do not need to load additional character sets. If you want to use characters that are not provided by your hardware character set, load one of the MS-DOS character sets included with MS-DOS. An MS-DOS character set is a set of 256 characters that is stored in a character set information (.CPI) file. You can use an MS-DOS character set instead of your hardware character set by including several commands in your CONFIG.SYS and AUTOEXEC.BAT files.

---

**Note**  Monochrome and CGA monitors and many printers cannot use MS-DOS character sets. See your hardware documentation to determine whether MS-DOS character sets are supported.

---

MS-DOS provides six character sets that you can use in addition to, or instead of, the hardware character set that comes with your computer. All MS-DOS character sets have the first 128 characters in common. These are standard ASCII characters. However, each character set has a different set of national language characters.

Before you use a character set, you must load it into memory. You can load more than one character set into memory, but only one character set can be active at a time. If you load one or more MS-DOS character sets, you can easily switch between them and your hardware character set.

For each of the countries supported by MS-DOS, you can use two MS-DOS character sets: a preferred character set and an alternate character set, each of which is represented by a number. If you want to change the character set, you must use one of the two character set numbers that are valid for the new country setting.

The following table lists the six MS-DOS character sets:

| Language | Number | Description |
|----------|--------|-------------|
| Canadian-French | 863 | Includes characters for English and Canadian-French |
| Multilingual (Latin I) | 850 | Includes characters for most of the languages that use the Latin alphabet |
| Nordic | 865 | Includes characters for English, Norwegian, and Danish |
| Portuguese | 860 | Includes characters for English and the Portuguese of Portugal |

| Language | Number | Description |
|----------|--------|-------------|
| English | 437 | Includes characters for English and most other European languages |
| Slavic (Latin II) | 852 | Includes characters for the Slavic languages that use the Latin alphabet |

See the appendix "Keyboard Layouts and Character Sets" for tables that list the characters in each character set.

# An Overview of the Procedures for Changing Character Sets

The following is an overview of the procedures you must carry out to change character sets. Each step includes a reference to more detailed instructions on how to complete it.

▶ **To change character sets**

1. In your CONFIG.SYS file, include a **device** command that loads the DISPLAY.SYS device driver. The DISPLAY.SYS device driver prepares MS-DOS to display the characters in a character set on your monitor. For instructions on adding this command to your CONFIG.SYS file, see the following section, "Preparing Your Monitor for Character Sets."

2. In your AUTOEXEC.BAT file, include the **nlsfunc** command, which starts the Nlsfunc program. Nlsfunc is a memory-resident program that loads country-specific information for national language support (NLS). For instructions on loading the Nlsfunc program, see "Loading National Language Support for Character Sets" later in this chapter.

3. In your AUTOEXEC.BAT file, include the **mode con cp prep** command, which loads the character set (code page) information (.CPI) file. For instructions on loading the character set information file, see "Loading a Character Set into Memory" later in this chapter.

4. Use the **chcp** command to make the character set active. You can specify this command in your AUTOEXEC.BAT file or at the command prompt. For instructions on making the character set active, see "Making a Character Set Active" later in this chapter.

---

**Note**  If you want to change your keyboard layout, specify the **keyb** command after you have changed the character set. If you want to change country-specific conventions, you can use the **country** command either before or after you load the character set. For more information about the **keyb** command, see "Changing the Keyboard Layout" earlier in this chapter. For more information about the **country** command, see "Changing Country-Specific Conventions" earlier in this chapter.

---

# Preparing Your Monitor for Character Sets

To display MS-DOS character sets on an EGA, VGA, or LCD monitor, you must install the DISPLAY.SYS device driver. If you have an EGA or VGA monitor, you can load up to six MS-DOS character sets. If you have an LCD monitor, you can load only one MS-DOS character set. If you have a monochrome or CGA monitor, you cannot display MS-DOS character sets.

You load the DISPLAY.SYS device driver by including a **device** command in your CONFIG.SYS file. The **device** command line that loads the DISPLAY.SYS device driver provides the following information:

- The kind of monitor you have. You can specify EGA or LCD. The EGA parameter supports both EGA and VGA monitors. If you omit this parameter, MS-DOS checks your hardware to determine what kind of monitor you have.

- The hardware character set your computer uses. The most common hardware character set is the one for the United States (437). If you omit this parameter, you will be unable to switch between your hardware character set and your MS-DOS character set.

- The number of MS-DOS character sets you want to use. For a VGA or EGA monitor, this number can be 1 through 6. For an LCD monitor, it must be 1. If you omit this parameter, the default number, 1, is used. This parameter doesn't specify which character set to use; it simply reserves space for it.

For example, suppose the DISPLAY.SYS file is in the C:\DOS directory, and your VGA monitor uses hardware character set 437. To prepare your monitor for one MS-DOS character set, you would include the following command in your CONFIG.SYS file:

**device=c:\dos\display.sys con=(ega,437,1)**

The part of the command line that begins with **device=** specifies that MS-DOS should load the device driver named DISPLAY.SYS, which is located in the C:\DOS directory. The part of the command line that begins with **con=** specifies the type of monitor and hardware character set you have and how many MS-DOS character sets you want to reserve space for. Note that you specify EGA even though you have a VGA monitor.

---

**Note**  If you load both DISPLAY.SYS and a third-party keyboard and monitor (console) driver (such as NANSI.SYS), the **device** command that loads the third-party driver must appear before the **device** command that loads DISPLAY.SYS in your CONFIG.SYS file. Otherwise, the third-party driver may disable DISPLAY.SYS.

---

For more information about loading the DISPLAY.SYS device driver, type **help display.sys** at the command prompt.

# Loading National Language Support for Character Sets

MS-DOS cannot recognize and switch between character sets unless you load the Nlsfunc program into memory. To do this, include the following command in your AUTOEXEC.BAT file:

**nlsfunc**

The **nlsfunc** command must appear before any commands that load or switch character sets.

For more information about the **nlsfunc** command, type **help nlsfunc** at the command prompt.

# Loading a Character Set into Memory

Loading the DISPLAY.SYS device driver prepares your monitor to display a character set, but does not load the character set you want to use. To load a character set, use the **mode con cp prep** command (**con** specifies that you want to load a character set for your console, or monitor and keyboard, and **cp prep** specifies that you want to prepare a code page, or character set). The **mode con cp prep** command retrieves the character set you want from the code page information (.CPI) file in which it is stored and loads it into memory. After the character set is in memory, you can make it active and use it.

For example, to load character set 850 from C:\DOS\EGA.CPI into memory, type the following command at the command prompt or in your AUTOEXEC.BAT file:

**mode con cp prep=((850)c:\dos\ega.cpi)**

This command line specifies the following:

- The code(s) of the character set(s) you want to load—in this case, 850. You can load as many character sets as you reserved space for in the **device** command line that loads the DISPLAY.SYS device driver (included in your CONFIG.SYS file). Use parentheses around the code(s) for the character set(s) you want to load. For a list of character set codes, see "Country, Keyboard, and Character Set Codes" later in this chapter.

- The file in which the character set is stored—in this case, C:\DOS\EGA.CPI. All character set (code page) information files have a .CPI extension. The EGA and VGA character sets are stored in the EGA.CPI file; the LCD character sets are stored in the LCD.CPI file.

All the parameters in the **mode con cp prep** command line that appear after the equal sign must be enclosed within parentheses.

If you reserved space for more than one character set in the **device** command line that loads the DISPLAY.SYS device driver in your CONFIG.SYS file, you can use the **mode con cp prep** command to load more than one character set. For example, the following command loads character sets 850 and 865:

**mode con cp prep=((850 865)c:\dos\ega.cpi)**

Use a space to separate the two character sets.

For more information about the **mode con cp prep** command, type **help mode (set device code pages)** at the command prompt.

# Making a Character Set Active

After you install the DISPLAY.SYS device driver, load the Nlsfunc program, and load the character set into memory, you must make the character set active. To make a character set active for all devices, use the **chcp** (change code page) command.

---

**Note**  You cannot make a character set active if a device uses only a hardware character set or if you have not loaded the character set for the device. In addition, you cannot change the character set if it is incompatible with the keyboard of a particular country. For example, the Danish keyboard can be used only with character sets 850 and 865. If you are using the Danish keyboard layout, you cannot change the character set to 437, because character set 437 is incompatible with the Danish keyboard.

---

You can use the **chcp** command to make a character set active for every device that can use it. For example, to make character set 850 active for every device, type the following at the command prompt:

**chcp 850**

You can also include the **chcp** command in your AUTOEXEC.BAT file.

If the character set has not been loaded using the procedure described in the preceding section, "Loading a Character Set into Memory," MS-DOS displays a message similar to the following:

```
Code page 850 not prepared for all devices
```

For more information about the **chcp** command, type **help chcp** at the command prompt.

# Viewing Information About Character Sets

If you have specified a keyboard layout using the **keyb** command, you can view information about the character sets your keyboard and monitor are using by typing the following at the command prompt:

**keyb**

MS-DOS then displays a message indicating which character sets your keyboard and monitor are using.

For example, suppose you are using a German keyboard layout and character set 850. When you type **keyb** at the command prompt, MS-DOS displays the following message:

```
Current keyboard code: GR code page:850
Current CON code page: 850
```

To view the number of the active character set, type the following at the command prompt:

**chcp**

You can also view information about character sets by using the **mode** command. The **mode** command lists the active character set and the hardware character set for all your devices, including the monitor and keyboard (console or **con**); parallel printer ports LPT1, LPT2, and LPT3; and any existing serial ports, such as COM1. For example, suppose you have loaded character sets for LPT1 and your keyboard and monitor. To view information about the character sets, type the following at the command prompt:

**mode**

If there is more than one screen of information, use the | **more** switch with the **mode** command. To use the | **more**, switch with the mode command, type the following at the command prompt:

**mode | more**

When "—More—" appears at the bottom of your screen, press any key to see the next screen of information.

The **mode** command displays information similar to the following:

```
Status for device LPT1:
-----------------------
LPT1: not rerouted
Retry=NONE

Code page operation not supported on this device.

Status for device CON:
----------------------

Active code page for device CON is 850
Hardware code pages:
  code page 437
Prepared code pages:
  code page 850

Status for device COM1:
-----------------------
Retry=NONE
```

*CON* refers to the console, or the keyboard and monitor. The *active code page* is the character set that is currently active. In this case, the active character set is 850. The *hardware code page* is the character set that came with your keyboard and monitor. In this case, the hardware character set is 437. A *prepared code page* is an MS-DOS character set that has been loaded into memory. In this case, character set 850 is loaded for the keyboard and monitor.

# Country, Keyboard, and Character Set Codes

When you change your country settings, you must specify which country-specific conventions, keyboard layout, and character set(s) you want to use. You indicate which settings you want to use by specifying an alphabetic or numeric code. When you carry out the procedures in this chapter, refer to the following table to determine which codes you need to specify.

| Language/country | Country code | Keyboard code | Preferred character set | Alternate character set |
|---|---|---|---|---|
| Belgian | 032 | be | 850 | 437 |
| Canadian-French | 002 | cf | 863 | 850 |
| Croatian | 038 | yu | 852 | 850 |
| Czech | 042 | cz | 852 | 850 |
| Danish | 045 | dk | 850 | 865 |
| Dutch | 031 | nl | 850 | 437 |
| English (International) | 061 | + | 437 | 850 |
| English (United Kingdom) | 044 | uk | 437 | 850 |
| English (United States) | 001 | us | 437 | 850 |
| Finnish | 358 | su | 850 | 437 |
| French (France) | 033 | fr | 850 | 437 |
| French (Switzerland) | 041 | sf | 850 | 437 |
| German (Germany) | 049 | gr | 850 | 437 |
| German (Switzerland) | 041 | sg | 850 | 437 |
| Hungarian | 036 | hu | 852 | 850 |
| Italian | 039 | it | 850 | 437 |
| Norwegian | 047 | no | 850 | 865 |
| Polish | 048 | pl | 852 | 850 |
| Portuguese (Brazil) | 055 | br | 850 | 437 |
| Portuguese (Portugal) | 351 | po | 850 | 860 |
| Serbian/Yugoslavian | 038 | yu | 852 | 850 |
| Slovak | 042 | sl | 852 | 850 |
| Slovenian | 038 | yu | 852 | 850 |
| Spanish (Latin America) | 003 | la | 850 | 437 |
| Spanish (Spain) | 034 | sp | 850 | 437 |
| Swedish | 046 | sv | 437 | 850 |

# Configuring Your Computer for International Use

To use country-specific conventions; to prepare, load, activate, and display different character sets; and to use the keyboard layout for another language, you must carry out all the procedures in the following table. For an example of how to use the listed commands in your CONFIG.SYS file, AUTOEXEC.BAT file, or at the command prompt, see the following section, "Example: Changing All Your Country-Specific Settings."

| To do this | Use this command | In this file |
|---|---|---|
| Change country-specific conventions | **country** | CONFIG.SYS |
| Prepare your monitor to display different character sets | **device** | CONFIG.SYS |
| Load National Language Support for character sets | **nlsfunc** | AUTOEXEC.BAT |
| Load the character set into memory | **mode con cp prep** | AUTOEXEC.BAT |
| Make the character set active | **chcp** | AUTOEXEC.BAT or command prompt |
| Change the layout of characters on your keyboard | **keyb** | AUTOEXEC.BAT or command prompt |

# Example: Changing All Your Country-Specific Settings

▶  **To change all your country-specific settings**

1.  Add the following commands to your CONFIG.SYS file:

    **country**=*country code*,,[*drive*][*path*]**country.sys**
    **device**=[*drive*][*path*]**display.sys con**=(*monitor,hardware character set,number of character sets*)

    For *country code*, specify the code for the country-specific conventions you want to use. Note that two commas separate the country code from the drive and path of the COUNTRY.SYS file. For *drive* and *path*, specify the drive letter and path of the COUNTRY.SYS file. For *drive* and *path* in the **device** command line, specify the drive letter and path of the DISPLAY.SYS file. For *monitor*, specify EGA or LCD. The EGA parameter supports both EGA and VGA monitors. For *hardware character set*, specify the hardware character set your computer uses. For *number of character sets*, specify how many MS-DOS character sets you want to be able to use.

2.  Add the following commands to your AUTOEXEC.BAT file:

**nlsfunc**
**mode con cp prep=((**_character set_**)[**_drive_**][**_path_**]**_character set information file_**)**
**chcp** _character set_
**keyb** _keyboard code_**,,[**_drive_**][**_path_**]keyboard.sys**

For _character set_, specify the code(s) of the character set(s) you want to load. If you specify more than one character set, separate them by a space. For _[drive][path]character set information file_, specify the drive, path, and filename of the character set information (.CPI) file. The EGA and VGA character sets are stored in the EGA.CPI file; the LCD character sets are stored in the LCD.CPI file. For _character set_, specify the code for the character set you want to make active. You must specify one of the character sets that you specified in the **mode** command line. For _keyboard code_, specify the code for the keyboard layout you want to use. For _drive_ and _path_ in the **keyb** command line, specify the drive and path of the KEYBOARD.SYS file.

Note that two commas separate the keyboard code from the drive and path of the KEYBOARD.SYS file.

For example, suppose you want to use the country-specific conventions, keyboard layout, and character set for Germany. The table in "Country, Keyboard, and Character Set Codes," earlier in this chapter, shows the following codes for Germany:

| Language/country | Country code | Keyboard code | Preferred character set | Alternate character set |
| --- | --- | --- | --- | --- |
| German (Germany) | 049 | gr | 850 | 437 |

Suppose you have a VGA monitor, your hardware character set is 437, and the COUNTRY.SYS, DISPLAY.SYS, KEYBOARD.SYS, and EGA.CPI files are all located in the C:\DOS directory.

You would add the following commands to your CONFIG.SYS file:

**country=049,,c:\dos\country.sys**
**device=c:\dos\display.sys con=(ega,437,1)**

You would add the following commands to your AUTOEXEC.BAT file:

**nlsfunc**
**mode con cp prep=((850)c:\dos\ega.cpi)**
**chcp 850**
**keyb gr,,c:\dos\keyboard.sys**

For more information about editing your CONFIG.SYS and AUTOEXEC.BAT files, see the chapter "Configuring Your System."

# Explanation of Error Messages

This section lists some of the most common error messages you may receive when you customize your international settings and describes how to correct each error.

## You receive the "Code page specified has not been prepared" message.

If you receive this error message, the keyboard code you specified with the **keyb** command is incompatible with your active character set. Before you change keyboard layouts, you must make sure that the active character set is valid for the new keyboard layout.

For each language, there are two valid character sets: a preferred character set, which is the default, and an alternate character set. When you specify the **keyb** command, MS-DOS checks to see if the active character set matches the preferred character set for the new keyboard layout.

When you see the "Code page specified has not been prepared" message, you have two options:

- You can change to the preferred character set for that keyboard layout. For instructions, see "Changing Character Sets" earlier in this chapter.

- If the active character set is the alternate character set for the keyboard layout you chose, you can specify it with the **keyb** command. To determine whether your active character set is the alternate character set for the keyboard layout you want to use, carry out the following procedure.

▶ **To identify which character set is active**

1. Type the following at the command prompt:

    **chcp**

    A message similar to the following appears:

    ```
    Active code page: 437
    ```

2. Consult the table in "Country, Keyboard, and Character Set Codes" earlier in this chapter to determine which two character sets are compatible with the keyboard layout you want to use.

    If the active character set is listed in the table as the alternate character set for the keyboard layout you want to use, carry out the following procedure.

▶ **To make your keyboard layout compatible with the alternate character set**

- Include the number of the alternate character set with the **keyb** command.

  For example, suppose you want to use the keyboard layout for France, but the active character set is 437. When you check the table, you see that the preferred character set for France is 850, but the alternate character set is 437. You can avoid having to switch to the preferred character set by including the number of the alternate character set with the **keyb** command. For example, suppose your KEYBOARD.SYS file is located in the DOS directory on drive C. To specify the keyboard layout for France and use alternate character set 437, you would type the following command:

  **keyb fr,437,c:\dos\keyboard.sys**

# You receive the "Invalid code page" message.

The character set, or code page, you selected is not valid with the keyboard layout you selected. For example, the German keyboard can be used only with character sets 850 and 437. If you are using the German keyboard layout, you cannot change the character set to 852, because character set 852 is not compatible with the German keyboard.

If you want to change both the keyboard layout and the character set, make sure you change the character set to one that is compatible with the keyboard code before changing the keyboard layout. If you are changing your international settings in your AUTOEXEC.BAT file, make sure the commands that change your character set appear before the **keyb** command.

# You receive the "Code page operation not supported on this device" message.

If this message appeared after you specified the **mode con cp prep** command, make sure your CONFIG.SYS file includes a **device** command that loads the DISPLAY.SYS device driver. For more information, see "Preparing Your Monitor for Character Sets" earlier in this chapter.

# You receive the "Code page *number* not prepared for all devices" message.

The character set you specified has not been loaded into memory, so you cannot use it yet. Before you can use this character set, you must load it into memory using the **mode con cp prep** command described in the section "Loading a Character Set into Memory" earlier in this chapter.

# You receive the "Failure to access code page font file" message.

The .CPI (character set information) file, also called a font file, specified in the **mode con cp prep** command is incorrect. For example, you may have typed VGA.CPI instead of EGA.CPI for your VGA monitor or specified the path or filename incorrectly. Check the command to make sure you typed the correct path and filename.

# You receive the "Font file contents invalid" message.

Most likely, you typed the wrong name for your .CPI (character set information) file, also called a font file. Make sure the font file you specified in the **mode con cp prep** command is either EGA.CPI or LCD.CPI. If you specified the correct file, there may be something wrong with it, in which case you should copy the original file from your MS-DOS Setup disks to your hard disk.

Files copied from your MS-DOS Setup disks must first be decompressed. For more information about decompressing files, see the topic "You need to copy Setup files directly to your computer" in the chapter "Diagnosing and Solving Problems."

# You receive the "Device error during prepare" message.

You may have specified too many character sets with the **mode con cp prep** command. You can specify only the number of character sets that are reserved by the **device** command that loads the DISPLAY.SYS device driver in your CONFIG.SYS file.

A P P E N D I X   A

# Summary of MS-DOS Commands

This appendix lists and briefly describes all the commands and device drivers available in MS-DOS 6. The list includes commands you can use to modify your CONFIG.SYS file, write batch programs, and change international settings.

For more information about MS-DOS commands, use MS-DOS Help. MS-DOS Help provides detailed information about each command, including syntax, notes about how each command works, and examples of how to use each command.

▶ **To get information about a command by using MS-DOS Help**

- At the command prompt, type **help** followed by a space and the command name.

    For example, for information about the **dir** command, type the following at the command prompt:

    **help dir**

For more information about using MS-DOS Help, see the chapter "MS-DOS Basics."

## MS-DOS 6 Commands

The following commands and device drivers are included with MS-DOS 6. Commands appear in bold type. Unless otherwise specified, you can type these commands at the command prompt. Device drivers appear in uppercase letters and are listed by filename. Unless otherwise specified, you load device drivers by using a **device** or **devicehigh** command in your CONFIG.SYS file.

For more information about these commands and device drivers, use MS-DOS Help, as described in the previous section.

| Command or device driver | Purpose |
| --- | --- |
| ANSI.SYS | Defines functions that change display graphics, control cursor movement, and reassign keys. This device driver must be loaded by a **device** or **devicehigh** command in your CONFIG.SYS file. |
| **append** | Enables programs to open data files in specified directories as if the files were in the current directory. Do not use this command when you are running Windows. |
| **attrib** | Displays or changes file attributes. |
| **break** | Sets or clears extended CTRL+C checking. You can use this command at the command prompt or in your CONFIG.SYS file. |
| **buffers** | Allocates memory for a specified number of disk buffers when your computer starts. You can use this command only in your CONFIG.SYS file. |
| **call** | Calls one batch program from another without causing the first batch program to stop. |
| **cd** | Displays the name of the current directory or changes the current directory. |
| **chcp** | Displays the number of the active character set (code page). You can also use this command to change the active character set for all devices that support character-set switching. |
| **chdir** | See the **cd** command. |
| **chkdsk** | Checks the status of a disk and displays a status report. Can also fix disk errors. Do not use **chkdsk** with the **/f** switch when you are running Windows. |
| **choice** | Prompts the user to make a choice in a batch program. Displays a specified prompt and pauses for the user to choose from among a specified set of keys. This command is useful only in batch programs. |
| **cls** | Clears the screen. |
| **command** | Starts a new instance of the MS-DOS command interpreter. |
| **copy** | Copies one or more files to the location you specify. |
| **country** | Enables MS-DOS to use country-specific conventions for displaying dates, times, and currency; for determining the order by which characters are sorted; and for determining which characters can be used in filenames. You can use this command only in your CONFIG.SYS file. |

| Command or device driver | Purpose |
| --- | --- |
| **ctty** | Changes the terminal device used to control your computer. |
| **date** | Displays the date and prompts you to change the date if necessary. |
| **dblspace** | Starts the DoubleSpace program, which sets up or configures compressed drives. You cannot use this command when you are running Windows. |
| DBLSPACE.SYS | Moves DBLSPACE.BIN to its final location in memory. (DBLSPACE.BIN is the portion of MS-DOS that provides access to compressed drives.) |
| **debug** | Starts the Debug program, which you can use to test and debug executable files. |
| **defrag** | Reorganizes the files on a disk to optimize disk performance. Do not use this command when you are running Windows. |
| **del** (**erase**) | Deletes the files you specify. |
| **deloldos** | Deletes the OLD_DOS.1 directory and the files it contains from your hard disk. If you have more than one OLD_DOS directory, the command deletes all OLD_DOS directories and their files. |
| **deltree** | Deletes a directory and all the files and subdirectories that are in it. |
| **device** | Loads the device driver you specify into memory. You can use this command only in your CONFIG.SYS file. |
| **devicehigh** | Loads the device driver you specify into upper memory. You can use this command only in your CONFIG.SYS file. |
| **dir** | Displays a list of the files and subdirectories that are in the directory you specify. |
| **diskcomp** | Compares the contents of two floppy disks. |
| **diskcopy** | Copies the entire contents of one floppy disk to another floppy disk. |
| DISPLAY.SYS | Enables you to display international character sets on EGA, VGA, and LCD monitors. This device driver must be loaded by a **device** or **devicehigh** command in your CONFIG.SYS file. |
| **dos** | Specifies that MS-DOS should maintain a link to the upper memory area, load part of itself into the high memory area (HMA), or both. You can use this command only in your CONFIG.SYS file. |

| Command or device driver | Purpose |
| --- | --- |
| **doskey** | Loads the Doskey program into memory. The Doskey program recalls MS-DOS commands and enables you to edit command lines and create and run macros. |
| **dosshell** | Starts MS-DOS Shell, a graphical interface for MS-DOS. |
| DRIVER.SYS | Creates a logical drive that you can use to refer to a physical floppy disk drive. This device driver must be loaded by a **device** or **devicehigh** command in your CONFIG.SYS file. |
| **drivparm** | Defines parameters for devices such as disk and tape drives when you start MS-DOS. You can use this command only in your CONFIG.SYS file. |
| **echo** | Displays or hides the text in batch programs when the program is running. Also indicates whether the command-echoing feature is on or off. |
| **edit** | Starts MS-DOS Editor, a text editor you can use to create and edit ASCII text files. |
| EGA.SYS | Saves and restores the display when the MS-DOS Shell Task Swapper is used with EGA monitors. This device driver must be loaded by a **device** or **devicehigh** command in your CONFIG.SYS file. |
| **emm386** | Enables or disables EMM386 expanded-memory support on a computer with an 80386 or higher processor. Do not use this command when you are running Windows. |
| EMM386.EXE | Provides access to the upper memory area and uses extended memory to simulate expanded memory. This device driver must be loaded by a **device** command in your CONFIG.SYS file and can be used only on computers with an 80386 or higher processor. |
| **erase** | See the **del** command. |
| **exit** | Quits the MS-DOS command interpreter (COMMAND.COM) and returns to the program that started the command interpreter, if one exists. |
| **expand** | Decompresses a compressed file. |
| **fasthelp** | Displays a list of all MS-DOS commands and gives a brief explanation of each. |

| Command or device driver | Purpose |
| --- | --- |
| fastopen | Starts the Fastopen program, which improves performance on computers with large directories. Fastopen decreases the amount of time that MS-DOS takes to open frequently used files. Do not use this command when you are running Windows. |
| fc | Compares two files and displays the differences between them. |
| fcbs | Specifies the number of file control blocks (FCBs) that MS-DOS can have open at the same time. You can use this command only in your CONFIG.SYS file. |
| fdisk | Starts the Fdisk program, which configures a hard disk for use with MS-DOS. |
| files | Specifies the number of files that MS-DOS can access at one time. You can use this command only in your CONFIG.SYS file. |
| find | Searches for a specific string of text in a file or files. |
| for | Runs a specified command for each file in a set of files. You can use this command in batch programs or at the command prompt. |
| format | Formats a disk for use with MS-DOS. |
| goto | Directs MS-DOS to a line in a batch program that is marked by a label you specify. You can use this command only in batch programs. |
| graphics | Loads a program into memory that enables MS-DOS to print the information displayed on your screen. Use the **graphics** command only if you are using a color or graphics adapter. |
| help | Starts MS-DOS Help. |
| HIMEM.SYS | Manages the use of extended memory. This device driver must be loaded by a **device** command in your CONFIG.SYS file. |
| if | Performs conditional processing in batch programs. You can use this command only in batch programs. |
| include | Includes the contents of one configuration block within another. You can use this command only in your CONFIG.SYS file. |
| install | Loads a memory-resident program into memory. You can use this command only in your CONFIG.SYS file. |

| Command or device driver | Purpose |
| --- | --- |
| interlnk | Starts the Interlnk program, which connects two computers by means of parallel or serial ports and enables the computers to share disks and printer ports. |
| INTERLNK.EXE | Redirects commands on Interlnk drives and printer ports to drives and printer ports on the Interlnk server. This device driver must be loaded by a **device** or **devicehigh** command in your CONFIG.SYS file. |
| intersvr | Starts the Interlnk server. |
| keyb | Starts the Keyb program, which configures a keyboard for a specific language. |
| label | Creates, changes, or deletes the volume label (name) of a disk. |
| lastdrive | Specifies the maximum number of drives you can access. You can use this command only in your CONFIG.SYS file. |
| lh | See the **loadhigh** command. |
| loadfix | Ensures that a program is loaded above the first 64 kilobytes (K) of conventional memory. |
| loadhigh (lh) | Loads a program into upper memory. |
| md | Creates a directory or subdirectory. |
| mem | Displays the amount of used and free memory on your computer. |
| memmaker | Starts the MemMaker program, which optimizes your computer's memory by configuring device drivers and memory-resident programs to run in the upper memory area. Do not use this command when you are running Windows. |
| menucolor | Sets the text and background colors for the startup menu. You can use this command only within a menu block in your CONFIG.SYS file. |
| menudefault | Specifies the default menu item on the startup menu and sets a time-out value if desired. You can use this command only within a menu block in your CONFIG.SYS file. |
| menuitem | Defines up to nine items on the startup menu. You can use this command only within a menu block in your CONFIG.SYS file. |
| mkdir | See the **md** command. |

| Command or device driver | Purpose |
|---|---|
| **mode** | Configures a printer, serial port, or display adapter; sets the typematic rate; redirects printer output from a parallel port to a serial port; prepares, selects, refreshes, or displays the numbers of the character sets (code pages) for parallel printers or the keyboard and screen; displays the status of all the devices installed on your computer. |
| **more** | Displays one screen of output at a time. |
| **move** | Moves one or more files to the location you specify. Can also be used to rename files and directories. |
| **msav** | Starts the Microsoft Anti-Virus program, which scans your computer for known viruses. |
| **msbackup** | Starts the Microsoft Backup program, which backs up or restores one or more files from one disk onto another. |
| **mscdex** | Provides access to CD-_ _ _ _ 1 drives. |
| **msd** | Starts the Microsoft D_ _ _ ics program, which provides detailed tec_ _ _ _ _ _ormation about your computer. |
| **nlsfunc** | Starts the Nlsfunc p_ _ _ _ _ _ _ch loads country-specific informatio_ _ _ _ _ _ _ _language support (NLS). Do not use _ _ _ _ _ _ _ _d when you are running Windows. |
| **numlock** | Specifies whether _ _ _ _ _ _ _ _ K setting on your numeric keypad i_ _ _ _ _ _ _ _FF. You can use this command only w_ _ _ _ _ _ _ck in your CONFIG.SYS fil_. |
| **path** | Indicates which _ _ _ _ _ _ _ _ OS should search for executable fi_ _ _ _ _ _ _ _ _. |
| **pause** | Suspends proces_ _ _ _ _ _ _ gram and displays a message that p_ _ _ _ _ _ s any key to continue. You c_ _ _ _ _ _ d only within batch programs |
| **power** | Turns power m_ _ _ _ _ _ _ _ff, reports the status of power _ _ _ _ _ _ _ _ ts levels of power conservation. |
| POWER.EXE | Reduces powe_ _ _ _ _ _ _ _ pplications and devices are id_ _ _ _ _ _ _ _ ust be loaded by a **device** or d_ _ _ _ _ _ _ _ your CONFIG.SYS _ _ _. |
| **print** | Prints a text fi_ _. |
| **prompt** | Changes the a_ _ _ _ _ _ _ _ _ _and prompt. |

| Command or device driver | Purpose |
|---|---|
| **qbasic** | Starts MS-DOS QBasic, a program that reads instructions written in the Basic computer language and interprets them into executable computer code (programs). |
| RAMDRIVE.SYS | Uses part of your computer's random-access memory (RAM) to simulate a hard disk drive. This device driver must be loaded by a **device** or **devicehigh** command in your CONFIG.SYS file. |
| **rd** | Deletes (removes) a directory. |
| **rem** | Enables you to include comments (remarks) or prevent commands in a batch program or the CONFIG.SYS file from running. |
| **ren** | Changes the name of the file or files you specify. |
| **rename** | See the **ren** command. |
| **replace** | Replaces files in a destination directory with files in a source directory that have the same name. |
| **restore** | Restores files that were backed up by using the **backup** command from previous versions of MS-DOS. |
| **rmdir** | See the **rd** command. |
| **set** | Displays, sets, or removes MS-DOS environment variables. You can use this command in your CONFIG.SYS file in addition to your AUTOEXEC.BAT file or at the command prompt. |
| **setver** | Displays the version table. Reports a version number (earlier than 6.0) to programs or device drivers that were designed for earlier versions of MS-DOS. |
| SETVER.EXE | Loads the MS-DOS version table into memory. This device driver must be loaded by a **device** or **devicehigh** command in your CONFIG.SYS file. |
| **share** | Starts the Share program, which installs file-sharing and locking capabilities on your disks and network drives. |
| **shell** | Specifies the name and location of the command interpreter you want MS-DOS to use. You can use this command only in your CONFIG.SYS file. |
| **shift** | Changes the position of replaceable parameters in a batch program. You can use this command only in batch programs. |

| Command or device driver | Purpose |
| --- | --- |
| **smartdrv** | When specified at the command prompt or in your AUTOEXEC.BAT file, creates a disk cache in extended memory. The cache speeds up access to your hard disk. Do not use this command when you are running Windows. |
| SMARTDRV.EXE | When loaded with a **device** command in your CONFIG.SYS file, this device driver provides compatibility for hard-disk controllers that cannot work with EMM386 and Microsoft Windows running in enhanced mode. |
| **sort** | Reads input, sorts data, and writes the results to the screen, a file, or another device. |
| **stacks** | Supports the dynamic use of data stacks to handle hardware interrupts. You can use this command only in your CONFIG.SYS file. |
| **submenu** | Defines an item on a startup menu that, when selected, displays another set of choices. You can use this command only within a menu block in your CONFIG.SYS file. |
| **subst** | Associates a path with a drive letter. Do not use this command when you are running Windows. |
| **switches** | Specifies special options in MS-DOS. This command can be used only in your CONFIG.SYS file. |
| **sys** | Creates a startup disk by copying hidden MS-DOS system files and the MS-DOS command interpreter (COMMAND.COM) to the disk. |
| **time** | Displays the system time or sets your computer's internal clock. |
| **tree** | Graphically displays the structure of a directory. |
| **type** | Displays the contents of a text file. |
| **undelete** | Restores files that were previously deleted by using the **del** command. |
| **unformat** | Restores a disk that was erased by using the **format** command. |
| **ver** | Displays the MS-DOS version number. |
| **verify** | Directs MS-DOS to verify that your files are written correctly to a disk, and displays the status of verification. You can use this command either at the command prompt or in your CONFIG.SYS file. |

| Command or device driver | Purpose |
| --- | --- |
| **vol** | Displays the volume label and serial number for a disk, if the disk has them. |
| **vsafe** | Continuously monitors your computer for viruses and displays a warning when it finds one. Do not use this command when you are running Windows. |
| **xcopy** | Copies directories, their subdirectories, and files (except hidden and system files). |

# Device Drivers

You can load the following device drivers in your CONFIG.SYS file by using the **device** or **devicehigh** command:

| | |
| --- | --- |
| ANSI.SYS | INTERLNK.EXE |
| DBLSPACE.SYS | POWER.EXE |
| DISPLAY.SYS | RAMDRIVE.SYS |
| DRIVER.SYS | SETVER.EXE |
| EGA.SYS | |

You can load the following device drivers in your CONFIG.SYS file by using only the **device** command:

EMM386.EXE

SMARTDRV.EXE

HIMEM.SYS

---

**Caution**  The COUNTRY.SYS and KEYBOARD.SYS files are not device drivers. If you try to load them by using the **device** or **devicehigh** command, your system will stop responding. To use COUNTRY.SYS or KEYBOARD.SYS, use the **country** command or the **keyb** command, respectively, in your CONFIG.SYS file.

---

# Commands That Cannot Be Used with Windows

Do not use the following commands when you are running Windows. Carry out the command from the MS-DOS command prompt before you start or after you quit Windows.

| | | |
|---|---|---|
| **append** | **fastopen** | **smartdrv** |
| **dblspace** | **memmaker** | **subst** |
| **defrag** | **mscdex** | **vsafe** |
| **emm386** | **nlsfunc** | |

**Note**   You cannot use the **chkdsk** command with the **/f** switch when you are running Windows.

# Commands Used in CONFIG.SYS Files

You can use the following commands in your CONFIG.SYS file:

| | | |
|---|---|---|
| **break** | **files** | **rem** |
| **buffers** | **include** | **set** |
| **country** | **install** | **shell** |
| **device** | **lastdrive** | **stacks** |
| **devicehigh** | **menucolor** | **submenu** |
| **dos** | **menudefault** | **switches** |
| **drivparm** | **menuitem** | **verify** |
| **fcbs** | **numlock** | |

# Commands Used in Batch Programs

You can use the following commands in batch programs:

| | | |
|---|---|---|
| **call** | **for** | **pause** |
| **choice** | **goto** | **rem** |
| **echo** | **if** | **shift** |

# Commands Used to Change International Settings

You can use the following commands to change international settings such as country codes, keyboard layouts, and character sets (code pages):

chcp          mode
country       nlsfunc
keyb

APPENDIX B

# Accessibility to MS-DOS for Individuals with Disabilities

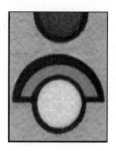

Microsoft is committed to making its products and services easier for everyone to use. This appendix provides information about the following products and services, which make MS-DOS more accessible for people with disabilities:

- Microsoft support services for individuals who are deaf or hard-of-hearing.
- AccessDOS, a product that makes using MS-DOS easier for people with motion or hearing disabilities.
- Keyboard layouts designed for people who type with only one hand.
- Microsoft software documentation on audio cassettes and floppy disks.
- Information about other products and services for people with disabilities.

---

**Note** The information in this appendix applies only to MS-DOS users in the United States. If you are outside the United States, your MS-DOS 6 package contains a subsidiary information card that lists telephone numbers and addresses for Microsoft Product Support Services. Contact your subsidiary to find out whether products and services similar to those described in this appendix are available in your area.

---

# Support Services for Individuals Who Are Deaf or Hard-of-Hearing

Through a text telephone (TT or TDD) service, Microsoft provides users who are deaf or hard-of-hearing with complete access to Microsoft's product and customer support services.

You can contact Microsoft support services by using a text telephone by dialing (206) 635-4948 between 6:00 A.M. and 6:00 P.M. Pacific time. Microsoft's product support services are subject to Microsoft's prices, terms, and conditions in place at the time the service is used.

# AccessDOS Features

Microsoft distributes AccessDOS, which provides users who are movement or hearing disabled with better access to computers that run MS-DOS. AccessDOS includes utilities that:

- Provide for single-fingered typing of SHIFT, CTRL, and ALT key combinations.
- Ignore accidental keystrokes.
- Adjust the rate at which a character is repeated when you hold down a key, or turn off character-repeating entirely.
- Prevent extra characters from being typed if you unintentionally press a key more than once.
- Enable you to control the mouse pointer by using the keyboard.
- Enable you to control the computer's keyboard and mouse by using an alternate input device.
- Provide a visual cue when the computer makes sounds.
- Enable you to turn off these utilities if they are not needed.
- Provide extensive online Help.

AccessDOS, which was developed by the Trace R&D Center at the University of Wisconsin-Madison, is available on the MS-DOS Supplemental Disk. You can order the Supplemental Disk directly from Microsoft or, if you have a modem, you can download MS-DOS Supplemental Disk components from the following network services:

- CompuServe ®
- GEnie ™
- Microsoft OnLine
- Microsoft Download Service (MSDL), which you can reach by calling (206) 936-MSDL (936-6735) any time except between 1:00 A.M. and 2:30 A.M. Pacific time. Use the following communications settings:

  | For this setting | Specify |
  |---|---|
  | Baud rate | 1200, 2400, or 9600 |
  | Parity | None |
  | Data bits | 8 |
  | Stop bits | 1 |

- Various user-group bulletin boards (such as the bulletin-board services on the Association of PC User Groups network)

If you are in the United States and want to order the MS-DOS Supplemental Disk directly from Microsoft, see the coupon at the back of this guide, or call Microsoft Customer Sales and Service at (800) 426-9400 (voice) or (206) 635-4948 (text telephone).

At the time this book was printed, AccessDOS was available only in the English language.

---

**Note**  Some computer manufacturers preinstall AccessDOS. To determine whether AccessDOS is already on your computer, type **dir ados.exe /s** at the command prompt.

---

# Keyboard Layouts for Single-Handed Users

Microsoft distributes a data file that contains keyboard layouts for people who have difficulty using the standard QWERTY layout. The file contains three Dvorak layouts: one for two-handed users, one for people who type only with their left hand, and one for people who type only with their right hand. The Dvorak keyboard layout makes the most frequently typed characters on a keyboard more accessible.

These layouts are included on the MS-DOS Supplemental Disk. For information about obtaining the MS-DOS Supplemental Disk, see the preceding section.

The following illustrations show the three Dvorak keyboard layouts:

**Two-handed Dvorak**

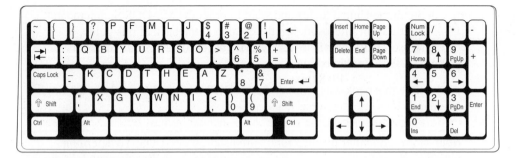

**Left single-handed Dvorak**

**Right single-handed Dvorak**

# Documentation on Audio Cassettes and Floppy Disks

People who cannot use printed documentation can obtain most of Microsoft's publications from Recording for the Blind, Inc. Recording for the Blind distributes these documents to registered members of their distribution service, either on audio cassettes or on floppy disks. Recording for the Blind's collection contains more than 80,000 titles, including Microsoft product documentation and books from Microsoft Press ®. You can contact Recording for the Blind at the following address:

Recording for the Blind, Inc.
20 Roszel Road
Princeton, NJ  08540

Telephone: (800) 221-4792
Fax: (609) 987-8116

# Getting More Information About Products and Services

For more information about Microsoft products and services for people with disabilities, contact Microsoft Customer Sales and Service at (800) 426-9400 (voice) or (206) 635-4948 (text telephone).

The Trace R&D Center at the University of Wisconsin-Madison produces a book and a compact disc that describe products that help people with disabilities use computers. The book, titled *Trace ResourceBook*, provides descriptions and photographs of about 2,000 products. The compact disc provides a database of more than 17,000 products and other information for people with disabilities. It is issued twice a year and should also be available in many public libraries by early 1993.

You can contact the Trace R&D Center by using the following address or telephone numbers:

Trace R&D Center
S-151 Waisman Center
1500 Highland Avenue
Madison, WI 53705–2280

Voice telephone: (608) 263-2309
Text telephone: (608) 263-5408

For general information and recommendations about how computers can help specific individuals, consult a trained evaluator who can best match the individual's needs with available solutions.

If you are in the United States, you can obtain information about resources in your area by contacting the National Information System, an information and referral center for people with disabilities, at the following address:

National Information System (NIS)
Center for Developmental Disabilities
University of South Carolina, Benson Bldg.
Columbia, SC 29208

Or, call or fax the National Information System by using the following numbers:

| Location | Voice/Text Telephone | Fax |
| --- | --- | --- |
| United States (excluding South Carolina) | (800) 922-9234 | (803) 777-6058 |
| South Carolina | (800) 922-1107 | (803) 777-6058 |
| Outside the United States | (803) 777-6222 | (803) 777-6058 |

This service is available only in the English language.

A P P E N D I X   C

# Keyboard Layouts and Character Sets

This appendix includes the following information:

- Illustrations of 20 keyboard layouts
- Instructions for using keys that have more than two characters on them
- Instructions for creating accented characters on a Brazilian keyboard
- Instructions for typing control characters and extended characters
- Tables that illustrate the characters that make up the six character sets supplied with MS-DOS

For information about changing your keyboard layout or character set, see the chapter "Customizing for International Use."

# Keyboard Layouts

**Belgium**

Canada

Croatia/Slovenia/Serbia  (Yugoslavia)

Czech  Republic

**Denmark**

**France**

**Germany**

**Hungary**

**Italy**

**Latin America**

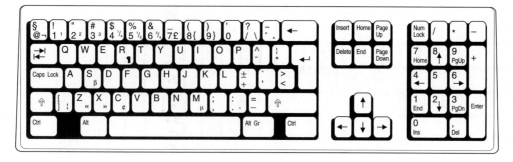

**Netherlands**

**Norway**

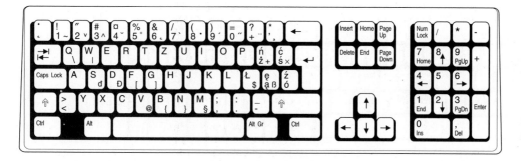

**Poland**

**Portugal**

**Slovakia**

**Spain**

**Sweden/Finland**

**Switzerland**

**United Kingdom**

United States

# Using Keys That Have More Than Two Characters on Them

Some keyboards include individual keys that you can use to type three different characters. To type the lower-left character, press the key. To type the upper-left character, press SHIFT and the character key. To type the lower-right character, use the key combinations listed in the following table.

| Keyboard | Lower-right character (standard keyboard) | Lower-right character (enhanced keyboard) | Upper-right character (all keyboards) |
|---|---|---|---|
| Canada | ALT+SHIFT | ALT+GR | None |
| Denmark | ALT | ALT+GR | ALT+SHIFT |
| Norway | ALT | ALT+GR | ALT+SHIFT |
| Sweden/Finland | ALT | ALT+GR | ALT+SHIFT |
| All others | ALT+CTRL | ALT+GR | None |

# Creating Accented Characters on a Brazilian Keyboard

If you specify the keyboard code for Brazilian Portuguese (**br**), you can create accented characters even though there is no separate Brazilian keyboard layout. To create accented characters, carry out the following procedures:

▶ **To create a character with an acute accent**

- Type an apostrophe ('), and then type the character above which the acute accent should appear.

▶ **To create a character with a diaeresis**

- Type a double quotation mark ("), and then type the character above which the diaeresis should appear.

▶ **To create a character with a tilde**

- Type the tilde (~), and then type the character above which the tilde should appear.

▶ **To create a cedilla**

- Type an apostrophe ('), and then type the letter **c**.

If you type an invalid key sequence, your computer will beep and MS-DOS will display the two characters separately.

# Character Set (Code Page) Tables

MS-DOS can use up to 256 different characters when you are displaying, printing, and working with text. MS-DOS includes six sets of 256 characters, which are called *character sets* or *code pages*. You refer to each character set by a number. For example, the English character set is number 437.

Each character in a character set is also numbered. MS-DOS reserves characters 0 through 31 for control characters. The keys on your keyboard represent characters 32 through 126. Characters 127 through 255 are *extended characters*.

To type extended characters and the control characters that MS-DOS uses, carry out the following procedure.

▶ **To type an extended or control character**

1. Determine which character set is active by typing the following at the command prompt:

   **chcp**

   A message such as the following appears:

   ```
   Active code page: 437
   ```

2. Turn to the character set table later in this appendix that matches your active character set (code page). Find the character you want to type and note the number that appears to the left of it.

3. Press the NUM LOCK key if it is not already active.

4. Hold down the ALT key and, on the numeric keypad, type the number that corresponds to the character you want.

For example, to type the Î character when using character set 437, hold down ALT while you type **140** on the numeric keypad.

You can type only the characters that are available in the active character set. To change the active character set, carry out the procedures in "Changing Character Sets" in the chapter "Customizing for International Use."

The following tables show which characters are available for each of the six character sets included with MS-DOS 6.

| | | | | | | | |
|---|---|---|---|---|---|---|---|
| 0 | 32 | 64 @ | 96 ` | 128 Ç | 160 á | 192 L | 224 α |
| 1 ☺ | 33 ! | 65 A | 97 a | 129 ü | 161 í | 193 ⊥ | 225 ß |
| 2 ☻ | 34 " | 66 B | 98 b | 130 é | 162 ó | 194 ⊤ | 226 Γ |
| 3 ♥ | 35 # | 67 C | 99 c | 131 â | 163 ú | 195 ├ | 227 π |
| 4 ♦ | 36 $ | 68 D | 100 d | 132 ä | 164 ñ | 196 ─ | 228 Σ |
| 5 ♣ | 37 % | 69 E | 101 e | 133 à | 165 Ñ | 197 ┼ | 229 σ |
| 6 ♠ | 38 & | 70 F | 102 f | 134 å | 166 ª | 198 ╞ | 230 μ |
| 7 • | 39 ' | 71 G | 103 g | 135 ç | 167 º | 199 ╟ | 231 τ |
| 8 ◘ | 40 ( | 72 H | 104 h | 136 ê | 168 ¿ | 200 ╚ | 232 Φ |
| 9 ○ | 41 ) | 73 I | 105 i | 137 ë | 169 ⌐ | 201 ╔ | 233 Θ |
| 10 ◙ | 42 * | 74 J | 106 j | 138 è | 170 ¬ | 202 ╩ | 234 Ω |
| 11 ♂ | 43 + | 75 K | 107 k | 139 ï | 171 ½ | 203 ╦ | 235 δ |
| 12 ♀ | 44 , | 76 L | 108 l | 140 î | 172 ¼ | 204 ╠ | 236 ∞ |
| 13 ♪ | 45 - | 77 M | 109 m | 141 ì | 173 ¡ | 205 = | 237 φ |
| 14 ♫ | 46 . | 78 N | 110 n | 142 Ä | 174 « | 206 ╬ | 238 ε |
| 15 ☼ | 47 / | 79 O | 111 o | 143 Å | 175 » | 207 ⊥ | 239 ∩ |
| 16 ► | 48 0 | 80 P | 112 p | 144 É | 176 ░ | 208 ╨ | 240 ≡ |
| 17 ◄ | 49 1 | 81 Q | 113 q | 145 æ | 177 ▒ | 209 ╥ | 241 ± |
| 18 ↕ | 50 2 | 82 R | 114 r | 146 Æ | 178 ▓ | 210 ╥ | 242 ≥ |
| 19 ‼ | 51 3 | 83 S | 115 s | 147 ô | 179 │ | 211 ╙ | 243 ≤ |
| 20 ¶ | 52 4 | 84 T | 116 t | 148 ö | 180 ┤ | 212 ╘ | 244 ⌠ |
| 21 § | 53 5 | 85 U | 117 u | 149 ò | 181 ╡ | 213 ╒ | 245 ⌡ |
| 22 ▬ | 54 6 | 86 V | 118 v | 150 û | 182 ╢ | 214 ╓ | 246 ÷ |
| 23 ↨ | 55 7 | 87 W | 119 w | 151 ù | 183 ╖ | 215 ╫ | 247 ≈ |
| 24 ↑ | 56 8 | 88 X | 120 x | 152 ÿ | 184 ╕ | 216 ╪ | 248 ° |
| 25 ↓ | 57 9 | 89 Y | 121 y | 153 Ö | 185 ╣ | 217 ┘ | 249 · |
| 26 → | 58 : | 90 Z | 122 z | 154 Ü | 186 ║ | 218 ┌ | 250 · |
| 27 ← | 59 ; | 91 [ | 123 { | 155 ¢ | 187 ╗ | 219 █ | 251 √ |
| 28 ∟ | 60 < | 92 \ | 124 | | 156 £ | 188 ╝ | 220 ▄ | 252 ⁿ |
| 29 ↔ | 61 = | 93 ] | 125 } | 157 ¥ | 189 ╜ | 221 ▌ | 253 ² |
| 30 ▲ | 62 > | 94 ^ | 126 ~ | 158 ₧ | 190 ╛ | 222 ▐ | 254 ■ |
| 31 ▼ | 63 ? | 95 _ | 127 ⌂ | 159 ƒ | 191 ┐ | 223 ▀ | 255 |

**437  United States**

| | | | | | | | | | | | | | | |
|---|---|---|---|---|---|---|---|---|---|---|---|---|---|---|
| 0 | | 32 | | 64 | @ | 96 | ` | 128 | Ç | 160 | á | 192 | L | 224 | Ó |
| 1 | ☺ | 33 | ! | 65 | A | 97 | a | 129 | ü | 161 | í | 193 | ⊥ | 225 | ß |
| 2 | ☻ | 34 | " | 66 | B | 98 | b | 130 | é | 162 | ó | 194 | T | 226 | Ô |
| 3 | ♥ | 35 | # | 67 | C | 99 | c | 131 | â | 163 | ú | 195 | ├ | 227 | Ò |
| 4 | ♦ | 36 | $ | 68 | D | 100 | d | 132 | ä | 164 | ñ | 196 | ─ | 228 | õ |
| 5 | ♣ | 37 | % | 69 | E | 101 | e | 133 | à | 165 | Ñ | 197 | ┼ | 229 | Õ |
| 6 | ♠ | 38 | & | 70 | F | 102 | f | 134 | å | 166 | ª | 198 | ã | 230 | µ |
| 7 | • | 39 | ' | 71 | G | 103 | g | 135 | ç | 167 | º | 199 | Ã | 231 | Þ |
| 8 | ◘ | 40 | ( | 72 | H | 104 | h | 136 | ê | 168 | ¿ | 200 | ╚ | 232 | þ |
| 9 | ○ | 41 | ) | 73 | I | 105 | i | 137 | ë | 169 | ® | 201 | ╔ | 233 | Ú |
| 10 | ◙ | 42 | * | 74 | J | 106 | j | 138 | è | 170 | ¬ | 202 | ╩ | 234 | Û |
| 11 | ♂ | 43 | + | 75 | K | 107 | k | 139 | ï | 171 | ½ | 203 | ╦ | 235 | Ù |
| 12 | ♀ | 44 | , | 76 | L | 108 | l | 140 | î | 172 | ¼ | 204 | ╠ | 236 | ý |
| 13 | ♪ | 45 | - | 77 | M | 109 | m | 141 | ì | 173 | ¡ | 205 | = | 237 | Ý |
| 14 | ♫ | 46 | . | 78 | N | 110 | n | 142 | Ä | 174 | « | 206 | ╬ | 238 | ¯ |
| 15 | ☼ | 47 | / | 79 | O | 111 | o | 143 | Å | 175 | » | 207 | ¤ | 239 | ´ |
| 16 | ► | 48 | 0 | 80 | P | 112 | p | 144 | É | 176 | ░ | 208 | ð | 240 | - |
| 17 | ◄ | 49 | 1 | 81 | Q | 113 | q | 145 | æ | 177 | ▒ | 209 | Ð | 241 | ± |
| 18 | ↕ | 50 | 2 | 82 | R | 114 | r | 146 | Æ | 178 | ▓ | 210 | Ê | 242 | ‗ |
| 19 | ‼ | 51 | 3 | 83 | S | 115 | s | 147 | ô | 179 | │ | 211 | Ë | 243 | ¾ |
| 20 | ¶ | 52 | 4 | 84 | T | 116 | t | 148 | ö | 180 | ┤ | 212 | È | 244 | ¶ |
| 21 | § | 53 | 5 | 85 | U | 117 | u | 149 | ò | 181 | Á | 213 | ı | 245 | § |
| 22 | ▬ | 54 | 6 | 86 | V | 118 | v | 150 | û | 182 | Â | 214 | Í | 246 | ÷ |
| 23 | ↨ | 55 | 7 | 87 | W | 119 | w | 151 | ù | 183 | À | 215 | Î | 247 | ¸ |
| 24 | ↑ | 56 | 8 | 88 | X | 120 | x | 152 | ÿ | 184 | © | 216 | Ï | 248 | ° |
| 25 | ↓ | 57 | 9 | 89 | Y | 121 | y | 153 | Ö | 185 | ╣ | 217 | ┘ | 249 | ¨ |
| 26 | → | 58 | : | 90 | Z | 122 | z | 154 | Ü | 186 | ║ | 218 | ┌ | 250 | · |
| 27 | ← | 59 | ; | 91 | [ | 123 | { | 155 | ø | 187 | ╗ | 219 | █ | 251 | ¹ |
| 28 | ∟ | 60 | < | 92 | \ | 124 | ¦ | 156 | £ | 188 | ╝ | 220 | ▄ | 252 | ³ |
| 29 | ↔ | 61 | = | 93 | ] | 125 | } | 157 | Ø | 189 | ¢ | 221 | ¦ | 253 | ² |
| 30 | ▲ | 62 | > | 94 | ^ | 126 | ~ | 158 | × | 190 | ¥ | 222 | Ì | 254 | ■ |
| 31 | ▼ | 63 | ? | 95 | _ | 127 | ⌂ | 159 | ƒ | 191 | ┐ | 223 | ▀ | 255 | |

**850  Multilingual (Latin I)**

| | | | | | | | | | | | | | | | |
|---|---|---|---|---|---|---|---|---|---|---|---|---|---|---|---|
| 0 | | 32 | | 64 | @ | 96 | ` | 128 | Ç | 160 | á | 192 | └ | 224 | Ó |
| 1 | ☺ | 33 | ! | 65 | A | 97 | a | 129 | ü | 161 | í | 193 | ┴ | 225 | ß |
| 2 | ☻ | 34 | " | 66 | B | 98 | b | 130 | é | 162 | ó | 194 | ┬ | 226 | Ô |
| 3 | ♥ | 35 | # | 67 | C | 99 | c | 131 | â | 163 | ú | 195 | ├ | 227 | Ń |
| 4 | ♦ | 36 | $ | 68 | D | 100 | d | 132 | ä | 164 | Ą | 196 | ─ | 228 | ń |
| 5 | ♣ | 37 | % | 69 | E | 101 | e | 133 | ů | 165 | ą | 197 | ┼ | 229 | ň |
| 6 | ♠ | 38 | & | 70 | F | 102 | f | 134 | ć | 166 | Ž | 198 | Ă | 230 | Š |
| 7 | • | 39 | ' | 71 | G | 103 | g | 135 | ç | 167 | ž | 199 | ă | 231 | š |
| 8 | ◘ | 40 | ( | 72 | H | 104 | h | 136 | ł | 168 | Ę | 200 | ╚ | 232 | Ŕ |
| 9 | ○ | 41 | ) | 73 | I | 105 | i | 137 | ë | 169 | ę | 201 | ╔ | 233 | Ú |
| 10 | ◙ | 42 | * | 74 | J | 106 | j | 138 | Ő | 170 | | 202 | ╩ | 234 | ŕ |
| 11 | ♂ | 43 | + | 75 | K | 107 | k | 139 | ő | 171 | ź | 203 | ╦ | 235 | Ű |
| 12 | ♀ | 44 | , | 76 | L | 108 | l | 140 | î | 172 | Č | 204 | ╠ | 236 | ý |
| 13 | ♪ | 45 | - | 77 | M | 109 | m | 141 | Ź | 173 | ş | 205 | ═ | 237 | Ý |
| 14 | ♫ | 46 | . | 78 | N | 110 | n | 142 | Ä | 174 | « | 206 | ╬ | 238 | ţ |
| 15 | ☼ | 47 | / | 79 | O | 111 | o | 143 | Ć | 175 | » | 207 | ¤ | 239 | ´ |
| 16 | ► | 48 | 0 | 80 | P | 112 | p | 144 | É | 176 | ░ | 208 | đ | 240 | ─ |
| 17 | ◄ | 49 | 1 | 81 | Q | 113 | q | 145 | Ĺ | 177 | ▒ | 209 | Đ | 241 | ˝ |
| 18 | ↕ | 50 | 2 | 82 | R | 114 | r | 146 | ĺ | 178 | ▓ | 210 | Ď | 242 | ˛ |
| 19 | ‼ | 51 | 3 | 83 | S | 115 | s | 147 | ô | 179 | │ | 211 | Ë | 243 | ˇ |
| 20 | ¶ | 52 | 4 | 84 | T | 116 | t | 148 | ö | 180 | ┤ | 212 | ď | 244 | ˘ |
| 21 | § | 53 | 5 | 85 | U | 117 | u | 149 | Ľ | 181 | Á | 213 | Ň | 245 | § |
| 22 | ▬ | 54 | 6 | 86 | V | 118 | v | 150 | ľ | 182 | Â | 214 | Í | 246 | ÷ |
| 23 | ↨ | 55 | 7 | 87 | W | 119 | w | 151 | Ś | 183 | Ě | 215 | Î | 247 | ¸ |
| 24 | ↑ | 56 | 8 | 88 | X | 120 | x | 152 | ś | 184 | Ş | 216 | ě | 248 | ° |
| 25 | ↓ | 57 | 9 | 89 | Y | 121 | y | 153 | Ö | 185 | ╣ | 217 | ┘ | 249 | ¨ |
| 26 | → | 58 | : | 90 | Z | 122 | z | 154 | Ü | 186 | ║ | 218 | ┌ | 250 | ˙ |
| 27 | ← | 59 | ; | 91 | [ | 123 | { | 155 | Ť | 187 | ╗ | 219 | █ | 251 | ű |
| 28 | ∟ | 60 | < | 92 | \ | 124 | ¦ | 156 | ť | 188 | ╝ | 220 | ▄ | 252 | Ř |
| 29 | ↔ | 61 | = | 93 | ] | 125 | } | 157 | Ł | 189 | Ż | 221 | Ţ | 253 | ř |
| 30 | ▲ | 62 | > | 94 | ^ | 126 | ~ | 158 | × | 190 | ż | 222 | Ů | 254 | ■ |
| 31 | ▼ | 63 | ? | 95 | _ | 127 | ⌂ | 159 | č | 191 | ┐ | 223 | ▀ | 255 | |

**852   Slavic (Latin II)**

| | | | | | | | | | | | | | | |
|---|---|---|---|---|---|---|---|---|---|---|---|---|---|---|---|
| 0 | | 32 | | 64 | @ | 96 | ` | 128 | Ç | 160 | á | 192 | L | 224 | α |
| 1 | ☺ | 33 | ! | 65 | A | 97 | a | 129 | ü | 161 | í | 193 | ⊥ | 225 | ß |
| 2 | ☻ | 34 | " | 66 | B | 98 | b | 130 | é | 162 | ó | 194 | ┬ | 226 | Γ |
| 3 | ♥ | 35 | # | 67 | C | 99 | c | 131 | â | 163 | ú | 195 | ├ | 227 | π |
| 4 | ♦ | 36 | $ | 68 | D | 100 | d | 132 | ã | 164 | ñ | 196 | ─ | 228 | Σ |
| 5 | ♣ | 37 | % | 69 | E | 101 | e | 133 | à | 165 | Ñ | 197 | ┼ | 229 | σ |
| 6 | ♠ | 38 | & | 70 | F | 102 | f | 134 | Á | 166 | ª | 198 | ╞ | 230 | μ |
| 7 | • | 39 | ' | 71 | G | 103 | g | 135 | ç | 167 | º | 199 | ╟ | 231 | τ |
| 8 | ◘ | 40 | ( | 72 | H | 104 | h | 136 | ê | 168 | ¿ | 200 | ╚ | 232 | Φ |
| 9 | ○ | 41 | ) | 73 | I | 105 | i | 137 | Ê | 169 | Ò | 201 | ╔ | 233 | Θ |
| 10 | ◙ | 42 | * | 74 | J | 106 | j | 138 | è | 170 | ¬ | 202 | ╩ | 234 | Ω |
| 11 | ♂ | 43 | + | 75 | K | 107 | k | 139 | Í | 171 | ½ | 203 | ╦ | 235 | δ |
| 12 | ♀ | 44 | , | 76 | L | 108 | l | 140 | Ô | 172 | ¼ | 204 | ╠ | 236 | ∞ |
| 13 | ♪ | 45 | - | 77 | M | 109 | m | 141 | ì | 173 | ¡ | 205 | = | 237 | ø |
| 14 | ♫ | 46 | . | 78 | N | 110 | n | 142 | Ã | 174 | « | 206 | ╬ | 238 | ε |
| 15 | ☼ | 47 | / | 79 | O | 111 | o | 143 | Â | 175 | » | 207 | ╧ | 239 | ∩ |
| 16 | ► | 48 | 0 | 80 | P | 112 | p | 144 | É | 176 | ░ | 208 | ╨ | 240 | ≡ |
| 17 | ◄ | 49 | 1 | 81 | Q | 113 | q | 145 | À | 177 | ▒ | 209 | ╤ | 241 | ± |
| 18 | ↕ | 50 | 2 | 82 | R | 114 | r | 146 | È | 178 | ▓ | 210 | ╥ | 242 | ≥ |
| 19 | ‼ | 51 | 3 | 83 | S | 115 | s | 147 | ô | 179 | │ | 211 | ╙ | 243 | ≤ |
| 20 | ¶ | 52 | 4 | 84 | T | 116 | t | 148 | õ | 180 | ┤ | 212 | ╘ | 244 | ⌠ |
| 21 | § | 53 | 5 | 85 | U | 117 | u | 149 | ò | 181 | ╡ | 213 | ╒ | 245 | ⌡ |
| 22 | ▬ | 54 | 6 | 86 | V | 118 | v | 150 | Ú | 182 | ╢ | 214 | ╓ | 246 | ÷ |
| 23 | ↨ | 55 | 7 | 87 | W | 119 | w | 151 | ù | 183 | ╖ | 215 | ╫ | 247 | ≈ |
| 24 | ↑ | 56 | 8 | 88 | X | 120 | x | 152 | Ì | 184 | ╕ | 216 | ╪ | 248 | ° |
| 25 | ↓ | 57 | 9 | 89 | Y | 121 | y | 153 | Õ | 185 | ╣ | 217 | ┘ | 249 | · |
| 26 | → | 58 | : | 90 | Z | 122 | z | 154 | Ü | 186 | ║ | 218 | ┌ | 250 | · |
| 27 | ← | 59 | ; | 91 | [ | 123 | { | 155 | ¢ | 187 | ╗ | 219 | █ | 251 | √ |
| 28 | ∟ | 60 | < | 92 | \ | 124 | ¦ | 156 | £ | 188 | ╝ | 220 | ▄ | 252 | ⁿ |
| 29 | ↔ | 61 | = | 93 | ] | 125 | } | 157 | Ù | 189 | ╜ | 221 | ▌ | 253 | ² |
| 30 | ▲ | 62 | > | 94 | ^ | 126 | ~ | 158 | ₧ | 190 | ╛ | 222 | ▐ | 254 | ■ |
| 31 | ▼ | 63 | ? | 95 | _ | 127 | ⌂ | 159 | Ó | 191 | ┐ | 223 | ▀ | 255 | |

**860  Portuguese**

| 0 | | 32 | | 64 | ℮ | 96 | ` | 128 | Ç | 160 | ¡ | 192 | L | 224 | α |
|---|---|----|---|----|---|----|---|-----|---|-----|---|-----|---|-----|---|
| 1 | ☺ | 33 | ! | 65 | A | 97 | a | 129 | ü | 161 | ´ | 193 | ⊥ | 225 | ß |
| 2 | ☻ | 34 | " | 66 | B | 98 | b | 130 | é | 162 | ó | 194 | T | 226 | Γ |
| 3 | ♥ | 35 | # | 67 | C | 99 | c | 131 | â | 163 | ú | 195 | ├ | 227 | π |
| 4 | ♦ | 36 | $ | 68 | D | 100 | d | 132 | Â | 164 | ¨ | 196 | — | 228 | Σ |
| 5 | ♣ | 37 | % | 69 | E | 101 | e | 133 | à | 165 | ‿ | 197 | ┼ | 229 | σ |
| 6 | ♠ | 38 | & | 70 | F | 102 | f | 134 | ¶ | 166 | ³ | 198 | ╞ | 230 | μ |
| 7 | • | 39 | ' | 71 | G | 103 | g | 135 | ç | 167 | ˙ | 199 | ‖ | 231 | τ |
| 8 | ◘ | 40 | ( | 72 | H | 104 | h | 136 | ê | 168 | Î | 200 | ╚ | 232 | Φ |
| 9 | ○ | 41 | ) | 73 | I | 105 | i | 137 | ë | 169 | ⌐ | 201 | ╔ | 233 | Θ |
| 10 | ◙ | 42 | * | 74 | J | 106 | j | 138 | è | 170 | ¬ | 202 | ╩ | 234 | Ω |
| 11 | ♂ | 43 | + | 75 | K | 107 | k | 139 | ï | 171 | ½ | 203 | ╦ | 235 | δ |
| 12 | ♀ | 44 | , | 76 | L | 108 | l | 140 | î | 172 | ¼ | 204 | ╠ | 236 | ∞ |
| 13 | ♪ | 45 | - | 77 | M | 109 | m | 141 | = | 173 | ¾ | 205 | = | 237 | ø |
| 14 | ♫ | 46 | . | 78 | N | 110 | n | 142 | À | 174 | « | 206 | ╬ | 238 | ∈ |
| 15 | ☼ | 47 | / | 79 | O | 111 | o | 143 | § | 175 | » | 207 | ⊥ | 239 | ∩ |
| 16 | ► | 48 | 0 | 80 | P | 112 | p | 144 | É | 176 | ░ | 208 | ╨ | 240 | ≡ |
| 17 | ◄ | 49 | 1 | 81 | Q | 113 | q | 145 | È | 177 | ▒ | 209 | ╤ | 241 | ± |
| 18 | ↕ | 50 | 2 | 82 | R | 114 | r | 146 | Ê | 178 | ▓ | 210 | π | 242 | ≥ |
| 19 | ‼ | 51 | 3 | 83 | S | 115 | s | 147 | ô | 179 | │ | 211 | ╙ | 243 | ≤ |
| 20 | ¶ | 52 | 4 | 84 | T | 116 | t | 148 | Ë | 180 | ┤ | 212 | ╘ | 244 | ⌠ |
| 21 | § | 53 | 5 | 85 | U | 117 | u | 149 | Ï | 181 | ╡ | 213 | ╒ | 245 | ⌡ |
| 22 | ▬ | 54 | 6 | 86 | V | 118 | v | 150 | û | 182 | ╢ | 214 | π | 246 | ÷ |
| 23 | ↨ | 55 | 7 | 87 | W | 119 | w | 151 | ù | 183 | ╖ | 215 | ╫ | 247 | ≈ |
| 24 | ↑ | 56 | 8 | 88 | X | 120 | x | 152 | ◌ | 184 | ╕ | 216 | ╪ | 248 | ° |
| 25 | ↓ | 57 | 9 | 89 | Y | 121 | y | 153 | Ô | 185 | ╣ | 217 | ┘ | 249 | ∙ |
| 26 | → | 58 | : | 90 | Z | 122 | z | 154 | Ü | 186 | ║ | 218 | ┌ | 250 | · |
| 27 | ← | 59 | ; | 91 | [ | 123 | { | 155 | ¢ | 187 | ╗ | 219 | █ | 251 | √ |
| 28 | ∟ | 60 | < | 92 | \ | 124 | ¦ | 156 | £ | 188 | ╝ | 220 | ▄ | 252 | ⁿ |
| 29 | ↔ | 61 | = | 93 | ] | 125 | } | 157 | Ù | 189 | ╜ | 221 | ▌ | 253 | ² |
| 30 | ▲ | 62 | > | 94 | ^ | 126 | ~ | 158 | Û | 190 | ╛ | 222 | ▐ | 254 | ■ |
| 31 | ▼ | 63 | ? | 95 | _ | 127 | ⌂ | 159 | ƒ | 191 | ┐ | 223 | ▀ | 255 | |

**863   Canadian-French**

| | | | | | | | |
|---|---|---|---|---|---|---|---|
| 0 | 32 | 64 @ | 96 ` | 128 Ç | 160 á | 192 L | 224 α |
| 1 ☺ | 33 ! | 65 A | 97 a | 129 ü | 161 í | 193 ⊥ | 225 ß |
| 2 ☻ | 34 " | 66 B | 98 b | 130 é | 162 ó | 194 T | 226 Γ |
| 3 ♥ | 35 # | 67 C | 99 c | 131 â | 163 ú | 195 ├ | 227 π |
| 4 ♦ | 36 $ | 68 D | 100 d | 132 ä | 164 ñ | 196 — | 228 Σ |
| 5 ♣ | 37 % | 69 E | 101 e | 133 à | 165 Ñ | 197 ┼ | 229 σ |
| 6 ♠ | 38 & | 70 F | 102 f | 134 å | 166 ª | 198 ╞ | 230 µ |
| 7 • | 39 ' | 71 G | 103 g | 135 ç | 167 º | 199 ╟ | 231 τ |
| 8 ◘ | 40 ( | 72 H | 104 h | 136 ê | 168 ¿ | 200 ╚ | 232 Φ |
| 9 ○ | 41 ) | 73 I | 105 i | 137 ë | 169 ⌐ | 201 ╔ | 233 Θ |
| 10 ◙ | 42 * | 74 J | 106 j | 138 è | 170 ¬ | 202 ╩ | 234 Ω |
| 11 ♂ | 43 + | 75 K | 107 k | 139 ï | 171 ½ | 203 ╦ | 235 δ |
| 12 ♀ | 44 , | 76 L | 108 l | 140 î | 172 ¼ | 204 ╠ | 236 ∞ |
| 13 ♪ | 45 - | 77 M | 109 m | 141 ì | 173 ¡ | 205 = | 237 ø |
| 14 ♫ | 46 . | 78 N | 110 n | 142 Ä | 174 « | 206 ╬ | 238 ∈ |
| 15 ☼ | 47 / | 79 O | 111 o | 143 Å | 175 ⌂ | 207 ⊥ | 239 ∩ |
| 16 ► | 48 0 | 80 P | 112 p | 144 É | 176 ░ | 208 ╨ | 240 ≡ |
| 17 ◄ | 49 1 | 81 Q | 113 q | 145 æ | 177 ▒ | 209 ╤ | 241 ± |
| 18 ↕ | 50 2 | 82 R | 114 r | 146 Æ | 178 ▓ | 210 ╥ | 242 ≥ |
| 19 ‼ | 51 3 | 83 S | 115 s | 147 ô | 179 │ | 211 ╙ | 243 ≤ |
| 20 ¶ | 52 4 | 84 T | 116 t | 148 ö | 180 ┤ | 212 ╘ | 244 ⌠ |
| 21 § | 53 5 | 85 U | 117 u | 149 ò | 181 ╡ | 213 ╒ | 245 ⌡ |
| 22 ▬ | 54 6 | 86 V | 118 v | 150 û | 182 ╢ | 214 ╓ | 246 ÷ |
| 23 ↨ | 55 7 | 87 W | 119 w | 151 ù | 183 ╖ | 215 ╫ | 247 ≈ |
| 24 ↑ | 56 8 | 88 X | 120 x | 152 ÿ | 184 ╕ | 216 ╪ | 248 ° |
| 25 ↓ | 57 9 | 89 Y | 121 y | 153 Ö | 185 ╣ | 217 ┘ | 249 · |
| 26 → | 58 : | 90 Z | 122 z | 154 Ü | 186 ║ | 218 ┌ | 250 · |
| 27 ← | 59 ; | 91 [ | 123 { | 155 ø | 187 ╗ | 219 █ | 251 √ |
| 28 ∟ | 60 < | 92 \ | 124 ¦ | 156 £ | 188 ╝ | 220 ▄ | 252 ⁿ |
| 29 ↔ | 61 = | 93 ] | 125 } | 157 Ø | 189 ╜ | 221 ▌ | 253 ² |
| 30 ▲ | 62 > | 94 ^ | 126 ~ | 158 ₧ | 190 ╛ | 222 ▐ | 254 ■ |
| 31 ▼ | 63 ? | 95 _ | 127 ⌂ | 159 ƒ | 191 ┐ | 223 ▀ | 255 |

**865  Nordic**

APPENDIX D

# Obtaining New Virus Signatures

Anti-virus programs use *virus signatures* to detect known computer viruses. A virus signature is a series of hexadecimal codes that uniquely identify a virus. By periodically updating your signature file, you can enable Microsoft Anti-Virus to detect new viruses. It is important to use only signature files written for Microsoft Anti-Virus. If you use a signature file written for another anti-virus program, you might receive a message indicating the presence of a virus, even if your computer is not infected.

## Updating Your Virus Signatures

New viruses are discovered regularly. As viruses are discovered, their signatures are posted on a bulletin board system (BBS), which is available 24 hours a day, 7 days a week. New signatures update only the ability of Microsoft Anti-Virus to *detect* new viruses; they do not enable you to *remove* new viruses. To fully protect your computer from unknown viruses and enable Microsoft Anti-Virus to remove them, you must update the Anti-Virus program. A coupon for a special Anti-Virus update offer is included at the back of this guide.

You must have a user identification code for the BBS to get an update. If you do not have a user identification code, carry out both the following procedures. If you have a user identification code, skip to the next procedure.

▶ **To obtain a user identification code for the BBS**

1. Change your communications settings to the following: 8 data bits, no parity, and 1 stop bit. You can select any speed up to 9600 baud.

2. Dial (503) 531-8100.

3. The first screen prompts you for information about your ANSI graphics display. If you want ANSI graphics, select Y, and then press ENTER.

4. When you are prompted for a user identification code, type the following at the prompt:

   **new**

5. The screen prompts you to indicate if the word "ANSI" is blinking. If the word is blinking, select Y and then press ENTER. If it is not blinking, select N and then press ENTER.

6. Type your full name, your company name (if applicable), your mailing address, and your daytime telephone number (including the area code). This information is used if it is necessary to contact you regarding your BBS account.

7. Choose your computer type.

8. Type the user identification code you want to use.

   Your user identification code can be 3 to 29 characters long, including spaces, numbers, and punctuation. To make your user identification code easy to remember, use a combination of your first and last name—for example, the first three letters of your first name and your full last name.

9. Type the password you want to use.

   Your password will be displayed after you type it. Make a record of your password when you are prompted to do so. You cannot get password information if you forget or lose the password you have chosen.

---

**Note**  You can change your user account information at any time, including your password. To do this, choose option A from the BBS menu, and then choose option E to edit your account information. You can change the screen display length by using this option (the default is 24 lines and 80 columns).

---

If you have a user identification code for the BBS, carry out the following procedure to obtain new virus signatures.

▶ **To obtain new virus signatures from the BBS**

1. If you have not logged on to the BBS, change your communications settings to the following: 8 data bits, no parity, and 1 stop bit. You can select any speed up to 9600 baud.

2. Dial (503) 531-8100.

3. Type your user identification code, and then press ENTER.

4. Type your password, and then press ENTER.

5. From the list that is displayed, choose option D (Download Anti-Virus Signature Files).

6. From the Download Signature Files list, choose one of the following options:

   - R (Readme First)—Lists options that enable you to display or download a readme file that contains instructions on using the signature files after you download them.

   - W (Windows)—Displays protocols you can choose from to download the signature files for Anti-Virus for Windows.

   - D (MS-DOS)—Displays protocols you can choose from to download the signature files for Anti-Virus for MS-DOS.

7. After selecting the W (Windows) or D (MS-DOS) option, select a download protocol supported by your modem.

8. Download the file.

9. After you have downloaded the file, press X, and then press ENTER to exit the BBS.

   Or, press C to display the Download Signature Files list again.

10. To log off, press Y.

   When the NO CARRIER message appears, quit your communications program.

11. Use the downloaded signature files as instructed in the Readme First file.

APPENDIX E

# Limited Warranties

This appendix contains information about the warranties that cover Microsoft products. The country or region in which you acquired your Microsoft product determines which warranty applies to you. This appendix includes warranties for the following countries or regions:

- Australia, New Zealand, Papua New Guinea
- Benelux (Dutch)
- Benelux (French)
- Brazil
- Canada (English)
- Canada (French)
- Commonwealth of Independent States
- Denmark
- England, Scotland, Wales, Ireland
- Finland
- France
- Germany, Switzerland, Austria, Liechtenstein
- Italy
- Latin America
- Mexico
- Norway
- Spain
- Sweden
- USA or any other country

To determine the warranty coverage for your Microsoft product, turn to the warranty for the country or region in which you acquired the product.

## If you acquired your Microsoft® product in AUSTRALIA, NEW ZEALAND, or PAPUA NEW GUINEA, the following limited warranty applies to you:

To the full extent permitted by the Commonwealth, State, Territory or other law or laws applicable to this Agreement, any conditions or warranties imposed by such legislation are hereby excluded. Insofar as liability under or pursuant to any legislation, whether of Commonwealth, State, Territory or other government, may not be excluded, such liability is limited to:

(i)  replacement of the SOFTWARE (and any accompanying hardware, if supplied by Microsoft); or,

(ii) correction of defects in the SOFTWARE at the exclusive option of Microsoft.

You acknowledge that no promise, representation or warranty or undertaking has been made or given by Microsoft or any person or company on its behalf in relation to the profitability of or any other consequences or benefits to be obtained from the delivery or use of the SOFTWARE and any accompanying Microsoft supplied hardware, SOFTWARE manuals, and written materials. You have relied upon your own skill and judgment in deciding to acquire the SOFTWARE and any accompanying hardware, SOFTWARE manuals, and written materials for use by you. This Agreement constitutes the entire agreement and understanding between you and Microsoft in relation to the supply of SOFTWARE and any accompanying hardware, SOFTWARE manuals, and written materials from Microsoft.

Except as and to the extent that it is hereinbefore provided, under no circumstances shall Microsoft or any related company be liable for any loss, damage or injury (including without limitation any loss of profit, indirect, consequential or incidental loss, damage or injury) arising from the supply or use of the SOFTWARE and any accompanying hardware and written materials or any failure by Microsoft or any related company to perform any obligation or observe any terms of this Agreement.

This Agreement is governed by the laws of New South Wales, Australia.

Should you have any questions concerning this Agreement, or if you desire to contact Microsoft for any reason, please use the address information enclosed in this product to contact the Microsoft subsidiary serving your country or write: Microsoft Customer Sales and Service, One Microsoft Way, Redmond, Washington 98052-6399.

# Indien u uw Microsoft®-produkt in de BENELUX hebt gekocht, geldt de volgende beperkte garantie voor u:

**BEPERKTE GARANTIE** — Microsoft garandeert dat (a) de SOFTWARE in hoofdzaak functioneert overeenkomstig de bijbehorende produkthandboek(en) gedurende een periode van 90 dagen na de datum van ontvangst; en (b) enig door Microsoft geleverde hardware behorende bij de SOFTWARE geen gebreken vertoont wat betreft het materiaal en vakmanschap bij normaal gebruik en onderhoud gedurende een periode van een jaar na de datum van ontvangst. Impliciete garanties op de SOFTWARE en hardware zijn beperkt tot respectievelijk 90 dagen en één (1) jaar.

**VERHAALSMOGELIJKHEDEN VAN KLANTEN** — De gehele aansprakelijkheid van Microsoft en uw enige verhaalsmogelijkheid is, ter keuze van Microsoft, ofwel (a) terugbetaling van de aankoopprijs of (b) reparatie of vervanging van de SOFTWARE of hardware die niet voldoet aan de beperkte garantie van Microsoft en die geretourneerd wordt aan Microsoft met een kopie van de aanschafbon. Deze beperkte garantie geldt niet indien het gebrek in de SOFTWARE of hardware het gevolg is van een ongeluk, misbruik of verkeerd gebruik. Voor vervangende SOFTWARE wordt garantie verleend voor de resterende tijd van de oorspronkelijke garantietermijn of 30 dagen, welke van de twee het langst is.

**GEEN ANDERE GARANTIES** — MICROSOFT VERLEENT GEEN ANDERE GARANTIE, NOCH UITDRUKKELIJK NOCH IMPLICIET, DAARONDER MEDEBEGREPEN MAAR NIET BEPERKT TOT IMPLICIETE GARANTIES BETREFFENDE VERKOOPBAARHEID OF GESCHIKTHEID VOOR EEN BEPAALDE TOEPASSING, MET BETREKKING TOT DE SOFTWARE, DE DAARBIJ BEHORENDE PRODUKTHANDBOEK(EN) EN DOCUMENTATIEMATERIAAL, EN ENIGE DAARBIJ BEHORENDE HARDWARE. DEZE BEPERKTE GARANTIE GEEFT U SPECIFIEKE RECHTEN.

**GEEN AANSPRAKELIJKHEID VOOR GEVOLGSCHADE** — IN GEEN GEVAL IS MICROSOFT OF HAAR LEVERANCIERS AANSPRAKELIJK VOOR SCHADE (DAARONDER MEDEBEGREPEN MAAR NIET BEPERKT TOT SCHADEVERGOEDING VOOR WINSTDERVING, BEDRIJFSONDERBREKING, VERLIES VAN BEDRIJFSINFORMATIE OF ANDER GELDELIJK VERLIES) WELKE ONSTAAN IS DOOR HET GEBRUIK VAN OF ENIGE VERHINDERING TOT GEBRUIK VAN DIT MICROSOFT PRODUKT, OOK INDIEN MICROSOFT OP DE HOOGTE GESTELD IS VAN HET RISICO VAN DERGELIJKE SCHADE. IN IEDER GEVAL ZAL DE AANSPRAKELIJKHEID VAN MICROSOFT KRACHTENS ENIGE BEPALING VAN DEZE OVEREENKOMST BEPERKT ZIJN TOT HET DAADWERKELIJK DOOR U VOOR DE SOFTWARE BETAALDE BEDRAG.

Op deze overeenkomst is het recht van Nederland van toepassing.

Indien u vragen hebt met betrekking tot deze overeenkomst of indien u om een of andere reden contact met Microsoft wilt opnemen, schrijft u dan naar de dichtstbijzijnde Microsoft-vestiging (raadpleeg de ingesloten adresinformatie) of naar Microsoft Customer Sales and Service, One Microsoft Way, Redmond, Washington 98052-6399.

## L'acquisition du produit Microsoft® au BENELUX est gouvernée par les limites de garantie suivantes :

**LIMITES DE GARANTIE** — Microsoft garantit (a) la performance générale du LOGICIEL conformément aux indications données par le(s) manuel(s) pour une durée de quatre-vingt-dix (90) jours à compter de la date de réception ; (b) la bonne qualité du matériel fourni par Microsoft et accompagnant le LOGICIEL ainsi que sa fabrication soignée pour une durée d'un (1) an à compter de la date de réception dans des conditions normales d'emploi et d'entretien. Toutes garanties tacites concernant le LOGICIEL et le matériel sont limitées à une durée de quatre-vingt-dix (90) jours pour le logiciel et à un (1) an pour le matériel.

**RECOURS DU CONSOMMATEUR** — En cas de responsabilité de la part de Microsoft, les recours du consommateur consisteront au gré de Microsoft soit dans (a) le remboursement du prix payé à l'achat, soit dans (b) la réparation ou le remplacement du LOGICIEL ou du matériel qui ne répondrait pas aux termes de la garantie limitée de Microsoft après le retour à Microsoft du LOGICIEL ou du matériel accompagné d'une copie du reçu. Cette garantie sera nulle si la non-performance du LOGICIEL ou du matériel est le résultat d'un accident, d'un abus ou d'une utilisation erronée quelconque. Tout LOGICIEL offert en remplacement sera garanti jusqu'à expiration de la garantie d'origine du premier LOGICIEL ou pendant une durée de trente (30) jours, la période la plus longue étant applicable.

**LIMITATIONS DE LA GARANTIE** — MICROSOFT REFUSE D'APPLIQUER TOUTES AUTRES GARANTIES EXPRESSES OU TACITES, Y COMPRIS, MAIS SANS Y ETRE LIMITE, LES GARANTIES TACITES CONCERNANT LA BONNE QUALITE ET L'UTILISATION SPECIFIQUE A LAQUELLE LE LOGICIEL, LE(S) MANUEL(S), DOCUMENT(S) ECRIT(S) ET TOUT MATERIEL L'ACCOMPAGNANT SONT DESTINES. CETTE GARANTIE RESTREINTE N'EXCLUT PAS LES DROITS AUX TERMES DE LA LOI.

**EXCLUSION DE RESPONSABILITE EN CAS DE DOMMAGE INDIRECT** — EN AUCUN CAS, MICROSOFT OU SES FOURNISSEURS NE SERONT RESPONSABLES D'UN DOMMAGE DIRECT, INDIRECT, INCIDENT OU SUBSEQUENT (Y COMPRIS ET SANS Y ETRE LIMITE, TOUT DOMMAGE POUR MANQUE A GAGNER, INTERRUPTION, PERTE DE DONNEES OU TOUT AUTRE DOMMAGE ECONOMIQUE) RESULTANT DE TOUTE UTILISATION OU DE TOUTE IMPOSSIBILITE D'UTILISER LE PRODUIT MICROSOFT, MEME SI LA POSSIBILITE D'UN TEL DOMMAGE A DEJA ETE PORTEE A LA CONNAISSANCE DE MICROSOFT. DANS TOUS LES CAS, LA RESPONSABILITE DE MICROSOFT, CONFORMEMENT AUX TERMES DE CE CONTRAT, SERA LIMITEE AU MONTANT DU PRIX D'ACHAT PAYE POUR LE LOGICIEL.

Le présent accord est régi par le droit des Pays-Bas.

Au cas où vous auriez des questions concernant cette licence ou que vous désiriez vous mettre en rapport avec Microsoft pour quelque raison que ce soit, veuillez contacter la succursale Microsoft desservant votre pays, dont l'adresse est fournie dans ce produit, ou écrire à : Microsoft Customer Sales and Service, One Microsoft Way, Redmond, Washington 98052-6399.

## Caso V.Sa. adquiriu seu produto Microsoft® no BRASIL, o seguinte Contrato de garantia limitada aplica-se a V.Sa.:

**GARANTIA LIMITADA** — A Microsoft garante que (a) o SOFTWARE desempenhará suas funções substancialmente em conformidade com seu(s) manual(is), por um período de 90 (noventa) dias a contar da data da entrega; (b) qualquer hardware fornecido pela Microsoft juntamente com o SOFTWARE estará isento de defeitos de fabricação e em relação aos materiais empregados, por um período de 1 (hum) ano, a contar da data da entrega, sob condições normais de utilização e manutenção. Quaisquer garantias implícitas com relação ao SOFTWARE e ao hardware ficam limitadas a 90 (noventa) dias e 1 (hum) ano, respectivamente.

**DIREITOS DO CLIENTE** — A responsabilidade integral da Microsoft, e o único direito de V.Sa. será, a critério da Microsoft, (a) a devolução do preço pago ou, alternativamente, (b) o conserto ou substituição do SOFTWARE ou hardware, sujeito aos termos da Garantia Limitada e à devolução dos mesmos à Microsoft com a cópia do recibo. Esta Garantia Limitada ficará prejudicada e não gerará efeitos se o defeito do SOFTWARE ou hardware resultar de acidente, utilização abusiva ou inadequada. Qualquer SOFTWARE substituído será garantido pelo prazo remanescente da garantia original ou por 30 (trinta) dias, no caso deste último prazo ser mais extenso.

**GARANTIAS ÚNICAS** — AS GARANTIAS SUPRA SÃO AS ÚNICAS GARANTIAS, QUER EXPRESSAS, QUER IMPLÍCITAS. FICAM EXCLUÍDAS, INCLUSIVE, EXEMPLIFICATIVAMENTE, QUAISQUER GARANTIAS IMPLÍCITAS DE COMERCIALIZAÇÃO E ADEQUAÇÃO PARA DETERMINADA APLICAÇÃO, COM RELAÇÃO AO SOFTWARE, SEUS MANUAIS E AOS MATERIAIS ESCRITOS E QUALQUER HARDWARE QUE ACOMPANHE O MESMO. ESTA GARANTIA LIMITADA LHE CONFERE DIREITOS ESPECÍFICOS.

**LIMITAÇÃO DE RESPONSABILIDADE (DANOS INDIRETOS)** — EM NENHUMA HIPÓTESE A MICROSOFT OU SEUS FORNECEDORES SERÃO RESPONSÁVEIS POR QUAISQUER OUTROS DANOS (INCLUINDO, MAS NÃO LIMITADOS, A LUCROS CESSANTES, INTERRUPÇÃO DE NEGÓCIOS, PERDA DE INFORMAÇÕES E OUTROS PREJUÍZOS PECUNIÁRIOS) DECORRENTES DO USO, OU DA IMPOSSIBILIDADE DE USAR ESTE PRODUTO MICROSOFT, AINDA QUE A MICROSOFT TENHA SIDO ALERTADA QUANTO À POSSIBILIDADE DESTES DANOS. EM QUALQUER CASO, A RESPONSABILIDADE INTEGRAL DA MICROSOFT SOB ESTE CONTRATO LIMITAR-SE-Á AO VALOR EFETIVAMENTE PAGO POR V.SA. PELO SOFTWARE.

Este Contrato é regido pelas leis da República Federativa do Brasil.

Caso V.Sa. possua dúvida em relação a este Contrato de Licença ou deseje entrar em contato com a Microsoft, utilize as informações de endereçamento que se encontram neste produto para contactar a subsidiária Microsoft no seu país ou escreva para: Microsoft Customer Sales, One Microsoft Way, Redmond, Washington 98052-6399.

## If you acquired your Microsoft® product in CANADA, the following limited warranty applies to you:

**LIMITED WARRANTY** — Microsoft warrants that (a) the SOFTWARE will perform substantially in accordance with the accompanying Product Manual(s) for a period of 90 days from the date of receipt; and (b) any Microsoft supplied hardware accompanying the SOFTWARE will be free from defects in materials and workmanship under normal use and service for a period of one year from the date of receipt. Any implied warranties on the SOFTWARE and hardware are limited to 90 days and one (1) year, respectively.

**CUSTOMER REMEDIES** — Microsoft's entire liability and your exclusive remedy shall be, at Microsoft's option, either (a) return of the price paid or (b) repair or replacement of the SOFTWARE or hardware that does not meet Microsoft's Limited Warranty and which is returned to Microsoft with a copy of your receipt. This Limited Warranty is void if failure of the SOFTWARE or hardware has resulted from accident, abuse, or misapplication. Any replacement SOFTWARE will be warranted for the remainder of the original warranty period or 30 days, whichever is longer.

**NO OTHER WARRANTIES** — MICROSOFT DISCLAIMS ALL OTHER WARRANTIES, EITHER EXPRESS OR IMPLIED, INCLUDING BUT NOT LIMITED TO IMPLIED WARRANTIES OF MERCHANTABILITY AND FITNESS FOR A PARTICULAR PURPOSE, WITH RESPECT TO THE SOFTWARE, THE ACCOMPANYING PRODUCT MANUAL(S) AND WRITTEN MATERIALS, AND ANY ACCOMPANYING HARDWARE. THIS LIMITED WARRANTY GIVES YOU SPECIFIC LEGAL RIGHTS.

**NO LIABILITY FOR CONSEQUENTIAL DAMAGES** — IN NO EVENT SHALL MICROSOFT OR ITS SUPPLIERS BE LIABLE FOR ANY OTHER DAMAGES WHATSOEVER (INCLUDING, WITHOUT LIMITATION, DAMAGES FOR LOSS OF BUSINESS PROFITS, BUSINESS INTERRUPTION, LOSS OF BUSINESS INFORMATION, OR OTHER PECUNIARY LOSS) ARISING OUT OF THE USE OF OR INABILITY TO USE THIS MICROSOFT PRODUCT, EVEN IF MICROSOFT HAS BEEN ADVISED OF THE POSSIBILITY OF SUCH DAMAGES. IN ANY CASE, MICROSOFT'S ENTIRE LIABILITY UNDER ANY PROVISION OF THIS AGREEMENT SHALL BE LIMITED TO THE AMOUNT ACTUALLY PAID BY YOU FOR THE SOFTWARE.

This Agreement is governed by the laws of the Province of Ontario, Canada. Each of the parties hereto irrevocably attorns to the jurisdiction of the courts of the Province of Ontario and further agrees to commence any litigation which may arise hereunder in the courts located in the Judicial District of York, Province of Ontario.

Should you have any questions concerning this Agreement, or if you desire to contact Microsoft for any reason, please use the address information enclosed in this product to contact the Microsoft subsidiary serving your country or write: Microsoft Customer Sales and Service, One Microsoft Way, Redmond, Washington 98052-6399.

## Si vous avez acquis votre produit Microsoft® au CANADA, la garantie limitée suivante vous concerne :

**GARANTIE LIMITEE** — Microsoft garantit que (a) la performance du LOGICIEL sera substantiellement en conformité avec le(s) manuel(s) de produits qui accompagne(nt) le LOGICIEL pour une période de quatre-vingt-dix (90) jours à compter de la date de réception ; et (b) tout matériel fourni par Microsoft accompagnant le LOGICIEL sera exempt de défaut de matière première ou de vice de fabrication dans des conditions normales d'utilisation et d'entretien pour une période d'un an à compter de la date de réception. Toute garantie implicite concernant le LOGICIEL et le matériel est limitée à quatre-vingt-dix (90) jours et un (1) an, respectivement.

**RECOURS DU CLIENT** — La seule obligation de Microsoft et votre recours exclusif seront, au choix de Microsoft, soit (a) le remboursement du prix payé ou (b) la réparation ou le remplacement du LOGICIEL ou du matériel qui n'est pas conforme à la Garantie Limitée de Microsoft et qui est retourné à Microsoft avec une copie de votre reçu. Cette Garantie Limitée est nulle si le défaut du LOGICIEL ou du matériel est causé par un accident, un traitement abusif ou une mauvaise application. Tout LOGICIEL de remplacement sera garanti pour le reste de la période de garantie initiale ou pour trente (30) jours, selon laquelle de ces deux périodes est la plus longue.

**AUCUNE AUTRE GARANTIE** — MICROSOFT DESAVOUE TOUTE AUTRE GARANTIE, EXPRESSE OU IMPLICITE, Y COMPRIS MAIS NE SE LIMITANT PAS AUX GARANTIES IMPLICITES DU CARACTERE ADEQUAT POUR LA COMMERCIALISATION OU UN USAGE PARTICULIER EN CE QUI CONCERNE LE LOGICIEL, LE(S) MANUEL(S) DE PRODUITS, LA DOCUMENTATION ECRITE ET TOUT MATERIEL QUI L'ACCOMPAGNENT. CETTE GARANTIE LIMITEE VOUS ACCORDE DES DROITS JURIDIQUES SPECIFIQUES.

**PAS D'OBLIGATION POUR LES DOMMAGES INDIRECTS** — MICROSOFT OU SES FOURNISSEURS N'AURONT D'OBLIGATION EN AUCUNE CIRCONSTANCE POUR TOUT AUTRE DOMMAGE QUEL QU'IL SOIT (Y COMPRIS, SANS LIMITATION, LES DOMMAGES ENTRAINES PAR LA PERTE DE BENEFICES, L'INTERRUPTION DES AFFAIRES, LA PERTE D'INFORMATION COMMERCIALE OU TOUTE AUTRE PERTE PECUNIAIRE) DECOULANT DE L'UTILISATION OU DE L'IMPOSSIBILITE D'UTILISATION DE CE PRODUIT MICROSOFT, ET CE, MEME SI MICROSOFT A ETE AVISE DE LA POSSIBILITE DE TELS DOMMAGES. EN TOUT CAS, LA SEULE OBLIGATION DE MICROSOFT EN VERTU DE TOUTE DISPOSITION DE CETTE CONVENTION SE LIMITERA AU MONTANT EN FAIT PAYE PAR VOUS POUR LE LOGICIEL.

La présente Convention est régie par les lois de la province d'Ontario, Canada. Chacune des parties à la présente reconnaît irrévocablement la compétence des tribunaux de la province d'Ontario et consent à instituer tout litige qui pourrait découler de la présente auprès des tribunaux situés dans le district judiciaire de York, province d'Ontario.

Au cas où vous auriez des questions concernant cette licence ou que vous désiriez vous mettre en rapport avec Microsoft pour quelque raison que ce soit, veuillez contacter la succursale Microsoft desservant votre pays, dont l'adresse est fournie dans ce produit, ou écrire à : Microsoft Customer Sales and Service, One Microsoft Way, Redmond, Washington 98052-6399.

# Если Вы приобрели продукцию корпорации Microsoft® на территории СОДРУЖЕСТВА НЕЗАВИСИМЫХ ГОСУДАРСТВ, то нижеследующая ограниченная гарантия относится к Вам:

**ОГРАНИЧЕННАЯ ГАРАНТИЯ** — Microsoft гарантирует Вам следующее: (а) ПРОГРАММА MICROSOFT будет нормально работать в соответствии с прилагаемой инструкцией по эксплуатации в течение шести (6) месяцев после приобретения, согласно дате на квитанции; (б) любые физические устройства (hardware), поставляемые Microsoft в комплекте с ПРОГРАММОЙ MICROSOFT будут при нормальном использовании и обслуживании гарантированы от дефектов в материале и изготовлении в течение одного (1) года со дня приобретения, согласно дате на квитанции. Любые предполагаемые гарантии на ПРОГРАММУ MICROSOFT и физические устройства ограничены шестью (6) месяцами и одним (1) годом соответственно.

**РЕКЛАМАЦИИ И КОМПЕНСАЦИИ** — Согласно ответственности Microsoft за данный продукт, а также Вашему праву на рекламации, предоставив копию квитанции, Вы можете выбрать по Вашему усмотрению следующее: (а) получить полный возврат уплаченной стоимости после возвращения ПРОГРАММЫ MICROSOFT или физических устройств; (б) получить пропорциональное снижение оплаченной стоимости; (в) получить исправленные или замененные ПРОГРАММУ MICROSOFT или физические устройства, не соответствующие условиям ограниченной гарантии Microsoft и возвращенные изготовителю. Данная ограниченная гарантия является недействительной, если неполадки в программе Microsoft или в физических устройствах появились в результате аварии, умышленного повреждения или нарушения инструкций по пользованию. Любая замененная ПРОГРАММА MICROSOFT будет содержать гарантию на оставшийся гарантийный срок или на 30 дней, в зависимости от того, какой срок длиннее.

**ОТКАЗ ОТ ДРУГИХ ГАРАНТИЙ** — MICROSOFT ОТКАЗЫВАЕТСЯ ОТ ВСЕХ ДРУГИХ ГАРАНТИЙ, КАК ЯВНЫХ, ТАК И ПРЕДПОЛАГАЕМЫХ, ВКЛЮЧАЯ (НО НЕ ОГРАНИЧИВАЯСЬ ТОЛЬКО ИМИ) ПРЕДПОЛАГАЕМЫЕ ГАРАНТИИ НА ПОКУПАТЕЛЬСКУЮ СПОСОБНОСТЬ И СООТВЕТСТВИЕ СПЕЦИАЛЬНЫМ ТРЕБОВАНИЯМ, ЧТО ОТНОСИТСЯ К ПРОГРАММЕ MICROSOFT, А ТАКЖЕ К НАХОДЯЩИМСЯ В КОМПЛЕКТЕ РУКОВОДСТВАМ ПО ЭКСПЛУАТАЦИИ, ПЕЧАТНЫМ МАТЕРИАЛАМ И ЛЮБЫМ ФИЗИЧЕСКИМ УСТРОЙСТВАМ. ЭТА ОГРАНИЧЕННАЯ ГАРАНТИЯ ПРЕДОСТАВЛЯЕТ ВАМ ОСОБЫЕ ЮРИДИЧЕСКИЕ ПРАВА.

**ОТКАЗ ОТ ОТВЕТСТВЕННОСТИ ЗА СОПУТСТВУЮЩИЕ УБЫТКИ** — MICROSOFT ИЛИ ЕГО ПОСТАВЩИКИ НИ ПРИ КАКИХ УСЛОВИЯХ НЕ НЕСУТ ОТВЕТСТВЕННОСТИ ЗА КАКОЙ-ЛИБО УЩЕРБ (ВКЛЮЧАЯ ВСЕ, БЕЗ ИСКЛЮЧЕНИЯ, СЛУЧАИ ПОТЕРИ ПРИБЫЛЕЙ, ПРЕРЫВАНИЯ ДЕЛОВОЙ АКТИВНОСТИ, ПОТЕРИ ДЕЛОВОЙ ИНФОРМАЦИИ ИЛИ ДРУГИХ ДЕНЕЖНЫХ ПОТЕРЬ), СВЯЗАННЫЙ С ИСПОЛЬЗОВАНИЕМ ИЛИ НЕВОЗМОЖНОСТЬЮ ИСПОЛЬЗОВАНИЯ ДАННОГО ПРОДУКТА MICROSOFT, ДАЖЕ ЕСЛИ MICROSOFT БЫЛ ИЗВЕЩЕН ЗАРАНЕЕ О ВОЗМОЖНОСТИ ТАКИХ ПОТЕРЬ. В ЛЮБОМ СЛУЧАЕ, СУММА ВОЗМЕЩЕНИЯ, СОГЛАСНО ДАННОМУ ДОГОВОРУ, НЕ МОЖЕТ ПРЕВЫШАТЬ СУММУ, ФАКТИЧЕСКИ УПЛАЧЕННУЮ ВАМИ ЗА ПРОГРАММУ MICROSOFT.

Если у Вас возникли какие-либо вопросы, касающиеся данного Соглашения, или если Вы хотите связаться с Microsoft по любому другому поводу, пожалуйста, используйте адрес, прилагаемый к данному продукту, чтобы связаться с филиалом Microsoft, обслуживающим Вашу страну, или пишите по адресу: Microsoft Customer Sales and Service, One Microsoft Way, Redmond, Washington 98052-6399.

# Hvis De har købt Deres Microsoft®-produkt i DANMARK, gælder følgende begrænset ansvar for Dem:

**BEGRÆNSET ANSVAR** — a) Microsoft står alene inde for, at softwaren i alt væsentligt vil fungere i overensstemmelse med de ledsagende håndbøger i en periode af 90 dage fra modtagelsen; b) og at al hardware, leveret af Microsoft, som ledsager softwaren, vil være fri for håndværks- og materialemæssige fejl under normal brug og servicering i en periode af et år fra modtagelsen. Enhver stiltiende garanti vedrørende softwaren og hardwaren er ligeledes begrænset til 90 dage respektive et år.

**BRUGERENS MISLIGHOLDELSESBEFØJELSER** — Microsofts totale ansvar og Deres eneste misligholdelsesbeføjelser er, efter Microsofts valg enten a) refundering af købesummen, eller; b) reparation eller omlevering af softwaren eller hardwaren, som ikke opfylder kravene i den ovenstående klausul om begrænset ansvar, når denne er blevet returneret til Microsoft vedlagt en kopi af Deres kvittering. De har dog intet krav under klausulen om begrænset ansvar, hvis manglerne ved softwaren eller hardwaren er opstået som et resultat af udefra kommende skade herpå samt bevidst eller ubevidst forkert brug.

**INGEN ANDRE GARANTIER** — MICROSOFT FRASKRIVER SIG UDTRYKKELIGT ALLE ANDRE GARANTIER, UDTRYKKELIGE SÅVEL SOM STILTIENDE — INKLUSIVE, MEN IKKE BEGRÆNSET TIL, STILTIENDE GARANTIER OM, AT PRODUKTERNE ER KURANTE ELLER KAN ANVENDES TIL SÆRLIGE FORMÅL — FOR SÅ VIDT ANGÅR SOFTWAREN, DE LEDSAGENDE HÅNDBØGER OG SKRIFTLIGT MATERIALE OG LEDSAGENDE HARDWARE.

**BEGRÆNSNINGER I ANSVARET** — MICROSOFT ELLER MICROSOFTS LEVERANDØRER SKAL PÅ INGEN ANDEN MÅDE VÆRE PLIGTIG AT BETALE NOGEN SOM HELST ERSTATNING (INKL., UDEN BEGRÆNSNINGER, ERSTATNING FOR DRIFTSTAB, FORSTYRRELSE AF VIRKSOMHED, TAB AF OPLYSNINGER FOR VIRKSOMHEDEN, ELLER ANDET TAB) , SOM OPSTÅR PÅ BAGGRUND AF BRUGEN ELLER DEN MANGLENDE BRUGBARHED AF DETTE MICROSOFT-PRODUKT SELV OM MICROSOFT MÅTTE VÆRE BLEVET NOTIFICERET OM RISIKOEN FOR SÅDAN ERSTATNING. UNDER ALLE OMSTÆNDIGHEDER SKAL MICROSOFTS FULDE ANSVAR UNDER ENHVER BESTEMMELSE I DENNE AFTALE VÆRE BEGRÆNSET TIL DET BELØB, SOM DE FAKTISK HAR BETALT FOR SOFTWAREN.

Denne aftale er underlagt retten i the State of Washington, U.S.A.

Hvis De har spørgsmål vedrørende denne licensaftale, eller hvis De ønsker at kontakte Microsoft i en anden forbindelse, kan De anvende vedlagte adresseliste og kontakte et Microsoft-datterselskab. De kan også kontakte Microsoft i USA på følgende adresse: Microsoft Customer Sales and Service, One Microsoft Way, Redmond, Washington 98052-6399.

## If you acquired your Microsoft® product in ENGLAND, SCOTLAND, WALES or IRELAND, the following limited warranty applies to you:

**LIMITED WARRANTY** — Microsoft warrants that (a) the SOFTWARE will perform substantially in accordance with the accompanying Product Manual(s) for a period of 90 days from the date of receipt; and (b) any Microsoft supplied hardware accompanying the SOFTWARE will be free from defects in materials and workmanship under normal use and service for a period of one year from the date of receipt. Any implied warranties on the SOFTWARE and hardware are limited to 90 days and one (1) year, respectively, or the shortest period permitted by applicable law, whichever is greater.

**CUSTOMER REMEDIES** — Microsoft's entire liability and your exclusive remedy shall be, at Microsoft's option, either (a) return of the price paid or (b) repair or replacement of the SOFTWARE or hardware that does not meet Microsoft's Limited Warranty and which is returned to Microsoft with a copy of your receipt. This Limited Warranty is void if failure of the SOFTWARE or hardware has resulted from accident, abuse, or misapplication. Any replacement SOFTWARE will be warranted for the remainder of the original warranty period or 30 days, whichever is longer.

**NO OTHER WARRANTIES** — TO THE MAXIMUM EXTENT PERMITTED BY APPLICABLE LAW, MICROSOFT DISCLAIMS ALL OTHER WARRANTIES, EITHER EXPRESS OR IMPLIED, INCLUDING BUT NOT LIMITED TO IMPLIED WARRANTIES OF MERCHANTABILITY AND FITNESS FOR A PARTICULAR PURPOSE, WITH RESPECT TO THE SOFTWARE, THE ACCOMPANYING PRODUCT MANUAL(S) AND WRITTEN MATERIALS, AND ANY ACCOMPANYING HARDWARE. THE LIMITED WARRANTY CONTAINED HEREIN GIVES YOU SPECIFIC LEGAL RIGHTS.

**NO LIABILITY FOR CONSEQUENTIAL DAMAGES** — TO THE MAXIMUM EXTENT PERMITTED BY APPLICABLE LAW, MICROSOFT AND ITS SUPPLIERS SHALL NOT BE LIABLE FOR ANY OTHER DAMAGES WHATSOEVER (INCLUDING, WITHOUT LIMITATION, DAMAGES FOR LOSS OF BUSINESS PROFITS, BUSINESS INTERRUPTION, LOSS OF BUSINESS INFORMATION, OR OTHER PECUNIARY LOSS) ARISING OUT OF THE USE OF OR INABILITY TO USE THIS MICROSOFT PRODUCT, EVEN IF MICROSOFT HAS BEEN ADVISED OF THE POSSIBILITY OF SUCH DAMAGES. IN ANY CASE, MICROSOFT'S ENTIRE LIABILITY UNDER ANY PROVISION OF THIS AGREEMENT SHALL BE LIMITED TO THE AMOUNT ACTUALLY PAID BY YOU FOR THE SOFTWARE.

This Agreement is governed by the laws of England.

Should you have any questions concerning this Agreement, or if you desire to contact Microsoft for any reason, please use the address information enclosed in this product to contact the Microsoft subsidiary serving your country or write: Microsoft Customer Sales and Services, One Microsoft Way, Redmond, Washington 98052-6399.

# Mikäli olette hankkineet Microsoft®-tuotteenne SUOMESTA, sovelletaan Teihin seuraavaa rajoitettua takuuta.

**RAJOITETTU TAKUU** — Microsoft takaa, että (a) OHJELMISTO suoriutuu olennaisilta osiltaan oheistetun tuoteoppaan (-oppaiden) mukaisesti vastaanottopäivästä 90 päivän aikana ja (b) missään Microsoftin OHJELMISTON mukana toimittamassa laitteistossa ei ole tavanomaisessa käytössä ja palveluksessa yhden vuoden aikana vastaanottopäivästä ilmeneviä materiaalivikoja ja laatuvirheitä. Kaikki oletettu vastuu on rajoitettu ohjelmiston osalta 90 päiväksi ja laitteiston osalta yhdeksi (1) vuodeksi.

**ASIAKKAAN OIKEUDET** — Microsoftin koko vastuu ja Teidän kaikki oikeutenne rajoittuvat, Microsoftin valinnan mukaan, joko (a) maksetun kauppahinnan palauttamiseen tai (b) niiden Microsoftille kuittijäljennöksen kanssa palautettujen ohjelmistojen tai laitteistojen, jotka eivät vastaa Microsoftin rajoitettua takuuta, korjauttamiseen tai uusimiseen. Tämä rajoitettu takuu on mitätön, jos ohjelmiston tai laitteiston vika on johtunut onnettomuudesta, väärinkäytöksestä tai ohjelmiston tai laitteiston väärinasentamisesta. Jokainen korvattu OHJELMISTO kuuluu takuun piiriin 30 päiväksi tai jäljellejääväksi alkuperäiseksi takuuajaksi riippuen siitä, kumpi niistä on pitempi.

**MUUT TAKUUT** — MICROSOFT TORJUU PÄTEMÄTTÖMINÄ KAIKKI MUUT TAKUUT JA VASTUUT, JOKO ILMAISTUT TAI OLETETUT, MUKAAN LUKIEN OLETETUT VASTUUT SOVELTUVUUDESTA JA SOPIVUUDESTA JOHONKIN ERITYISEEN TARKOITUKSEEN, KÄSITTÄEN OHJELMISTON, LIITETYN TUOTEOPPAAN (-OPPAIDEN), KIRJOITETUN MATERIAALIN JA KAIKKI LIITETYT LAITTEET. TÄMÄ RAJOITETTU TAKUU ANTAA TEILLE NIMENOMAISET OIKEUDET.

**VASTUU VÄLILLISISTÄ VAHINGOISTA** — MISSÄÄN TAPAUKSESSA MICROSOFT TAI SEN TOIMITTAJAT EIVÄT OLE VASTUUSSA MISTÄÄN MUISTA VAHINGOISTA (MUKAAN LUKIEN ILMAN RAJOITUSTA VAHINGOT, JOTKA JOHTUVAT LIIKETOIMINNAN VOITTOJEN MENETTÄMISESTÄ, LIIKETOIMINNAN KESKEYTTÄMISESTÄ, LIIKETOIMINNAN TIETOJEN MENETTÄMISESTÄ, TAI MUUSTA RAHALLISESTA MENETYKSESTÄ), JOTKA SYNTYVÄT MICROSOFT-TUOTTEEN KÄYTÖSTÄ TAI KYKENEMÄTTÖMYYDESTÄ KÄYTTÄÄ SITÄ, VAIKKA MICROSOFTIA ON VAROITETTU SELLAISTEN VAHINKOJEN MAHDOLLISUUDESTA. JOKA TAPAUKSESSA MICROSOFTIN VASTUU ON RAJOITETTU SIIHEN MÄÄRÄÄN, JONKA ITSE MAKSOITTE OHJELMISTOSTA.

Tähän sopimukseen sovelletaan Suomen lakia.

Jos Teillä on tätä sopimusta koskevia kysymyksiä tai haluatte jostain muusta syystä ottaa yhteyttä Microsoftiin, olkaa hyvä ja käyttäkää tässä tuotteessa olevia maatanne palvelevan tytäryhtiön yhteystietoja tai kirjoittakaa: Microsoft Customer Sales and Service, One Microsoft Way, Redmond, Washington 98052-6399.

## Si vous avez acheté votre produit Microsoft® en FRANCE, les limites de garantie suivantes vous concernent.

**LIMITES DE GARANTIE** — Microsoft garantit, sous réserve d'une exploitation dans des conditions normales d'utilisation, a) que le LOGICIEL permettra une utilisation conforme, pour l'essentiel, aux performances définies dans le(s) manuel(s) accompagnant le LOGICIEL, pendant une période de quatre-vingt-dix (90) jours suivant la date de son acquisition, et b) que les supports et matériels de Microsoft fournis avec le LOGICIEL sont exempts de vice de fabrication ; cette dernière garantie étant limitée à une année à compter de la date d'acquisition du LOGICIEL. Toute garantie intrinsèque, de quelque nature que ce soit, sera limitée à quatre-vingt-dix (90) jours pour le LOGICIEL et à un (1) an pour les supports et matériels et ce, sous les mêmes réserves.

**RECOURS DU CLIENT** — En cas de défectuosité, les obligations de Microsoft et les droits de l'utilisateur se limiteront, au choix de Microsoft, soit a) au remboursement du prix payé, soit b) à la réparation ou au remplacement du LOGICIEL ou du matériel non conforme à la garantie limitée de Microsoft qui est envoyé à Microsoft accompagné d'une copie du justificatif d'achat du LOGICIEL. Toutefois, la garantie limitée de Microsoft ne sera pas applicable au cas où la défectuosité résulterait d'un accident, d'un abus ou d'une mauvaise utilisation. Tout LOGICIEL de remplacement sera garanti pour la période de la garantie d'origine restant à courir, ou trente (30) jours suivant la date de remplacement au cas où cette dernière période serait plus longue.

**EXCLUSION DE TOUTE AUTRE GARANTIE** — MICROSOFT N'ASSUME AUCUNE GARANTIE DE QUELQUE NATURE ET A QUELQUE TITRE QUE CE SOIT, EXPLICITE OU IMPLICITE, EN RAPPORT AVEC LE LOGICIEL, LES MANUELS, LA DOCUMENTATION L'ACCOMPAGNANT OU TOUT SUPPORT OU MATERIEL FOURNI, ET NOTAMMENT DES GARANTIES POUR LA COMMERCIALISATION DE TOUS PRODUITS EN RAPPORT AVEC LE LOGICIEL, OU DE L'UTILISATION DU LOGICIEL POUR USAGE DETERMINE.

**ABSENCE DE RESPONSABILITE POUR LES DOMMAGES INDIRECTS** — EN AUCUN CAS MICROSOFT OU SES FOURNISSEURS NE POURRONT ETRE TENUS RESPONSABLES DE TOUT DOMMAGE DE QUELQUE NATURE QUE CE SOIT, NOTAMMENT PERTE D'EXPLOITATION, PERTE DE DONNEES OU TOUTE AUTRE PERTE FINANCIERE RESULTANT DE L'UTILISATION OU DE L'IMPOSSIBILITE D'UTILISER LE PRODUIT MICROSOFT, MEME SI MICROSOFT A ETE PREVENU DE L'EVENTUALITE DE TELS DOMMAGES. EN TOUT ETAT DE CAUSE, LA RESPONSABILITE DE MICROSOFT NE POURRA EN AUCUN CAS EXCEDER LE MONTANT EFFECTIVEMENT PAYE POUR L'ACQUISITION DU LOGICIEL. AFIN DE DETERMINER SI LA LIMITE DE RESPONSABILITE DE MICROSOFT A ETE ATTEINTE, IL SERA TENU COMPTE DE L'ENSEMBLE DES SOMMES QUI AURAIENT EVENTUELLEMENT ETE REGLEES PAR MICROSOFT A CE TITRE.

Le présent accord est régi par le droit français. Tout litige qui en résulterait sera de la compétence exclusive des tribunaux du siège social de la société Microsoft France.

Au cas où vous auriez des questions concernant cette licence ou que vous désiriez vous mettre en rapport avec Microsoft pour quelque raison que ce soit, veuillez contacter la succursale Microsoft desservant votre pays, dont l'adresse est fournie dans ce produit, ou écrire à : Microsoft Customer Sales and Service, One Microsoft Way, Redmond, Washington 98052-6399.

# Wenn Sie Ihr Microsoft®-Produkt in DEUTSCHLAND erworben haben, gilt für Sie die folgende beschränkte Garantie:

**BESCHRÄNKTE GARANTIE** — Microsoft garantiert (a) für einen Zeitraum von 90 Tagen ab Empfangsdatum, daß die SOFTWARE im wesentlichen gemäß dem begleitenden Produkthandbuch arbeitet, und (b) für einen Zeitraum von einem Jahr ab Empfangsdatum, daß eine die SOFTWARE begleitende, von Microsoft gelieferte Hardware bei normaler Benutzung und Wartung frei von Material- oder Verarbeitungsfehlern ist. Die Garantie ist bezüglich der SOFTWARE auf 90 Tage und bezüglich der Hardware auf ein (1) Jahr beschränkt. DIESE GARANTIE WIRD VON MICROSOFT ALS HERSTELLER DES PRODUKTES ÜBERNOMMEN; ETWAIGE GESETZLICHE GEWÄHRLEISTUNGS- ODER HAFTUNGSANSPRÜCHE GEGEN DEN HÄNDLER, VON DEM SIE IHR EXEMPLAR DER SOFTWARE BEZOGEN HABEN, WERDEN HIERDURCH WEDER ERSETZT NOCH BESCHRÄNKT.

**ANSPRÜCHE DES KUNDEN** — Die gesamte Haftung von Microsoft und Ihr alleiniger Anspruch besteht nach Wahl von Microsoft entweder (a) in der Rückerstattung des bezahlten Preises oder (b) in der Reparatur oder dem Ersatz der SOFTWARE oder der Hardware, die der beschränkten Garantie von Microsoft nicht genügt und zusammen mit einer Kopie Ihrer Quittung an Microsoft zurückgegeben wird. Diese beschränkte Garantie gilt nicht, wenn der Ausfall der SOFTWARE oder der Hardware auf einen Unfall, auf Mißbrauch oder auf fehlerhafte Anwendung zurückzuführen ist. Für eine Ersatz-SOFTWARE übernimmt Microsoft nur für den Rest der ursprünglichen Garantiefrist oder für 30 Tage eine Garantie, wobei der längere Zeitraum maßgebend ist.

**KEINE WEITERE GEWÄHRLEISTUNG** — MICROSOFT SCHLIESST FÜR SICH JEDE WEITERE GEWÄHRLEISTUNG BEZÜGLICH DER SOFTWARE, DER ZUGEHÖRIGEN HANDBÜCHER UND SCHRIFTLICHEN MATERIALIEN UND DER BEGLEITENDEN HARDWARE AUS.

**KEINE HAFTUNG FÜR FOLGESCHÄDEN** — WEDER MICROSOFT NOCH DIE LIEFERANTEN VON MICROSOFT SIND FÜR IRGENDWELCHE SCHÄDEN (UNEINGESCHRÄNKT EINGESCHLOSSEN SIND SCHÄDEN AUS ENTGANGENEM GEWINN, BETRIEBSUNTERBRECHUNG, VERLUST VON GESCHÄFTLICHEN INFORMATIONEN ODER VON DATEN ODER AUS ANDEREM FINANZIELLEN VERLUST) ERSATZPFLICHTIG, DIE AUFGRUND DER BENUTZUNG DIESES MICROSOFT-PRODUKTES ODER DER UNFÄHIGKEIT, DIESES MICROSOFT-PRODUKT ZU VERWENDEN, ENTSTEHEN, SELBST WENN MICROSOFT VON DER MÖGLICHKEIT EINES SOLCHEN SCHADENS UNTERRICHTET WORDEN IST. AUF JEDEN FALL IST DIE HAFTUNG VON MICROSOFT AUF DEN BETRAG BESCHRÄNKT, DEN SIE TATSÄCHLICH FÜR DAS PRODUKT BEZAHLT HABEN. DIESER AUSSCHLUSS GILT NICHT FÜR SCHÄDEN, DIE DURCH VORSATZ ODER GROBE FAHRLÄSSIGKEIT AUF SEITEN VON MICROSOFT VERURSACHT WURDEN. EBENFALLS BLEIBEN ANSPRÜCHE, DIE AUF UNABDINGBAREN GESETZLICHEN VORSCHRIFTEN ZUR PRODUKTHAFTUNG BERUHEN, UNBERÜHRT.

Sollten Sie Fragen zu diesem Vertrag haben, oder sollten Sie sich mit Microsoft aus irgendwelchen Gründen in Verbindung setzen wollen, verwenden Sie bitte die diesem Produkt beiligende Adresseninformation, um mit der für Ihr Land zuständigen Microsoft-Niederlassung Kontakt aufzunehmen, oder schreiben Sie an: Microsoft Customer Sales and Service, One Microsoft Way, Redmond, Washington 98052-6399.

## Ogni acquisto di prodotti Microsoft® in ITALIA è sottoposto ai seguenti limiti di garanzia:

**LIMITI DI GARANZIA** — La Microsoft garantisce che (a) il SOFTWARE funzionerà in sostanziale conformità con il (i) manuale (i) ed il materiale scritto di accompagnamento al prodotto per un periodo di 90 giorni dalla data di acquisto; e (b) ogni hardware (es. i dischetti) annesso al SOFTWARE sarà privo di difetti di materiale e di fabbricazione sotto uso e servizio normali, per un periodo di un anno dalla data di acquisto. Ogni garanzia implicita su SOFTWARE e hardware è limitata, rispettivamente, a 90 giorni ed un (1) anno.

**TUTELA DEL CLIENTE** — La responsabilità della Microsoft ed i rimedi esclusivi dell'utente saranno, a discrezione della Microsoft, (a) la restituzione del prezzo pagato; o (b) la riparazione o la sostituzione del SOFTWARE o dell'hardware che non rientrano nella Garanzia di cui sopra, purché siano restituiti alla Microsoft con una copia della fattura di acquisto o ricevuta fiscale regolarmente emessa in Italia. La presente Garanzia viene meno qualora il vizio del SOFTWARE o dell'hardware derivi da incidente, uso inidoneo od erronea applicazione. Ogni SOFTWARE sostitutivo sarà garantito per il rimanente periodo della garanzia originaria e in ogni caso per non meno di 30 giorni.

**ESCLUSIONE DI ALTRE GARANZIE** — LA MICROSOFT NON RICONOSCE ALCUNA ALTRA GARANZIA, ESPRESSA O IMPLICITA, COMPRESE, TRA LE ALTRE, LA GARANZIA DI COMMERCIABILITÀ ED IDONEITÀ PER UN FINE PARTICOLARE, RELATIVAMENTE AL SOFTWARE, AL MATERIALE SCRITTO DI ACCOMPAGNAMENTO ED AD OGNI HARDWARE ANNESSO.

**ESCLUSIONE DI RESPONSABILITÀ PER DANNI INDIRETTI** — IN NESSUN CASO LA MICROSOFT O I SUOI FORNITORI SARANNO RESPONSABILI PER I DANNI (INCLUSI, SENZA LIMITAZIONI, IL DANNO PER PERDITA O MANCATO GUADAGNO, INTERRUZIONE DELL'ATTIVITÀ, PERDITA DI INFORMAZIONI O ALTRE PERDITE ECONOMICHE) DERIVANTI DALL'USO DEL PRODOTTO MICROSOFT, ANCHE NEL CASO CHE LA MICROSOFT SIA STATA AVVERTITA DELLA POSSIBILITÀ DI TALI DANNI. IN OGNI CASO, LA RESPONSABILITÀ DELLA MICROSOFT AI SENSI DEL PRESENTE CONTRATTO SARÀ LIMITATA AD UN IMPORTO CORRISPONDENTE A QUELLO EFFETTIVAMENTE PAGATO PER IL SOFTWARE.

Chiunque desideri porre domande in ordine a questo Contratto, o contattare la Microsoft per qualunque ragione, può rivolgersi alla filiale Microsoft responsabile per il proprio paese all'indirizzo accluso in questo prodotto oppure scrivere a: Microsoft Customer Sales and Service, One Microsoft Way, Redmond, Washington 98052-6399.

## Si usted adquirió su producto Microsoft® en cualquier país de LATINOAMERICA (con excepción de Brasil y México), el uso del software se regirá por la siguiente garantía limitada:

**GARANTIA LIMITADA** — Microsoft garantiza (a) que el SOFTWARE podrá ser operado substancialmente de acuerdo a lo indicado por el o los manuales del producto incluido/s en el paquete, por un período de noventa (90) días contados a partir de la fecha de entrega; y (b) que cualquier equipamiento o parte de equipamiento provista por Microsoft que acompañe al SOFTWARE (en adelante "EQUIPAMIENTO") estará libre de defectos de material o de mano de obra, bajo condiciones de uso y servicio normales, por un período de un (1) año contado a partir de la fecha de entrega. Cualquier garantía implícita sobre el SOFTWARE o el EQUIPAMIENTO estará limitada a noventa (90) días y un (1) año respectivamente.

**RECURSOS DEL LICENCIATARIO** — La sola obligación de Microsoft y el único recurso de usted será, a opción de Microsoft, ya sea:
(a) rembolsar el precio pagado; o (b) reparar o reemplazar el SOFTWARE o el EQUIPAMIENTO que no esté de acuerdo con la Garantía Limitada Microsoft y que sea devuelto a Microsoft con una copia de su recibo. Esta Garantía Limitada será nula en caso de que la falla del SOFTWARE o del EQUIPAMIENTO resulte de accidente, abuso o uso indebido. Cualquier reemplazo del SOFTWARE estará garantizado por el resto del término de la garantía original o por el de treinta (30) días; el que resulte mayor.

**INEXISTENCIA DE OTRAS GARANTIAS** — MICROSOFT NO RECONOCE OTRAS GARANTIAS, EXPRESAS O IMPLICITAS, INCLUYENDO -PERO NO LIMITANDOSE A ELLAS- GARANTIAS IMPLICITAS DE COMERCIALIZACION Y ADECUACION A UN PROPOSITO EN ESPECIAL, CON RESPECTO AL SOFTWARE, EL O LOS MANUALES Y MATERIALES IMPRESOS, Y CUALQUIER EQUIPAMIENTO QUE LO ACOMPAÑE. ESTA GARANTIA LIMITADA LE OTORGA A USTED DERECHOS ESPECIFICOS.

**AUSENCIA DE RESPONSABILIDAD POR DAÑOS RESULTANTES** — EN NINGUN CASO MICROSOFT O SUS LICENCIANTES O PROVEEDORES SERAN RESPONSABLES POR CUALQUIER OTRO DAÑO (INCLUYENDO, SIN LIMITACION, DAÑOS POR PERDIDA DE GANANCIAS EN LOS NEGOCIOS, PERDIDA DE INFORMACION COMERCIAL U OTRA PERDIDA PECUNIARIA) RESULTANTE DEL USO O INCAPACIDAD DE USAR ESTE PRODUCTO MICROSOFT, AUN CUANDO MICROSOFT HAYA SIDO ADVERTIDO SOBRE LA POSIBILIDAD DE DICHOS DAÑOS. EN CUALQUIER CASO, LA COMPLETA RESPONSABILIDAD CONFORME A CUALQUIER CLAUSULA DE ESTE CONTRATO ESTARA LIMITADA AL MONTO REAL PAGADO POR USTED POR ESTE SOFTWARE.

Si usted tiene alguna duda acerca de este Acuerdo o si desea contactar, por cualquier motivo, con Microsoft, utilice por favor la información con la dirección que se adjunta con este producto para contactar con su subsidiaria Microsoft o escriba a: Microsoft Customer Sales and Service, One Microsoft Way, Redmond, Washington 98052-6399.

## Si usted adquirió su Producto Microsoft® en MÉXICO entonces le es aplicable la garantía limitada que aparece a continuación:

**GARANTIA LIMITADA** — Microsoft garantiza (a) que el SOFTWARE funcionará sustancialmente de acuerdo con el o los Manuales del Producto que acompañan al SOFTWARE, por un período de noventa (90) días a partir de la fecha de su entrega; y (b) que todo el equipo de computación que acompaña al SOFTWARE estará libre de defectos por lo que se refiere a sus materiales y mano de obra, bajo condiciones normales de uso y servicio, por un período de un (1) año a partir de la fecha de su entrega. Todas las garantías implícitas respecto del SOFTWARE y el equipo están limitadas a noventa (90) días y un (1) año, respectivamente.

**RECURSOS DEL CLIENTE** — La responsabilidad total que Microsoft tiene y el recurso único que usted tiene, a opción de Microsoft, es
(a) devolverle el precio pagado, o (b) reparar o restituir el SOFTWARE o equipo de computación que no se ajuste a la Garantía Limitada de Microsoft y que sea devuelto a Microsoft con una copia de su factura. Esta Garantía Limitada quedará sin efectos si el mal funcionamiento del SOFTWARE o equipo se debe a accidentes, abusos o aplicación indebida del mismo. Cualquier restitución del SOFTWARE estará garantizada por el resto del período de garantía original o treinta (30) días, lo que sea mayor.

**NINGUNA OTRA GARANTIA** — MICROSOFT DESCONOCE CUALQUIER OTRA GARANTIA EXPRESA O IMPLICITA, INCLUYENDO, SIN LIMITAR, LAS GARANTIAS IMPLICITAS O DE COMERCIALIZACION Y ADECUACION PARA UN FIN PARTICULAR CON RESPECTO AL SOFTWARE, EL O LOS MANUALES Y MATERIALES ESCRITOS QUE LE ACOMPAÑAN, Y CUALQUIER EQUIPO DE COMPUTACION QUE ASIMISMO VAYA INCLUIDO. ESTA GARANTIA LIMITADA LE CONFIERE DERECHOS ESPECIFICOS CONFORME A LA LEY.

**NINGUNA RESPONSABILIDAD POR DAÑOS INDIRECTOS** — EN NINGUN CASO, MICROSOFT O SUS PROVEEDORES SERAN RESPONSABLES POR DAÑOS DE CUALQUIER NATURALEZA (INCLUYENDO SIN LIMITAR, PERDIDAS DE UTILIDADES, INTERRUPCION DE OPERACIONES, PERDIDA DE INFORMACION COMERCIAL U OTROS DAÑOS PECUNIARIOS) QUE SE DERIVEN DEL USO O INCAPACIDAD DE USAR EL PRODUCTO MICROSOFT, AUN CUANDO MICROSOFT HAYA SIDO INFORMADA SOBRE LA POSIBILIDAD DE DICHOS DAÑOS. EN CUALQUIER CASO, LA RESPONSABILIDAD MAXIMA A CARGO DE MICROSOFT CONFORME A LAS ESTIPULACIONES DE ESTE CONTRATO ESTARA LIMITADA AL IMPORTE QUE EFECTIVAMENTE USTED HAYA PAGADO POR CONCEPTO DEL SOFTWARE.

Este Contrato estará regulado por las leyes de los Estados Unidos Mexicanos.

Si usted tiene alguna duda acerca de este Acuerdo o si desea contactar, por cualquier motivo, con Microsoft, utilice por favor la información con la dirección que se adjunta con este producto para contactar con su subsidiaria Microsoft o escriba a: Microsoft Customer Sales and Service, One Microsoft Way, Redmond, Washington 98052-6399.

# Hvis De har kjøpt Deres Microsoft®-produkt i NORGE, gjelder begrenset garanti i denne avtale:

**BEGRENSET GARANTI** — Microsoft garanterer at (a) PROGRAMVAREN funksjonerer i det vesentlige i overensstemmelse med medfølgende brukerveiledning(er) for en periode av 90 dager fra dato for mottagelsen; og at (b) ethvert utstyr som leveres av Microsoft og som følger PROGRAMVAREN ikke har materialmangler eller utførelsesmangler ved normal bruk og ytelse for en periode av ett år fra dato for mottagelsen. Enhver stilltiende garanti for PROGRAMVAREN og utstyr er begrenset til henholdsvis 90 dager og ett (1) år.

**KUNDENS RETTIGHETER** — Microsofts fulle ansvar og Deres eneste krav skal være, etter Microsofts valg, enten (a) tilbakebetaling av kjøpesummen eller (b) av hjelp eller omlevering av PROGRAMVAREN og utstyr som ikke tilfredsstiller Microsofts Begrensede Garanti og som er returnert til Microsoft sammen med en kopi av Deres faktura. Denne Begrensede Garanti gjelder ikke dersom mangler ved PROGRAMVAREN eller utstyret skyldes uhell, misbruk eller feilaktig anvendelse. Enhver omlevert PROGRAMVARE er garantert for den lengste periode av det gjenværende av garantiperioden eller 30 dager.

**INGEN ØVRIGE GARANTIER** — MICROSOFT FRASKRIVER SEG ETHVERT ØVRIG GARANTIANSVAR, ENTEN DETTE ER DIREKTE ELLER STILLTIENDE, HERUNDER, MEN IKKE BEGRENSET TIL, STILLTIENDE GARANTIER OM SALGBARHET OG ANVENDELIGHET FOR SÆRSKILTE FORMÅL. DENNE ANSVARSFRASKRIVELSE GJELDER MED HENSYN TIL PROGRAMVAREN, MEDFØLGENDE BRUKERVEILEDNING(ER) OG SKRIFTLIG MATERIALE, OG ETHVERT MEDFØLGENDE UTSTYR. DENNE BEGRENSEDE GARANTI GIR DEM SPESIFIKKE RETTIGHETER.

**ØVRIGE ANSVARSBEGRENSNINGER** — I INTET ØVRIG TILFELLE SKAL MICROSOFT ELLER DETS LEVERANDØRER ELLER RETTSFORGJENGERE VÆRE ANSVARLIG FOR TAP OG SKADER AV EN HVILKEN SOM HELST ART (HERUNDER, UTEN BEGRENSNING, TAP AV FORTJENESTE, DRIFTSAVBRUDD, TAP AV INFORMASJON I VIRKSOMHETEN ELLER ØVRIG ØKONOMISK TAP) SOM OPPSTÅR SOM FØLGE AV BRUKEN AV, ELLER MANGLENDE EVNE TIL Å BRUKE, DETTE MICROSOFT-PRODUKT. DETTE GJELDER SELV OM MICROSOFT ER BLITT INFORMERT OM MULIGHETEN FOR SLIKE SKADER ELLER TAP. UNDER ENHVER OMSTENDIGHET ER MICROSOFTS FULLE ANSVAR I HENHOLD TIL SAMTLIGE AV DENNE AVTALES BESTEMMELSER BEGRENSET TIL DET BELØP SOM DE FAKTISK HAR BETALT FOR PROGRAMVAREN.

**FORBRUKERKJØP** — Denne avtale gjelder med de begrensninger som følger av kjøpslovens ufravikelige bestemmelser i forbrukerkjøp, jfr. Lov av 13. mai 1988 nr. 27 om kjøp § 4.

For denne avtale gjelder norsk rett.

Hvis De har spørsmål vedrørende denne Avtale, eller hvis De ønsker å kontakte Microsoft av andre årsaker, bruker De adresseinformasjonen som følger med dette produktet for å kontakte Microsofts underkontor eller skriv til: Microsoft Customer Sales and Service, One Microsoft Way, Redmond, Washington 98052-6399.

## Si usted ha adquirido su producto Microsoft® en ESPAÑA, la presente garantía limitada le es de aplicación:

**GARANTIA LIMITADA** — Microsoft garantiza que (a) durante un período de noventa (90) días a contar desde la fecha de recepción, el SOFTWARE funcionará sustancialmente de acuerdo con lo especificado en el/los manual(es) que acompañan al Producto; y (b) durante un período de un (1) año desde su recepción, cualquier pieza de hardware suministrada por Microsoft que acompañe al SOFTWARE y que sea utilizada en condiciones normales de uso y servicio no contendrá defectos materiales ni de fabricación. Cualquier garantía implícita del SOFTWARE y del hardware se limitará a noventa (90) días y a un (1) año, respectivamente.

**INDEMNIZACION AL USUARIO** — La responsabilidad total de Microsoft y su única indemnización consistirá, a elección de Microsoft, en: (a) el reembolso del precio pagado, o (b) la reparación o reemplazo del SOFTWARE o hardware que no cumpla con la Garantía Limitada de Microsoft y sea devuelta a Microsoft con copia de su recibo. Esta Garantía Limitada será nula si los defectos del SOFTWARE o del hardware son consecuencia de accidente, abuso o mal uso. Cualquier SOFTWARE reemplazado estará garantizado por el período de tiempo que resultase mayor entre el que reste hasta el vencimiento de la garantía original o un período de treinta (30) días.

**INEXISTENCIA DE OTRAS GARANTIAS** — MICROSOFT RECHAZA CUALESQUIERA OTRAS GARANTIAS, TANTO IMPLICITAS COMO EXPLICITAS, INCLUYENDO, PERO NO LIMITANDOSE A LAS GARANTIAS IMPLICITAS DE SER APTO PARA EL COMERCIO Y ADECUADO PARA UN FIN PARTICULAR, RESPECTO DEL SOFTWARE, EL/LOS MANUAL(ES) DEL PRODUCTO Y OTROS DOCUMENTOS ESCRITOS, ASI COMO CUALQUIER HARDWARE QUE LE ACOMPAÑE. ESTA GARANTIA LIMITADA LE OTORGA A USTED DERECHOS ESPECIFICOS.

**INEXISTENCIA DE RESPONSABILIDAD POR DAÑOS INDIRECTOS** — EN NINGUN CASO MICROSOFT O SUS PROVEEDORES SERAN RESPONSABLES DE CUALESQUIERA DAÑOS (INCLUYENDOSE, SIN LIMITE, LOS QUE DERIVEN DE PERDIDA DE BENEFICIOS, INTERRUPCION DEL NEGOCIO, PERDIDA DE INFORMACION COMERCIAL O CUALESQUIERA OTRAS PERDIDAS PECUNIARIAS) QUE SE ORIGINEN COMO CONSECUENCIA DEL USO O LA IMPOSIBILIDAD DE USO DE ESTE PRODUCTO MICROSOFT, INCLUSO EN EL SUPUESTO DE QUE MICROSOFT HAYA SIDO INFORMADO DE LA POSIBILIDAD DE QUE DICHOS DAÑOS SE ORIGINEN. EN CUALQUIER CASO, LA RESPONSABILIDAD DE MICROSOFT CON RESPECTO A CUALQUIER CLAUSULA DE ESTE CONTRATO SE LIMITA A LA CANTIDAD EFECTIVAMENTE PAGADA POR USTED POR EL SOFTWARE.

Este Contrato se regirá por las leyes españolas.

Si usted tiene alguna duda acerca de este Acuerdo o si desea contactar, por cualquier motivo, con Microsoft, utilice por favor la información con la dirección que se adjunta con este producto para contactar con su subsidiaria Microsoft o escriba a: Microsoft Customer Sales and Service, One Microsoft Way, Redmond, Washington 98052-6399.

# Om Ni har förvärvat Er Microsoft®-produkt i SVERIGE, gäller följande begränsade garanti för Er:

**BEGRÄNSAD GARANTI** — Microsoft garanterar (a) att PROGRAMVARAN i allt väsentligt fungerar i enlighet med tillhörande produktmanual(er) för en period om 90 dagar från dagen för mottagandet; och (b) att av Microsoft som tillbehör till PROGRAMVARAN levererad hårdvara är fri från material- och tillverkningsfel under normal användning och service under 1 år från den dag Ni mottagit produkterna. Varje garanti, uttrycklig eller implicit, avseende PROGRAMVARAN eller hårdvara är begränsad till 90 dagar respektive ett (1) år.

**KÖPARENS RÄTT ENLIGT GARANTIN** — Microsofts ansvar på grund av garantin är, efter Microsofts val, begränsad till antingen (a) återbetalning av köpeskillingen eller (b) reparation eller utbyte av den PROGRAMVARA eller hårdvara som inte uppfyller Microsofts begränsade garanti och som returnerats till Microsoft AB tillsammans med en kopia på ert kvitto. Garantin gäller ej om fel eller brist i PROGRAMVARAN eller hårdvaran beror på olyckshändelse, eller oriktig användning eller hantering. Utbytt PROGRAMVARA omfattas av en garantitid motsvarande för den utbytta varan återstående garantiperiod, dock minst 30 dagar.

**INGA YTTERLIGARE GARANTIER** — MICROSOFTS ANSVAR ÄR BEGRÄNSAT ENLIGT OVAN OCH MICROSOFT ÅTAR SIG INGET ANNAT GARANTIANSVAR, VARE SIG UTTRYCKLIGT ELLER IMPLICIT, AVSEENDE PRODUKTERNAS LÄMPLIGHET FOR ETT SÄRSKILT ÄNDAMÅL, ELLER AVSEENDE PROGRAMVARAN, TILLHÖRANDE PRODUKTMANUAL(ER) OCH DET SKRIFTLIGA MATERIALET SAMT I FÖREKOMMANDE FALL TILLHÖRANDE HÅRDVARA.

**ANSVARSBEGRÄNSNING** — MICROSOFT ELLER DESS LEVERANTÖRER SVARAR ICKE FÖR SKADOR (INKLUSIVE, MEN UTAN BEGRÄNSNING TILL, UTEBLIVEN VINST, DRIFTSAVBROTT, FÖRLUST AV LAGRAD INFORMATION ELLER ANNAN EKONOMISK SKADA) TILL FÖLJD AV ANVÄNDNING ELLER FELAKTIG ANVÄNDNING AV DENNA MICROSOFT-PRODUKT. DETTA GÄLLER ÄVEN OM MICROSOFT HAR UPPMÄRKSAMMATS PÅ MÖJLIGHETERNA TILL SÅDANA SKADOR. MICROSOFTS TOTALA ANSVAR ENLIGT BESTÄMMELSERNA I DETTA AVTAL SKALL VIDARE ALLTID VARA BEGRÄNSAT TILL DEN FÖR PROGRAMVARAN ERLAGDA KÖPESKILLINGEN.

Svensk lag är tillämplig på detta avtal.

Om ni har frågor om detta licensavtal eller om ni behöver kontakta Microsoft i något annat ärende, kan ni använda den bifogade adressinformationen och kontakta Microsofts dotterbolag i ert land. Ni kan också kontakta Microsoft i USA på följande adress: Microsoft Customer Sales and Service, One Microsoft Way, Redmond, Washington 98052-6399.

## If you acquired your Microsoft® product in United States of America or ANY OTHER COUNTRY, the following limited warranty applies to you:

**LIMITED WARRANTY** — Microsoft warrants that (a) the SOFTWARE will perform substantially in accordance with the accompanying Product Manual(s) for a period of 90 days from the date of receipt; and (b) any Microsoft supplied hardware accompanying the SOFTWARE will be free from defects in materials and workmanship under normal use and service for a period of one year from the date of receipt. Any implied warranties on the SOFTWARE and hardware are limited to 90 days and one (1) year, respectively.

**CUSTOMER REMEDIES** — Microsoft's entire liability and your exclusive remedy shall be, at Microsoft's option, either (a) return of the price paid or (b) repair or replacement of the SOFTWARE or hardware that does not meet Microsoft's Limited Warranty and which is returned to Microsoft with a copy of your receipt. This Limited Warranty is void if failure of the SOFTWARE or hardware has resulted from accident, abuse, or misapplication. Any replacement SOFTWARE will be warranted for the remainder of the original warranty period or 30 days, whichever is longer.

**NO OTHER WARRANTIES** — MICROSOFT DISCLAIMS ALL OTHER WARRANTIES, EITHER EXPRESS OR IMPLIED, INCLUDING BUT NOT LIMITED TO IMPLIED WARRANTIES OF MERCHANTABILITY AND FITNESS FOR A PARTICULAR PURPOSE, WITH RESPECT TO THE SOFTWARE, THE ACCOMPANYING PRODUCT MANUAL(S) AND WRITTEN MATERIALS, AND ANY ACCOMPANYING HARDWARE. THIS LIMITED WARRANTY GIVES YOU SPECIFIC LEGAL RIGHTS.

**NO LIABILITY FOR CONSEQUENTIAL DAMAGES** — IN NO EVENT SHALL MICROSOFT OR ITS SUPPLIERS BE LIABLE FOR ANY OTHER DAMAGES WHATSOEVER (INCLUDING, WITHOUT LIMITATION, DAMAGES FOR LOSS OF BUSINESS PROFITS, BUSINESS INTERRUPTION, LOSS OF BUSINESS INFORMATION, OR OTHER PECUNIARY LOSS) ARISING OUT OF THE USE OF OR INABILITY TO USE THIS MICROSOFT PRODUCT, EVEN IF MICROSOFT HAS BEEN ADVISED OF THE POSSIBILITY OF SUCH DAMAGES. IN ANY CASE, MICROSOFT'S ENTIRE LIABILITY UNDER ANY PROVISION OF THIS AGREEMENT SHALL BE LIMITED TO THE AMOUNT ACTUALLY PAID BY YOU FOR THE SOFTWARE.

This Agreement is governed by the laws of the State of Washington, U.S.A.

Should you have any questions concerning this Agreement, or if you desire to contact Microsoft for any reason, please write: Microsoft Customer Sales and Service, One Microsoft Way, Redmond, Washington 98052-6399.

# Index

---

*You can start MS-DOS Help by typing **help** at the command prompt. To get help on a specific command, type **help** followed
by the command name—for example, **help copy**.

*You can start MS-DOS Help by typing **help** at the command prompt. To get help on a specific command, type **help** followed by the command name—for example, **help copy**.

---

---

*You can start MS-DOS Help by typing **help** at the command prompt. To get help on a specific command, type **help** followed
  by the command name—for example, **help copy**.

---

*You can start MS-DOS Help by typing **help** at the command prompt. To get help on a specific command, type **help** followed
  by the command name—for example, **help copy**.

---

*You can start MS-DOS Help by typing **help** at the command prompt. To get help on a specific command, type **help** followed
  by the command name—for example, **help copy**.

---

*You can start MS-DOS Help by typing **help** at the command prompt. To get help on a specific command, type **help** followed by the command name—for example, **help copy**.

# N

Naming
  directories 35–37
  disks (labeling when formatting) 30
  files 35–37
National Information System (NIS) 259
National language support (Nlsfunc program), loading 233
Network card, conflicting memory addresses 220
Network drives, limiting virus scanning to local drives 69
Networks
  deleted files, recovering 87
  startup files, order of commands in 148
NIS *See* National Information System
Nlsfunc command
  *See also* MS-DOS Help*
  loading national language support 233
Non–MS-DOS partitions, deleting 208–209
Norton Backup 51
"Not enough space to install MS-DOS" message 182
"Not enough space to install selected programs" message 193
"Not ready reading drive A" message 19
Novell disk partitions 189
Numlock command
  *See also* MS-DOS Help*
  creating a startup menu 107

# O

OLD_DOS directories
  deleting 3, 7
  restoring a previous version of DOS by using 179
Online documents x
Online Help
  Microsoft Anti-Virus 65
  Microsoft Backup 44
  Microsoft Undelete 89
  MS-DOS Help, how to use 37–40
  MS-DOS Setup 3
  MS-DOS Shell 42
Optimizing your system *See* Disk space; Memory
  management
Options command, DoubleSpace 129
OS/2, upgrading to MS-DOS 6
  described 5
  freeing disk space for setting up MS-DOS 6 183–184
  if you don't have OS/2 Dual Boot or OS/2 Boot
    Manager 5–6
  if you have OS/2 Boot Manager with DOS 6–8
  if you have OS/2 Boot Manager without DOS 8–9

OS/2, upgrading to MS-DOS 6 *(continued)*
  if you have OS/2 Dual Boot with DOS 6–8
  removing OS/2 and saving data 6, 8, 9
"Out-of-memory" messages 225–226

# P

PACKING.LST file 195
Parameters, using with commands 20
Partitions
  *See also* Configuring your hard disk
  Disk Manager 190
  Everex 189
  messages
    "Incompatible primary DOS partition" 188
    "Too many primary partitions" 188
  Novell 189
  Priam 189
  restrictions on repartitioning with Fdisk 204
  SpeedStor Bootall 190
  UNIX 189
  Vfeature 189
  XENIX 189
"Password-protection" message received during MS-DOS
  Setup 187
Path
  defined 34
  full path, defined 35
  how to specify 34–35
  limit on length of 35
  relative path, defined 35
  substituting *See* MS-DOS Help* for the Subst command
Path command *See* MS-DOS Help*
Pause command *See* MS-DOS Help*
Pausing a directory list 15
Ports, redirected by the Interlnk program 172
Power command
  *See also* MS-DOS Help*
  current power setting, displaying 175
Power program for laptop computers 174–175
POWER.EXE device driver
  *See also* MS-DOS Help*
  installing 174
Previous version of DOS, restoring 179
Priam disk partitions
  restrictions on repartitioning with Fdisk 204
  setting up MS-DOS 6 on computers with 189
Primary MS-DOS partition
  creating 212–213
  deleting 211–212

---

*You can start MS-DOS Help by typing **help** at the command prompt. To get help on a specific command, type **help** followed
  by the command name—for example, **help copy**.

*You can start MS-DOS Help by typing **help** at the command prompt. To get help on a specific command, type **help** followed by the command name—for example, **help copy**.

# T

*You can start MS-DOS Help by typing **help** at the command prompt. To get help on a specific command, type **help** followed
by the command name—for example, **help copy**.

---

*You can start MS-DOS Help by typing **help** at the command prompt. To get help on a specific command, type **help** followed by the command name—for example, **help copy**.

# Microsoft MS-DOS 6.2 Upgrade
# Low-Density (360K and 720K) Disk Offer

Your Microsoft® MS-DOS® 6.2 Upgrade includes either 5.25" high-density (1.2 MB) disks or 3.5" high-density (1.44 MB) disks. If your system requires 5.25" or 3.5" low-density disks, please mark your preferred disk size, and send this order form to the address below. There is no charge for ordering low-density disks. *No photocopies or facsimiles of this order coupon will be accepted.*

*Preferred disk size (limit of one disk set per order):*
❑ 5.25" low-density disks (Kit No. 147-099-313)
❑ 3.5" low-density disks (Kit No. 147-095-313)

## Print your name, shipping address, and phone number:

Name

Company name
(if company licenses product)
Shipping address

City                     State/Province              ZIP/Postal Code

Daytime phone (        )
(in case we have a question about your order)

## Send the completed order form to:

Microsoft MS-DOS 6.2 Upgrade Disk Offer
P. O. Box 3024
Bothell, WA 98041-3024
U.S.A.

**-OR-**

Microsoft Canada Order Centre
P.O. Box 3030
Malton Postal Station
Mississauga, ON L4T 4C2
Canada

If you have any questions about this offer, in the U.S. call the Microsoft Sales Information Center at (800) 426-9400 or in Canada, call the Microsoft Canada Order Centre at (800) 933-4750 before returning this coupon. Outside the United States and Canada, contact your local Microsoft subsidiary. Deaf and hard-of-hearing customers can reach Microsoft Text Telephone (TT/TDD) services at (800) 892-5234 in the U.S. or (905) 568-9641 in Canada. Please allow 2 to 4 weeks for delivery upon receipt of this order by Microsoft. Offer good while supplies last or until November 1, 1994. Offer good only in the 50 United States and Canada. This coupon is not transferable.

Microsoft and MS-DOS are registered trademarks of Microsoft Corporation.

# Microsoft® MS-DOS® 6.2 Resource Kit, Supplemental Disks, and Conversion Disk Offer

You can use this coupon to order the MS-DOS 6.2 Resource Kit, the MS-DOS 6.2 Supplemental disks, and the Conversion Disk for Users of Stacker®. The Resource Kit contains the following:

- The *MS-DOS 6.2 Technical Reference,* which includes a printed reference for all MS-DOS 6.2 commands as well as technical information about DoubleSpace™ and MemMaker. It also includes the specification for the Microsoft Real-Time Compression Interface, or MRCI. The MRCI specification is a compression-interface standard designed to make it easy for software and hardware vendors to take advantage of the disk compression technology included with MS-DOS 6.2.

- The Supplemental disks, which include files and tools (see item 2 on the following page for disk contents). You can also order the Supplemental disks separately.

The Conversion Disk for Users of Stacker includes a utility that automatically converts data that was compressed by Stacker compression software to the DoubleSpace format. To use the Conversion utility, your data must have been compressed by Stacker versions 2.0 through 3.0 (but not 3.1).

You can download the data on the Supplemental disks from the Microsoft Product Support Download Service (MSDL). To reach the MSDL, call (206) 936-6735 in the United States or (905) 507-3022 in Canada.

When you call the MSDL, use the following communications settings:

| For this setting | Specify |
| --- | --- |
| Baud rate | 1200, 2400, or 9600 |
| Parity | none |
| Data bits | 8 |
| Stop bits | 1 |

## How to order:

To order the Resource Kit, Supplemental disks, or Conversion Disk for Users of Stacker, fill out the form on the following page and send it to the following address. **Offer limited to one Resource Kit, set of Supplemental disks, *or* Conversion Disk per order.**

## Send the completed order form to:

Microsoft MS-DOS 6.2 Disk Offer
P.O. Box 3024
Bothell, WA 98041-3024
U.S.A.

—OR—

Microsoft Canada Order Centre
P.O. Box 3030
Malton Postal Station
Mississauga, ON L4T 4C2
Canada

# Microsoft MS-DOS 6.2 Resource Kit, Supplemental Disks, and Conversion Disk Offer

## 1. Print your name, shipping address, and phone number:

Name

Company name
(if company licenses product)

Shipping address

City            State/Prov.        ZIP/PC

Daytime phone (          )
(in case we have a question about your order)

## 2. Check the Supplemental disk feature(s) that prompted your order:

❑ Microsoft QuickBasic™ games and programs
❑ Files for use with IBM® ProPrinter® or IBM PC convertible
❑ Utilities to assist persons with disabilities
❑ Batch file for creating a bootable DoubleSpace floppy disk
❑ MS-DOS Shell
❑ MS-DOS commands (included in earlier versions of MS-DOS):

❑ ASSIGN.COM        ❑ GRAFTABL.COM
❑ BACKUP.EXE        ❑ JOIN.EXE
❑ COMP.EXE          ❑ MIRROR.COM
❑ CV.COM            ❑ MSHERC.COM
❑ EDLIN.EXE         ❑ PRINTFIX.COM
❑ EXE2BIN.EXE

## 3. Calculate cost and indicate method of payment:

❑ Microsoft MS-DOS 6.2 Resource Kit—including the Supplemental disks (U.S. $19.95 or CDN $24.95, plus freight and tax)
❑ 5.25" low-density disks (Kit No. 147-099-314)
❑ 3.5" low-density disks (Kit No. 147-095-314)

❑ Supplemental disks only (U.S. $5.00 or CDN $7.50)
❑ 5.25" low-density disks (Kit No. 147-099-312)
❑ 3.5" low-density disks (Kit No. 147-095-312)

❑ Conversion Disk for Users of Stacker (U.S. $5.00 or CDN $7.50)
❑ 5.25" low-density disk (Kit No. 147-099-315)
❑ 3.5" low-density disk (Kit No. 147-095-315)

| | |
|---|---|
| Cost (see above) | $ |
| Freight (U.S. $5.00/Canada $7.50) | $ |
| U.S. sales tax* (multiply cost by the sales tax rate) | $ |
| Canadian GST* (multiply cost by the GST rate) | $ |
| Canadian PST* (multiply cost & freight by the PST rate) | $ |
| **Total cost** | **$** |

\* In the U.S., add the applicable sales tax in the following states: AR, AZ, CA, CO, CT, DC, FL, GA, HI, IA, ID, IL, IN, KS, KY, LA, MA, MD, ME, MI, MN, MO, MS, NC, ND, NE, NJ, NM, NV, NY, OH, OK, PA, RI, SC, SD, TN, TX, UT, VA, VT, WA, WI, WV, and WY. In Canada, please add 7% GST. Also add PST on the total including freight if you are located in BC (7%) or Ontario (8%). Microsoft's GST Registration No. is R135625069. Microsoft reserves the right to correct tax rates and/or collect the sales tax assessed by additional states/provinces as required by law, without notice.

*Method of Payment***

❑ Check or money order enclosed    ❑ VISA (13 or 16 numbers)
❑ MasterCard (16 numbers)          ❑ American Express (15 numbers)

| | | | | | | | | | | | | | | | |
|---|---|---|---|---|---|---|---|---|---|---|---|---|---|---|---|
| 1 | 2 | 3 | 4 | 5 | 6 | 7 | 8 | 9 | 10 | 11 | 12 | 13 | 14 | 15 | 16 |

**Expiration date**

**Cardholder's signature**

**Please send payment in U.S. or Canadian funds. Do not send cash or purchase orders. Make checks payable to Microsoft. Note: Your check will be deposited immediately upon receipt by Microsoft.

---

If you have questions about this offer: in the U.S. call the Microsoft Sales Information Center at (800) 426-9400; in Canada, call the Microsoft Canada Order Centre at (800) 933-4750 before returning this coupon. Deaf and hard-of-hearing customers can reach Microsoft Text Telephone (TT/TTD) services at (800) 892-5234 in the U.S. or (905) 568-9641 in Canada. Please allow 2 to 4 weeks for delivery upon receipt of this order by Microsoft. Offer good while supplies last or until **November 1, 1994.** Offer good only in the 50 United States and Canada. This coupon is not transferable. No photocopies or facsimiles accepted.

Microsoft and MS-DOS are registered trademarks and DoubleSpace and Microsoft QuickBasic are trademarks of Microsoft Corporation. Stacker is a registered trademark of STAC Electronics.

# Protect your PC against new viruses. Get two anti-virus updates for as little as $9⁹⁵* each!

Your Microsoft® MS–DOS® 6 Upgrade includes a powerful virus protection program that detects and removes more than 800 viruses. Unfortunately, new viruses appear frequently. That's why you need an ongoing plan to keep your data safe.

To keep your virus protection current, Microsoft is pleased to offer you two anti-virus software updates for as little as $9.95 each. (Price to U.S. residents; see reverse side for prices in your country.)

Plus you'll also receive information about ongoing service plans. It's our way of making sure we take care of your data-protection needs today—and tomorrow.

To order your low-cost anti-virus update, just complete and send the attached coupon to the address for your country as indicated on the reverse side.

**Microsoft®**
Making it easier

## Virus Protection Update Order Form

Order your anti-virus update(s) now and save money! (See reverse side for your price.)

☐ **Yes! Please send me my anti-virus update(s).** I understand the first will ship now and the second will follow in 3-4 months. (Please allow 2-3 weeks for initial delivery.)

Name

Company                         Department

Street Address

City                            Country

Zip Code/Postal Code

Daytime Phone          Fax

**CA, CT, IL, MA, MD, MI, MN, NJ, NY, TX, VA add applicable sales tax. Canadian buyers add applicable GST. Our GST code is 129820296.

Choose one disk size:   ☐ 5.25 inch 360K   ☐ 3.5 inch 720K
Choose version:          ☐ MS-DOS           ☐ Windows™        |ENG|

**Please find your price on reverse side and enter below:**

☐ Price–One Update          _____
☐ Price–Two Updates         _____
Applicable Sales Tax**       _____
Total                        _____

Sales Tax Number: (if applicable) _____

**Payment Method:** ☐ Cheque/Eurocheque/Money Order Enclosed
(Make cheques payable to "Anti-Virus Update")
☐ VISA            ☐ MasterCard         ☐ EuroCard
☐ BankCard        ☐ American Express
☐ P.O. # _____

Card Number: | | | | | | | | | | | | | | | | |

Exp. Date : | | | - | | |

Signature _____

# Anti-Virus Update Offer Price Chart

Prices below include shipping, handling and local sales tax where applicable.

| If resident of | Respond to | Pay in | Price (one) | Price (two) | Payment method accepted |
|---|---|---|---|---|---|
| Germany (see 1 below) | Germany | DM | 39,00 | 78,00 | VISA, MC, EuroCard, AMEX, Personal Cheque, Eurocheque |
| France (see 1 below) | France | FF | 139,90 | 279,80 | VISA, MC, EuroCard, AMEX, Personal Cheque, Eurocheque |
| UK (see 1 below) | UK | £ | 14.95 | 29.90 | VISA, MC, EuroCard, AMEX, Personal Cheque, Eurocheque |
| Italy | Italy | DM* | 39.00 or 33.91 (See 2 below) | 78.00 or 67.83 (See 2 below) | VISA, Eurocheque |
| Denmark, Holland, Spain, Luxembourg, Belgium, Portugal, Greece, Ireland | Germany | DM* | 39.00 or 33.91 (See 2 below) | 78.00 or 67.83 (See 2 below) | VISA, MC, EuroCard, Amex, Eurocheque |
| Austria, Finland, Norway, Sweden, Africa, Switzerland | Germany | DM* | 33.91 | 67.83 | VISA, MC, EuroCard, AMEX, Eurocheque |
| Australia, New Zealand, Asia/Pacific | Australia | A$ | 33.90 | 67.80 | VISA, MC, BankCard, Money Order, Personal Cheque (Cheques accepted from Australia and New Zealand only) |
| South America, Central America, Mexico | USA | US$ | 14.95 | 29.90 | VISA, MC, AMEX, Money Order |
| Israel | Israel | IS | 35.00 | 60.00 | VISA, MC, Personal Cheque |
| Middle East | Middle East | DM* | 33.91 | 67.83 | VISA, MC, EuroCard, AMEX, Eurocheque |
| Eastern Europe | Germany | DM | 33.91 | 67.83 | Eurocheque |

## Please send your order to the address for your country as listed below:

**UNITED STATES**
AV Update
15220 Greenbrier Parkway #200
Beaverton, OR 97006-9937 • USA

**UNITED KINGDOM**
AV Update
P.O. Box 104
Camberley
Surrey GU17 7WZ • UK

**ITALY**
AV Update
Via Vittorio Veneto 24
20124 Milano - Italy

**GERMANY**
AV Update
Postfach 83 01 45
D-81701 Munich
Germany

**AUSTRALIA**
AV Update
P.O. Box 660 • Brookvale • NSW 2100
Australia

**MIDDLE EAST**
AV Update
P.O. Box 14135 • Dubai
United Arab Emirates

**FRANCE**
AV Update
1, Rond-Point de l'Europe
92257 La Garenne Colombes Cedex
France

**ISRAEL**
AV Update
P.O. Box 25055 • Haifa 31250
Israel

## Important Information

1. Attention: Due to VAT registration in Germany, France and the UK, the prices quoted are final prices. You cannot deduct any VAT.
   Residents of France and the UK: Attention: Credit card payments are subject to minimal exchange rate fluctuations due to central fulfilment.

2. Attention: Under the new EC-VAT system, we are required to charge sales tax (e.g. VAT, TVA, MOMS, FPA, IVA, BTW) as follows: The price for customers who cannot supply us with a VAT identification number is: DM 39.00/78.00 (including currently 15% VAT). The price for customers with a VAT identifcation number is: DM 33.91/67.83. Please quote your VAT ID number on the order form.

*The following shows approximately DM 39.00 in your equivalent currency at press time:

| Italy | DK | Holland | LUX | Belgium | Spain | Portugal | Greece | Ireland | CH | Austria | Finland | Norway | Sweden |
|---|---|---|---|---|---|---|---|---|---|---|---|---|---|
| 38,903 ITL | 150 DKK | 44 NLG | 802 LUF | 802 BEF | 2,784 ESB | 3,591 PTE | 5,228 GRD | 16 IEP | 36 CHF | 274 ATS | 141 FIM | 166 NOK | 185 SEK |